THE THEORY OF

Sex Allocation

MONOGRAPHS IN POPULATION BIOLOGY

EDITED BY ROBERT M. MAY

THE THEORY OF
Sex Allocation

ERIC L. CHARNOV

PRINCETON, NEW JERSEY

PRINCETON UNIVERSITY PRESS

1982

Library of Congress Cataloging in Publication Data will be
found on the last printed page of this book

This book has been composed in APS-5 Baskerville
by Science Press, Ephrata, Pennsylvania

Clothbound editions of Princeton University Press books are
printed on acid-free paper, and binding materials are chosen for
strength and durability

Printed in the United States of America by
Princeton University Press, Princeton, New Jersey

THIS BOOK IS DEDICATED TO
Gordon Orians,
who first taught me about selection thinking

AND TO
Dan Bunker,
whose standards of excellence
have proven a most valuable gift.

Contents

Acknowledgments

This book was begun in 1974 when Judith Myers (University of British Columbia) showed me an unpublished manuscript of hers dealing with evolution of the sex ratio. While her monograph was never published, it proved very important in my own work. It introduced me to sex ratio theory and suggested the wealth of data which lay unused in the literature. I disagree (and did in 1974) with many of the conclusions Myers reached, but the debt to her is large and I record it here.

In its initial stages this book was to be a joint effort by Jim Bull and myself. Then it was to consist of two major sections; first, the evolution of sex allocation, and second, the evolution of the sex determining mechanisms themselves. However, it rapidly became obvious that such a venture would be rather too long for a readable single book. For this reason, we have split the book into two. Jim Bull's book, entitled *The Evolution of Sex Determination and Sex Chromosomes*, should appear about a year after this one.

Many people helped during the writing of the book. I thank all who shared not-yet-published work, or who aided my journey through the wilderness we call "the literature." James J. Bull, John Maynard Smith, Steve Stearns, Brian Charlesworth, Deborah Charlesworth, Sam Skinner, Michael Ghiselin, and David Policansky read and commented on the entire manuscript. For comments on one or more chapters I thank Kamal Bawa, Brenda Casper, Carl Freeman, Dennis Crisp, Bill Newman, John Werren, Hans van den Assem, Jeff Waage, Robert Warner, Tim Clutton-Brock, Robert Colwell, and Tony Janetos. I have not always followed their advice, but the book is much improved due to their efforts. Kristen Hawkes gently forced me to expand the introductory chapters to become more representative of the theoretical perspective here called "selection thinking." Georgia Jeppesen provided good humor and a keen eye for mistakes in the manuscript. Kerry Matz drew almost all the figures and Maurine

ix

Vaughan cheerfully typed the many drafts. During most of the writing I was supported by the John Simon Guggenheim Memorial Foundation. The Biology Department of the University of Utah helped pay some of the bills. My own research reported here has occasionally been supported by the National Science Foundation.

For love, support, and for letting me share in her own work with "selection thinking" in psychology, I thank Maureen Ellis.

I am grateful to the following presses, journals, and individuals for permission to use certain material: Annual Reviews Inc. (*Ann. Rev. Ecol. and Syst.*), University of Chicago Press (*Amer. Natur.*), *Quarterly Review of Biology,* American Assn. Adv. Science (*Science*), *Nature,* Academic Press, W. D. Hamilton, D. Policansky, K. Bawa, J. Werren, J. Waage, P. McClure, K. E. Hoagland, J. Bull, R. Warner.

THE THEORY OF
Sex Allocation

CHAPTER ONE

Selection Thinking

This book is about the theory of natural selection applied in critical fashion to the biological problem of sex allocation, the allocation of resources to male versus female reproductive function. The problem will be defined more precisely in Chapter Two. Here I wish to discuss in a general way the use of natural selection as an explanatory principle. In attempting to understand, for example, the distribution of separate versus combined sexes (dioecy versus hermaphroditism), we seek theoretical predictions (e.g., when be a hermaphrodite?) in terms of the reproductive consequences of possible alternative states or the transition between states. In short, we ask when, or under what environmental, social, or life-history conditions natural selection favors one or the other form of sexuality. We test our theory by arranging experiments, geographic or taxonomic comparisons to see if selection acts as we think it does or if the sexuality is matched to the appropriate environmental condition. Thus we seek to understand sexuality in terms of the ultimate causes (the *why* questions) rather than the proximate mechanisms (the physiological *how* questions). Seeking answers to the way in which nature is structured, in terms of *why* questions, I shall term *selection thinking*.

The use of selection thinking begins with Darwin, whose twenty-plus volumes of work abound with it. The modern theory of population genetics, due essentially to Fisher, Haldane, and Wright has been very important, particularly in making more clear and precise how natural selection works and when forces in addition to selection might be important in altering the composition of a population. However, the key reference in selection thinking is undoubtedly the 1966 book by G. C. Williams, entitled

3

Adaptation and Natural Selection. In addition, Williams's 1957 paper on senescence may be taken to be the type specimen for the use of selection to understand a major biological problem. He blends together physiological and environmental constraints on development and life span, pleiotropy of reproductive function, and a precise definition of a soma (e.g., somatic as opposed to germ tissue). These factors are combined with one simple fitness observation to produce a theory of senescence. This observation states that reproduction later in life is worth less (in fitness terms) to an individual simply because the individual is less likely to be alive at the older age. The theory is one of tradeoffs: increased mortality (dysfunction) later in life for enhanced reproduction earlier. The theory is probably correct (Rose and Charlesworth, 1980). Having derived the consequences of his incredibly simple assumptions, Williams then applies the theory to a wide array of biological problems. The insights it provides are simply remarkable. Every student of biology should read the paper.

I use the term selection thinking, rather than adaptation, to emphasize that there is a lot more to the exercise than any simplistic notion that organisms are "designed well" (Gould, 1980). Indeed, the notion of good design itself requires a decision of just what the design is for. Population genetics, with appropriate definitions of fitness, suggests strong constraints as to what selection favors. Furthermore, by considering just how selection works, we are forced to realize that it essentially operates to modify preexisting structures. By doing so, selection may often not favor *A* over *B* simply because the intermediates between the two are not themselves selected for, even if *A* is in some absolute fitness sense better than *B*. A good example is provided by the evolution of livebearing (from egg laying) in reptiles, where selection must first favor the intermediates of longer egg retention in the female's body (Shine and Bull, 1979). We do not simply compare livebearing to egg laying, we ask how selection may act to modify one or the other system. Sometimes considering the process of transition is of key importance.

Probably the easiest example with which to see how selection

4

thinking differs from the simplistic notion of "well-designed organisms" (Gould, 1980) is in the realm of social behavior, where conflict of interest among the participants in an interaction is an essential component of the process. In the late 1940's, David Lack proposed a theory of clutch size applicable mostly to birds. The key idea was that the clutch size would be adjusted to an intermediate value which maximized the number of surviving young produced by the parents. Lack's hypothesis has generated a tremendous amount of research. However, in 1974 Robert Trivers noted that virtually all models for the evolution of life-history attributes (such as clutch size) assigned control to the parent. That is, the distribution of resources among offspring had classically been assumed to evolve to increase or maximize the parents' fitness. He pointed out that if we allow the offspring to control the resources it gets from the mother, selection operates on it to take more than the amount which the parent is selected to give. Thus, parent and offspring disagree over the quantity of resource to be given to the offspring. This perspective on life-history evolution was unknown prior to 1974 and raises many new questions, particularly for organisms, such as birds, with much parental care. Conflict of interest has proven important in understanding many other processes. Examples are male-female relations, animal fighting, and even interactions within an individual (i.e., intragenomic conflict—see Chapter Eight).

There are many other examples of the fruitful use of selection thinking. Recent books include Krebs and Davies (1978), Alexander and Tinkle (1981), and Wittenberger (1981). The first two are edited volumes. John Endler's 1978 monograph on the evolution of animal coloration shows how geographic comparisons (variation in the degree of danger from visually hunting predators) can be turned into a powerful test of selection hypotheses (also Endler, 1982; Reznick and Endler, 1982). His more recent work, using guppies, their predators, and laboratory streams of designated bottom composition, shows how predictable selection can be if the fitness constraints are well understood (Endler, 1980). These references testify to the revolution in biological thought engendered by the careful and deep use of the theory of natural selection, a product of only the last twenty or so years.

In reviewing the literature for this book, I was struck with the almost complete absence of the use of natural selection in viewing many of the phenomena. If any general perspective can be said to have dominated the field of sexuality, it is simply that of proximate mechanisms (e.g., Lepori, 1980). I believe that the best chances for a comprehensive theory lie in the critical use of selection thinking, as called for by Williams (1957, and especially 1966). This book is a first step toward such a theory.

CHAPTER TWO

Introduction
to Sex Allocation

This book is about natural selection and the evolution of *sex allocation*. It has three goals:

(1) To review the major theoretical results for sex allocation, using graphical arguments and basic calculus.
(2) From these results, to derive and test hypotheses on particular biological systems. In general, our tests must be able to exclude alternative hypotheses. By way of example, sex ratio shifts may be due to differential mortality, or to adaptive modification of the sex ratio.
(3) Finally, the book will point to biological systems which may lend themselves well to tests of hypotheses, even if we can give no tests at present.

Let me introduce the problem through a simple classification for forms of sexual reproduction, and five general questions. While certainly not exhaustive, the scheme used here is sufficient for our purposes. Most animal or plant species produce only two types of gametes (large-small). In hermaphroditic organisms, a single individual produces both large and small gametes in its lifetime. In dioecious (=gonochoric) organisms, males and females are separate throughout their lives. Hermaphroditism takes two forms: (1) *Sequential*—an individual functions early in life as one sex and then switches to the other sex for the rest of its life ($♀ \rightarrow ♂$ protogyny; $♂ \rightarrow ♀$ protandry). (2) *Simultaneous*—an individual produces both kinds of gametes in each breeding season (more or less at the same time).

7

In relation to the above scheme, the problem of *sex allocation* may be stated as follows.

(1) For a dioecious species, what is the equilibrium *sex ratio* (proportion of males among the offspring) maintained by natural selection?

(2) For a sequential hermaphrodite, what is the equilibrium *sex order* (male or female first?) and *time of sex change*?

(3) For a simultaneous hermaphrodite, what is the equilibrium allocation of resources to male versus female function in each breeding season?

(4) Under what conditions are the various states of hermaphroditism or dioecy evolutionarily stable? (e.g., when does selection favor genes for protandry over dioecy?) When is a *mixture* of sexual types stable?

(5) When does selection favor the ability of an individual to alter its allocation to male versus female function, in response to particular environmental or life history situations?

These problems are very similar to one another in that each involves working out an equilibrium under natural selection where the possible genotypes have different genetic contributions through male versus female function. Answers to the questions must, of course, consider the biology of the organisms—growth, morphology, mortality, competition (inter- and intra-specific), predation, patchiness in the environment, etc.—as well as possible genetic factors (inbreeding, autosomal versus cytoplasmic inheritance, etc.). These factors will be discussed throughout the book.

What is meant by the phrase, "the problems are very similar to one another," is that all of the five questions are really one question, phrased in different forms. Consider a typical diploid organism. R. A. Fisher (1930) noted the seemingly trivial fact that with respect to autosomal genes, each zygote gets half of its genome from its father, half from its mother. To put it simply: everyone has exactly one father and one mother. However, far from being trivial, this fact holds the key to understanding sex allocation in diploids. It is true regardless of whether we talk of

8

dioecy, simultaneous hermaphroditism, or sequential hermaphroditism. Half the autosomal genes come via male function, half via female. This has two implications. First, an individual's reproductive success through male function (sperm) is to be measured relative to the male function of other individuals (vice versa for female function). Second, since half the zygote genes come via each pathway, male and female function are in a real sense equivalent means to reproductive success. Consider, for example, dioecy and the sex ratio. If many daughters are being produced, then large reproductive gains accrue to the producers of the scarce sons. Selection then favors more sons. An equilibrium will be established where reproductive gains through male and female offspring are equilibrated. Note that the process generates its own natural selection. It is the scarcity of one sex which itself makes increased production of that sex worthwhile. This is frequency dependent natural selection, caused by the fact that everyone has one mother and one father.

The theoretical approach I use solves for a genetic equilibrium in a population. Maynard Smith (1976) has termed the equilibrium value of a trait an "Evolutionarily Stable Strategy (or an ESS)." Suppose we have a population made up of individuals who all have some attribute Z; we introduce into this population a rare genotype with alternative attribute $\hat{Z}$ and see whether the $\hat{Z}$ individuals are selected for or against (i.e., does the rare mutant spread?). If for some character of interest (e.g., primary sex ratio), there exists a Z such that all deviants are selected against, Z is termed an ESS. The classical example is selection on the primary sex ratio (Fisher, 1930) where the ESS is one-half males at conception in the simplest case. Thus a rare genotype producing an altered sex ratio in such a population is selected against. As will be shown, the ESS idea is a very useful way of asking such questions as: at what age do we expect a cohort of protandrous shrimp to change from ♂ to ♀? The answer is: at an age when, under the prevailing demographic and growth conditions, genotypes which switch at some other age contribute less genetic material to future generations. Framed in this way, the tools of population genetics can be used to provide answers and allow us to calculate the appropriate value. It is also possible that the ESS is not a single action (pure strategy) but is some array of actions, each of which takes place with some probability (mixed strategy). Finally, if the environment is nonuniform, the ESS may consist of a set of actions, with a particular one appropriate for a particular patch.

Before discussing some general equilibrium results for sex allocation, let us consider a specific ESS problem, one which very simply illustrates the method of argument. The question is: what sex ratio do we expect to find in a random mated plant population which has two sexual types, one a female, the other a simultaneous hermaphrodite? This population structure is termed *gynodioecious* by botanists, and the sex ratio problem was first considered by Lewis (1941). I will not repeat Lewis's genetic argument here and only note that he showed the equilibrium sex ratio (the ratio of females to hermaphrodites) to be independent of the particular genetic system, provided that fitness was a phenotypic character and inheritance was through nuclear genes. The fitness assumption means that a female's seed set depends upon her being a female and not on the particular genes she carries at the sex determining locus (or loci). As noted by Charnov et al. (1976) and Lloyd (1975a), the equilibrium sex ratio found by Lewis is that value which equalizes the reproductive gains of the two sexual types. To derive this value, we define as follows for discrete generations:

N = population size (very large);

P = proportion of the population which is female in the seed stage;

F_1 = seed set of female (probability of a female living to adulthood times her seed production);

F_2 = seed set for a hermaphrodite.

Let $W♀$, $W⚥$ be the fitness values for females and hermaphrodites respectively, letting fitness be the number of seeds to which an individual contributes genes. It follows that $W♀ = F_1$, while the

10

hermaphrodite's fitness is given by

$$W\hat{\varphi} = F_2 + \text{seeds via pollen for each } \hat{\varphi},$$

$$W\hat{\varphi} = F_2 + \frac{\text{seed set for the population}}{\text{number of } \hat{\varphi} \text{ in population}}.$$

Finally,

$$W\hat{\varphi} = F_2 + \frac{PF_1 + (1 - P)F_2}{(1 - P)}.$$

If we set $W\hat{\varphi} = W\varphi$, and solve for P, we obtain the ESS. The final result is very simple.

$$P/(1 - P) = 1 - 2W, \text{ where } W = F_2/F_1. \tag{2.1}$$

That is, the ratio of females to hermaphrodites is predicted to be a linear, decreasing function of the relative seed sets of the two types. Note how the "one mother, one father" fact entered into the calculation of $W\hat{\varphi}$ and how $W\hat{\varphi}$ thus depended upon P (i.e., fitness was frequency dependent). In equation 2.1, W must be $< \frac{1}{2}$ for P to take on positive values. For $W > \frac{1}{2}$, P must equal zero and no pure females are predicted. $W < \frac{1}{2}$ means that the female has more than double the seed set of the hermaphrodite. It is easy to see why this condition must be met for any females to be present. In a hermaphrodite population, each individual must on average contribute genes to two seed sets, one being its own seed production, the other being the seeds it fertilizes via pollen. If a hermaphrodite turns into a female, it immediately forfeits the seed set it would have gained via pollen. To make up for this loss, the female must at least replace the one seed set. This shows that $W < \frac{1}{2}$ is required for the first, rare morph to be selected to become a female. The female morph will then become more common, until the fitness of the typical hermaphrodite increases (via pollen) to equal the female's fitness. Webb (1981) showed qualitative agreement with this model for thirteen species of New Zealand apioid Umbelliferae (and discussed some added complications).

This example illustrates another attribute of sex allocation. In the calculations of $W\varphi$, $W\hat{\varphi}$, we assumed the inheritance was due to autosomal, nuclear genes. What would happen if the male sterility (=become a female) was inherited via cytoplasmic DNA passed only through eggs? For such a "gene," the male pathway (=sperm, pollen) does not exist. That is, everyone has a mother but no father. Here, selection would favor male sterility provided the female increased her seed set over the seed set of the hermaphrodite (Lewis, 1941). Under random mating, the trait might well spread to fixation resulting in extinction of the population. Clearly, there is *conflict of interest* between nuclear and maternally transmitted DNA over the prospect of being a female. The nuclear DNA requires at least a doubling of seed set, while cytoplasmic DNA requires only a very small increase in seed set. We might then expect to find a complex interaction over sex determination between these two types of DNA. Indeed, cytoplasmic inheritance of male sterilty is not uncommon in plants, and is usually found associated with nuclear genes (called "restorer genes") which "combat" the cytoplasmic genes to reinstate pollen production. Such systems are well studied in corn and sunflowers (e.g., Beard, 1981), where the cytoplasmic genes are managed for economic gain by the growers. Other conflict situations within sex allocation theory include worker-queen conflict over sex ratio in haplodiploid eusocial insects (Trivers and Hare, 1976) and sex chromosome–autosome conflict for sex ratio in diploids (Shaw, 1958; Hamilton, 1967). Some of these will be discussed later in the book.

Having posed the question of sex allocation in terms of diploids, where the one mother, one father theorem is easy to see, I will now hedge somewhat. In haplodiploid species males are haploid and females diploid. A male's sperm carries only the chromosomes inherited from its mother, whether or not there is fertilization of eggs destined to be males (Bull, 1979). Probably the most common situation is that found in Hymenoptera, where unfertilized, haploid eggs become males. Clearly, the diploid genes of the mother are not passed equally through grandchildren. To calculate the ESS sex ratio for such a situation we are forced to write population genetic equations, asking for a sex ratio such that a

12

mutant gene (affecting sex ratio) is selected against (but see Stubblefield, 1980, for an alternative approach). Hartl and Brown (1970) showed, however, that a frequency dependence very similar to the diploid situation also holds for haplodiploidy. The system is essentially one where the entire nuclear genome of the female is sex linked. She is the homogametic sex (XX). The sex ratio evolves as if the genes affecting it are all X-linked and only operate in the homogametic sex. Sex ratio ESS's for such a system are usually very close to those which would result from the corresponding assumption of diploidy and autosomal control (Hamilton, 1979, or Figure 5.1). For this reason, we shall often assume an autosomal model, which will be easier to develop, even when dealing with haplodiploidy.

I began this introduction with the suggestion that our five questions were really one question. This section expands on that notion. Again, it is useful to provide a simple example. This example is the first formal treatment of sex ratio evolution for diploids, from an early paper by Shaw and Mohler (1953). While R. A. Fisher (1930) clearly was the pathbreaker in sex ratio theory, Shaw and Mohler (1953) provide a very elegant discussion and, to my knowledge, the first explicit use of an ESS argument. Their method will be used throughout the book, and their basic sex ratio equation will be generalized to include most (diploid) sex allocation problems. The beauty of their argument is its utter simplicity. Consider a population of N reproductive females of a dioecious species with discrete generations. Each of these females will produce C eggs, a proportion r of them being sons. Suppose that a proportion S_m of the sons and S_f of the daughters survive to breed. Introduce into this population a single mutant female, who alters her sex ratio to $\hat{r}$. The question of interest is: will this female contribute *more* or *fewer* genes to the next generation, contrasted to a typical female in the population? Suppose that the population of reproductive adults, who are the offspring of our original $N+1$ females, themselves produce a total of K children (the grand-children of the original females). Half of the genes in these grandchildren came via males, half via females. Our mutant

13

female (here called "mom") will thus contribute genes to the following number of grandchildren through her sons:

$(\frac{1}{2})$ · (number of grandchildren)

· (proportion of reproductive males who are mom's sons).

(We multiply by $\frac{1}{2}$ since half the genes passed by mom's children did not come from her; they came from her mate, the children's father.) To write the above in symbols:

$$= \frac{1}{2}(K) \left[\frac{S_m\, C\, \hat{r}}{S_m\, C\, \hat{r} + N\, S_m\, C\, r} \right]. \tag{2.2}$$

The same argument obtains through her daughters:

$$= \frac{1}{2}(K) \left[\frac{S_f\, C\, (1 - \hat{r})}{S_f\, C\, (1 - \hat{r}) + N\, S_f\, C\, (1 - r)} \right]. \tag{2.3}$$

Finally, adding (2.2) and (2.3) gives us the total representation of mom's genes in grandchildren, her total fitness, W_t.

Provided N is large, this sum will be approximated well by

$$W_t = \frac{1}{2}(K) \left[\frac{S_f\, C\, (1 - \hat{r})}{N\, S_f\, C\, (1 - r)} + \frac{S_m\, C\, \hat{r}}{N\, S_m\, C\, r} \right]. \tag{2.4}$$

Before looking at the implications of equation. 2.4, let us first generalize the result. Define:

$\hat{m}$ = surviving sons from mom;

m = surviving sons from each additional female;

$\hat{f}$ = surviving daughters from mom;

f = same from other females.

With these in mind, W_t may be generally written as

$$W_t = (\frac{1}{2}) \left(\frac{K}{N} \right) \left(\frac{\hat{m}}{m} + \frac{\hat{f}}{f} \right), \tag{2.5}$$

or

$$W_t \propto \frac{\hat{m}}{m} + \frac{\hat{f}}{f}. \tag{2.6}$$

Equation 2.6 is the general form of the *Shaw-Mohler equation for*

14

sex ratio (and was first derived by MacArthur, 1965). Shaw and Mohler (1953) worked with equation 2.4, to which we now return. The $\frac{1}{2}(K/N)$ is simply a proportionality factor and the equation may be written as (canceling S_m, S_f, and C):

$$W_t \propto \frac{\hat{r}}{r} + \frac{(1 - \hat{r})}{1 - r}. \qquad (2.7)$$

But this is simply a linear equation in $\hat{r}$.

If mom is the same as all other females, $\hat{r} = r$ and equation 2.7 (where we simply replace $\propto$ with $=$) is equal to 2. Mom contributes more genes (than the average female) to grandchildren if $W_t > 2$. In Figure 2.1, I have graphed W_t as a function of $\hat{r}$ for two assumed r values, namely, $r = \frac{1}{4}$ or $\frac{3}{4}$. If $r = \frac{1}{4}$, W_t is a line with positive slope and all $\hat{r} > \frac{1}{4}$ have $W_t > 2$. That is, selection favors females who produce more sons. If $r = \frac{3}{4}$, the reverse

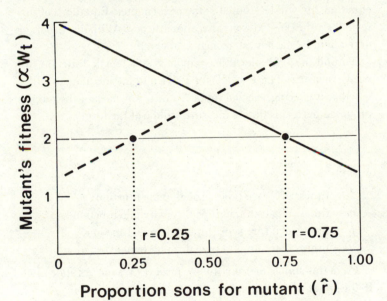

FIGURE 2.1. Fitness (W_t, equation 2.7) for a mutant female is plotted as a function of her sex ratio ($\hat{r}$) for two population sex ratios ($r = 0.25, 0.75$). She has the same fitness ($W_t = 2$) as a typical female when $\hat{r} = r$. The mutant is favored by selection if $W_t > 2$. For $r < 0.5$, $\hat{r} > r$ is favored (the reverse for $r > 0.5$). The ESS is $r = \frac{1}{2}$.

obtains and females with $\hat{r} < \frac{3}{4}$ are more fit. With reference to equation 2.7, if $r > \frac{1}{2}$, mothers are favored who produce an $\hat{r}$ smaller then r; for $r < \frac{1}{2}$ mothers are favored who produce an $\hat{r} > r$. In this way, selection moves the sex ratio toward $\frac{1}{2}$. If $r = \frac{1}{2}$, W_t does not change with $\hat{r}$. This is the ESS sex ratio. From this biological argument follows a surprising prediction. Note that r (or $\hat{r}$) is the sex ratio near or at conception and that the survival rates to adulthood (S_m, S_f) cancel out of the argument. That is, differential survival to adulthood for sons versus daughters does not alter the ESS primary sex ratio away from equality, at least in this simple situation. Nor does the mating system (monogamy versus polygamy) affect the result, since the arguments remain the same under each.

I have carried out this calculation in some detail because it is a prototype of many in the book. The more general sex ratio, equation 2.6, will be studied in the next chapter. Equations of this form are the key to sex allocation theory. Without proof or derivation, let me now state a general result.

To find the ESS allocation to male versus female function, we need a measure of fitness (W_t) for a rare mutant adequate to tell us whether it is being selected for or against. For most of the models proposed here, this fitness measure will be of the form

$$W_t = \frac{\hat{m}}{m} + \frac{\hat{f}}{f}, \qquad (2.8)$$

where

$\hat{m}$ = fitness of a rare type through male function;
m = fitness of a common type through male function;
$\hat{f}$ = fitness of a rare type through female function;
f = fitness of a common type through female function.

From this simple measure follow most results for sex allocation. If the mutant is identical to the common type $(\hat{m} = m, \hat{f} = f)$, $W_t = 2$; we may assign the common type a fitness of 2. The mutant is selected against if $W_t < 2$. The mutant is favored if $W_t > 2$, that is, if $\hat{m}/m + \hat{f}/f > 2$. If we write $\hat{m} = m + \Delta m$, $\hat{f} = f + \Delta f$, the rule becomes

$$\frac{\Delta m}{m} + \frac{\Delta f}{f} > 0, \qquad (2.9)$$

or (in words): *Selection favors a mutant gene which alters various life history parameters if the percent gain in fitness through one sex function exceeds the percent loss through the other sex function.*

This rule allows us to find the ESS allocation. Since Shaw and Mohler (1953) were the first to study equations of form (2.8), this book will designate that form *the Shaw-Mohler equation,* regardless of the sex allocation problem under consideration.

There is an alternative way to write this ESS result, at least for situations where there is no within-sex frequency dependence (Charnov, 1979a). It is very often the case that the ESS allocation of resources to male versus female function is that which maximizes the product of the fitness gain through male function (e.g., sons, pollen, time spent as a male) times the gain through female function (daughters, seeds, time as a female). Or, more simply: *selection maximizes m · f.* Actually, the principle proposed here is that selection will act to maximize $m \cdot f$, both in the choice of sexual states (e.g., hemaphroditism versus dioecy) and in the allocation to male versus female function within a sexual state. This product result will be discussed many times in the book. For example, Chapter Three shows how it may imply conditions where the ESS sex ratio consists of a mixture of two kinds of families (see Figure 3.6). Chapters Nine and Fourteen discuss it in relation to the stability of hermaphroditism versus dioecy. As noted above, some situations having within-sex frequency dependence of fitness values may not yield a product maximization in equilibrium. Chapter Eleven discusses an example from sex reversal in fish. In this case, we use the basic Shaw-Mohler (or equivalent) result, equation 2.8.

It will be useful here to apply the product theorem to a particular case, that of sex ratio under gynodioecy (equation 2.1). As previously defined, P is the proportion of the population which is female, and W is the fitness through female function (= seeds) of a hermaphrodite relative to a female. The female fitness (f) of

17

a typical (average) individual is $f = P + (1 - P)$ W. The male fitness (m) of a typical individual is $P \cdot 0 + (1 - P)1$ or $m = 1 - P$. We multiply the P by zero since females have no male fitness. Male fitness for a hermaphrodite is set equal to one, as hermaphrodites are the only male type present. If we form the $m \cdot f$ product, the rule is: choose P to maximize

$$[P + (1 - P)W] (1 - P). \tag{2.10}$$

Since W does not change with P, differentiation of equation 2.10 with respect to P shows the maximum to be when $P/(1 - P) = 1 - 2W$. This is again equation 2.1, now derived through the optimization principle.

In short, this book is mostly about biological predictions which follow from the Shaw-Mohler equation, or (very often) the equivalent result, a product theorem. I divide the work into three major sections. Since sex ratio is the classic question, I deal with it first. The next two sections treat sequential and simultaneous hermaphroditism, respectively. The organization is both conceptual and taxonomic, as there is simply no linear path through this body of knowledge. The outline for each section is laid out at its beginning. The final chapter considers possible future directions, in light of all the previous chapters. There are very few formal population genetic models (see Appendix). Most of the arguments are similar to the three examples provided in this introduction.

Dioecy and Sex Allocation

This section analyzes sex ratio evolution in dioecious organisms. The question of when dioecy is favored over various forms of hermaphroditism is deferred until Chapters Nine and Fourteen. The first chapter (Chapter Three) uses the simple Shaw-Mohler equation to look at sex ratio with discrete generations. The next two chapters introduce the complexities of individual differences in opportunities to rear sons versus daughters, and spatial population structure. Both these chapters retain the assumption of discrete generations. The next chapter (Chapter Six) introduces age structure to the life history. The final two chapters depart somewhat from the conceptual approach of the previous four. Chapter Seven briefly reviews sex ratio in vertebrates, while Chapter Eight considers some of the better-known examples of conflict situations for the sex ratio. All chapters discuss both theory and data.

CHAPTER THREE:

Sex Ratio
and Discrete Generations

This chapter does three things. First, I show how the Shaw-Mohler equation implies that the $m \cdot f$ product is maximized at the ESS. Second, I discuss the classic model of R. A. Fisher (1930) for the sex ratio. Third will be a discussion of a simple model for the sex ratio, proposed by Maynard Smith (1980). This model explicitly includes physiological limitations on the parent's ability to control the sex ratio, and suggests how to begin to incorporate such factors into our models. Both examples illustrate the product theorem.

I begin by examining some consequences of the Shaw-Mohler equation for sex ratio. The formal derivation of this equation for diploid or haplodiploid populations is in the Appendix. Recall that if we have a population with discrete generations, made up of individuals who rear on average m sons and f daughters (counted when the children are adults), selection will favor a mutant individual who produces a family with composition $\hat{m}, \hat{f}$ if and only if $W_t > 2$ where

$$W_t = \frac{\hat{m}}{m} + \frac{\hat{f}}{f}. \tag{3.1}$$

This equation contains a great deal of information, since the relations between m and f (or $\hat{m}, \hat{f}$) involve sex ratio, investment of resources in sons versus daughters, survivorship of offspring to adulthood, and other details. Suppose that we can represent the tradeoff between m and f (or $\hat{m}, \hat{f}$) as in Figure 3.1. We shall call this tradeoff a *fitness set* (Levins, 1968).

W_t may be used in the following way. In Figure 3.1, assume the population to be at m_0, f_0. To know if some other $\hat{m}, \hat{f}$ will be selected for, we ask if $\hat{m}/m_0 + \hat{f}/f_0$ has a value greater or less than 2. The equation of a line, with slope e, through any point x_0, y_0 is $y - y_0 = e(x - x_0)$. Through the point (m_0, f_0) draw a straight line with slope $- f_0/m_0$. Denote all points on this line as $\hat{m}, \hat{f}$. This line has the equation $\hat{m}/m_0 + \hat{f}/f_0 = 2$. All points above the line make $\hat{m}/m_0 + \hat{f}/f_0 > 2$; all points below make W_t less than 2. In Figure 3.1, construction of this line for the population values (m_0,

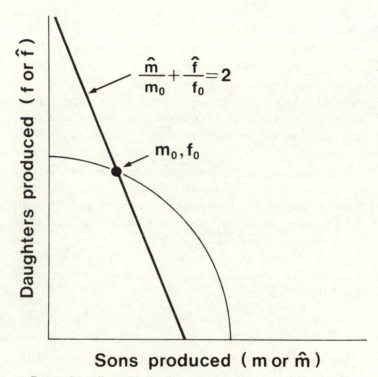

Sons produced (m or m̂)

FIGURE 3.1. All possible family compositions can be represented as a tradeoff between sons produced $(m, \hat{m})$ and daughters produced $(f, \hat{f})$. We guess some value (m_0, f_0) to be the ESS. This can be checked by constructing a line through m_0, f_0 with slope minus f_0/m_0. This line has equation $\hat{m}/m_0 + \hat{f}/f_0 = 2$, or $W_t = 2$ all along it. All points above the line have $W_t > 2$ and represent families which would be selected for in a population of mostly m_0, f_0. In this figure, with the population assumed to be at m_0, f_0, families with more sons are selected for.

f_0) shows that male-biased families (i.e., on the curve below m_0, f_0) fall to the outside of the line, and are selected for. Now, in Figure 3.2, the population values (m_0, f_0) are shifted toward males. Here, construction of the W_t line shows that families with greater female composition are selected for. In Figure 3.3, at some more intermediate family composition, no points on the tradeoff (or fitness) set fall to the outside of the line; thus this (m_0, f_0) is the ESS. I denote these values as m^*, f^*. Here, the slope of the tradeoff curve ($\partial f^*/\partial m^*$) is equal to the slope of the line ($-f^*/m^*$), or $\partial f^*/\partial m^* = -f^*/m^*$. *At this point $m^* \cdot f^*$ is maximized.* This geometrical argument also shows that if the population is not at

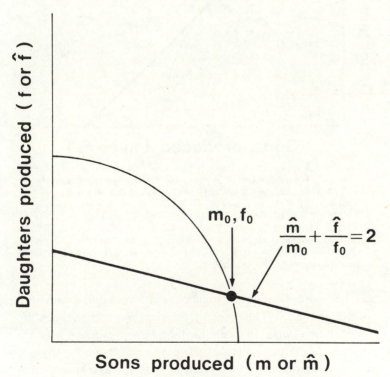

$$\frac{\hat{m}}{m_0} + \frac{\hat{f}}{f_0} = 2$$

FIGURE 3.2. In this figure (contrasted to Fig. 3.1) we guess the ESS family composition to be relatively male- (son-) biased (m_0, f_0). Construction of the $W_t = 2$ line shows that, in a population with families of mostly m_0, f_0, families more daughter-biased are selected for.

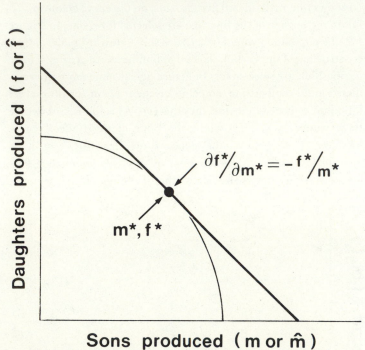

FIGURE 3.3. The tradeoff (fitness set) between sons and daughters is the same as in Figures 3.1 and 3.2. We guess the ESS family composition to be m^*, f^*. Here, construction of the $W_t = 2$ line shows that no points on the fitness set fall to the outside of the $W_t = 2$ line. Thus, in a population of mostly m^*, f^*, all other family compositions are selected against. If the fitness set is *convex* (bowed out), only one family (m^*, f^*) will be the ESS. If the population is not at m^*, f^*, selection favors families (Figs. 3.2 and 3.1) which move it toward m^*, f^*. The ESS values are such that $m^* \cdot f^*$ is maximized, or $\partial f^*/\partial m^* = -f^*/m^*$.

the ESS, selection favors mutants who move the population toward the ESS. This product theorem was first devised by MacArthur (1965). In plain English: *In a population at ESS, selection favors those females who control their clutch size, sex ratio, and allocation of resources among offspring so as to maximize the m · f product.*

The tradeoff curves in Figures 3.1–3.3 are *convex* (bowed outwards, Fig. 14.1). If the curve is *concave* (Fig. 3.4), application

24

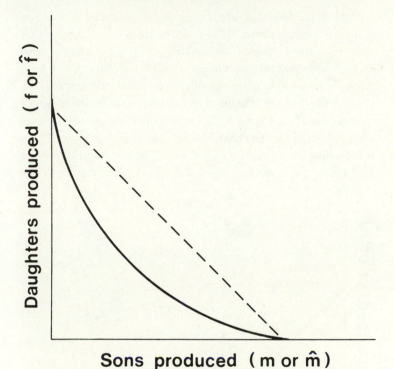

Daughters produced (f or f̂)

Sons produced (m or m̂)

FIGURE 3.4. If the fitness set is *concave* (bowed in), application of our geometrical argument (the $W_t = 2$ line) will lead to the conclusion that no single family composition is an ESS. However, the argument may be extended to include ESS's which consist of a mixture of two or more types of families. The dashed line shows a population which consists of a mixture of all-son, all-daughter families. Such a population may be anywhere on the line, depending upon the frequency of the two types. By considering populations which are mixtures, we may construct a new fitness set. It is easy to see that the boundary of this new set will here be the dashed line; that is, all other combinations of families will fall to the inside of the dashed line.

of this geometrical argument will lead to the result that there is no single family composition which is an ESS. However, suppose that our population consists of several kinds of families, each with offspring (m_i, f_i), in proportion h_i ($\Sigma h_i = 1$). The m in equation 3.1 is the average son production (i.e., $m = \Sigma h_i m_i$) and f the average daughter production. Our mutant is assumed to alter the

25

(m_i, f_i) or h_i. Selection now favors the *combination* of families which maximizes the $m \cdot f$ product (or $[\Sigma m_i h_i] \cdot [\Sigma f_i h_i]$). This conclusion also emerged from Speith's (1974) study and has been derived independently by Green (1982). In Figure 3.4, I have drawn a line between two families—all males, all females. All possible family combinations must fall within the boundary given by this line. Thus, Figure 3.5 is a new tradeoff set, which includes all possible (m, f). We can treat it just like the other tradeoff sets, constructing the $\hat{m}/m_0 + \hat{f}/f_0 = 2$ line. The end result is that the ESS consists of a mixture of all-son, all-daughter families. The

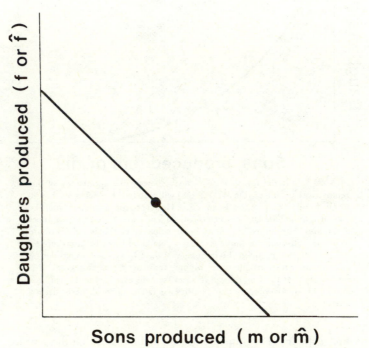

Sons produced (m or m̂)

FIGURE 3.5. This fitness set is the same as the dashed line of Figure 3.4. It represents various combinations of all-son, all-daughter families. We find the ESS (m^*, f^*—here represented as a dot) by the usual $W_t = 2$ argument. The ESS consists of half all-daughter families, half all-son families. It is the value which maximizes (hm) $(1 - h)f$ where $h =$ proportion all-son families (and m, f here refer to the offspring of such families). This maximizes $h(1 - h)$, or $h = \frac{1}{2}$.

26

frequency of each family is 0.5. More complex fitness sets may be treated the same way: turn the set into a convex set by drawing lines between points at the outside. Treat this new set just like the other; if the product maximization falls on the line connecting two families, the ESS is a mixture. An example is given in Figure 3.6.

The product theorem for sex ratio is a general statement about what selection favors at equilibrium, from the viewpoint of the

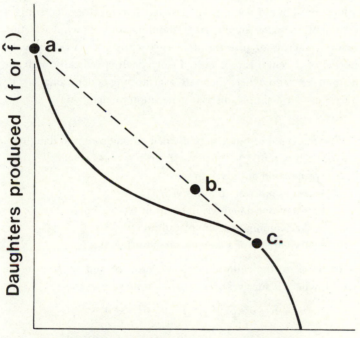

Sons produced (m or m̂)

FIGURE 3.6. A fitness set which is made up of concave and convex parts. In order to find the ESS, we connect points at the boundary of the set to form a new boundary which is a combination of convex and/or linear parts. Here we connect points a and c. We treat this new fitness set (= new boundary) in the same way as the old (i.e., the $W_t = 2$ argument, or maximize $m^* \cdot f^*$) to find the ESS. Here the ESS is at point b and implies a population which is a mixture of all-daughter families (point a) and families with the composition of point c.

27

mother (or the father). In order to use it to make biological predictions, the m-f tradeoff must be specified. Here I consider two special cases.

FISHER'S SEX RATIO MODEL

In 1930 R. A. Fisher proposed that natural selection would favor females who allocated equal resources to sons versus daughters. He further stated that differential, sex-specific mortality after the period of parental care would not influence this favored allocation. He did not specify: (i) what parental resources might consist of, (ii) what an offspring "should" cost (i.e., what selection favors in terms of investment in each child), or (iii) when the period of parental care is over. Fisher dealt specifically with the human sex ratio, where there are overlapping generations. Let us here consider a simple, discrete generation model.

Let

R = maternal resource to be divided among sons and daughters (for each parent);
q = proportion of r given to sons;
C_1 = cost of one son, in terms of R;
C_2 = cost of one daughter, in terms of R;
S_m = survivorship of a son to adulthood;
S_f = survivorship of a daughter to adulthood;

In this case the child is given its resource and set free in the world, where it survives at the appropriate rate. Now,

$$m = R \cdot q \cdot S_m/C_1, \quad f = R \cdot (1 - q) \cdot S_f/C_2,$$

or

$$m \cdot f = \frac{R^2 \cdot S_m \cdot S_f}{C_1 \cdot C_2} \cdot q(1 - q). \tag{3.2}$$

If S_m, S_f, C_1, and C_2 do not interact with q, then equation 3.2 becomes $m \cdot f \propto q(1 - q)$ which is maximized at $q = \frac{1}{2}$, or when equal resources are expended on sons versus daughters.

Where there is a linear tradeoff between the production of a son and a daughter, Fisher's theory is exact. Equal resources are to be invested in each sex, and the survivorship to adulthood (S_m, S_f) cancels out of the final answer. The primary sex ratio here is $r = C_2/(C_1 + C_2)$, or

$$\frac{r}{1 - r} = \frac{C_2}{C_1}. \tag{3.3}$$

In words this is

$$\frac{\text{number of sons}}{\text{number of daughters}} = \frac{\text{cost of one daughter}}{\text{cost of one son}}.$$

This model $(C_1 \neq C_2)$ is the simplest notion of sons and daughters being of unequal cost. Of course, there are other possibilities (Table 3.1 presents three). If one sex dies faster during the period of parental care, it is likely the "cheaper sex"

TABLE 3.1. Three interpretations of Fisher's (1930) concept that sons and daughters may be of unequal cost.

A son may cost less because . . .	Notes
(i) It requires less food than a daughter, and food limits the clutch size produced.	Mother and father agree on sex ratio, offspring disagrees with both (Trivers, 1974).
(ii) They die faster during the period of parental care, freeing resources for their sisters.	Same as above; sex ratio should be male biased early, but female biased near weaning.
(iii)* One (or a few) offspring is born at a time and a son imposes a smaller mortality or growth decrement upon its mother.	Mother wants more sons, but age reversal of the sex ratio ($\delta \rightarrow \female$) is predicted. Father's ESS sex ratio is equality, with no age effect. Offspring's ESS lies between the parents'.

*This model includes age structure and is developed in Chapter Six.

29

and more of it should be born, because a death during this period frees resources for investment in other offspring. The key idea is that of substitution cost. If a mother forfeits attempting to rear one daughter, how many sons can she produce? In the simple model, the answer is C_2/C_1. She can have one daughter, or C_2/C_1 sons. Sons and daughters are of unequal cost if they do not substitute one for one. It is a general result that selection favors overproduction of the cheaper sex, where cheaper is defined in terms of substitution cost. Various authors have considered discrete generation versions of Fisher's idea (Verner, 1965; Crow and Kimura,

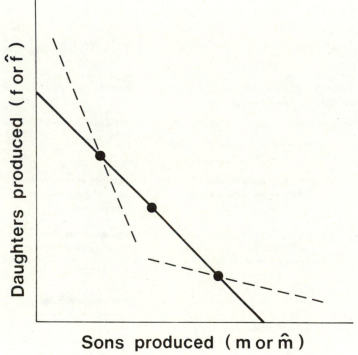

FIGURE 3.7. If the fitness set is linear, application of the $W_t = 2$ argument (dotted lines) produces a somewhat peculiar result. If the population is not at ESS, selection most strongly favors families made up solely of the sex in short supply. At ESS (center dot) the fitness set and the $W_t = 2$ line are the same. This suggests that any combination of families which average this ESS value is stable. However, as discussed in the text, a single family, which itself produces a mixture, is really the most likely ESS.

30

1970; Kolman, 1960; Bodmer and Edwards, 1960; Charnov, 1978) where substitution cost (or compensation for lost offspring) defines one sex to be cheaper.

Probably the vast majority of dioecious organisms invests equal resources in a son or a daughter; here the sex ratio is predicted to be ½ at fertilization. However, there is a deeper issue here. Consider Figure 3.7 where the son-daughter tradeoff is linear. If we repeat the W_t argument for this case we find that if the sex ratio is not ½, females are most favored who produce broods consisting only of the sex in short supply. But if the sex ratio is ½, it makes no difference what an individual female does, for all points on the tradeoff surface (fitness set) have $W_t = 2$. This suggests that the theory says something about the population sex ratio, but nothing about what an individual female should do (Williams, 1979). Thus, the ESS could be achieved in innumerable ways so long as the balance is half sons (for theoretical examples, see Shaw, 1958). However, there appear to be few examples in nature of balances achieved other than by an individual producing a mixed brood (e.g., XY-XX sex chromosome system). I think that this is basically for two reasons. First, individuals producing an equal sex ratio (at least on average) are probably favored in almost any finite population (e.g., Verner, 1965; Taylor and Sauer, 1980). That is, violation of the assumption of an infinite population will often reduce the EES to being an individual's strategy, rather than a population-wide balance. Second, the development of an individual into a male or a female is usually determined by genes carried by the individual in question. It is hard to think of a genetic system (except for haplodiploidy) that both meets this condition and generates equal numbers of all-son and all-daughter producing mothers.

MAYNARD SMITH'S SEX RATIO MODEL

As the Fisher example shows, use of the product theorem to calculate an ESS requires that one first assume some things about the possible tradeoff in family composition. These are assumptions about the factors under maternal control (e.g., her options to replace lost offspring, the cost to her in doing so, and so forth). For example, if the sex of the offspring cannot be controlled at conception, the parent may be limited to control at some later time. Maynard Smith (1980) has considered cases where the sex ratio is fixed at one-half at conception but where the parent has the option of disposing of a few offspring later on or investing more in one sex after conception. Some of his models involve a type of frequency dependence which makes the product theorem invalid (however, the ESS can be calculated from the Shaw-Mohler equation), so here I consider only the simplest case.

Suppose that the primary sex ratio is fixed at one-half and that it costs the mother some time and resource before she can know the sex of an offspring. At this instant she can rear the child or abort it. If she rears a son, it will cost her β additional units of resource, compared to one unit for a daughter ($\beta \geq 1$). The resource per offspring prior to identification of sex is α. Thus, each son reared to independence costs $\alpha + \beta$, while each daughter costs $\alpha + 1$. Let the total resource available be R units. Finally, let q_m proportion of the males be reared, and all of the daughters (since they are the cheaper sex, the ESS is to rear all of them). The number of sons and daughters reared will thus be:

m = (sons at conception) · (proportion reared)

f = (daughters at conception).

If C offspring are conceived, $C/2$ are sons ($C/2$ are daughters). This makes

$$m = \frac{C \cdot q_m}{2}, \quad f = \frac{C}{2} \text{ or } m \cdot f = \frac{C^2 \cdot q_m}{4}. \tag{3.4}$$

However, if all the resource (R) is used up,

$$R = C\alpha + (C/2)(q_m \cdot \beta + 1).$$

If we solve this for $C \cdot q_m/2$, and substitute into equation 3.4,

$$m \cdot f = \frac{C^2 \cdot q_m}{4} \propto \frac{q_m}{(2\alpha + q_m \cdot \beta + 1)^2}. \tag{3.5}$$

32

To maximize this with respect to q_m, we look at $\partial\log(m \cdot f)/\partial q_m$. There are two cases:

Case 1:

$\beta\text{-}1 < 2\alpha \rightarrow q_m = 1$; rear all sons.

Case 2:

$\beta\text{-}1 > 2\alpha \rightarrow q_m = \dfrac{1 + 2\alpha}{\beta}$; rear only some of the sons.

If β is small or α large, all offspring should be reared. Otherwise not all of the more expensive sex should be reared. The total resource invested in sons (versus daughters) is q. It follows that:

$$\frac{q}{1 - q} = \frac{\alpha + q_m \cdot \beta}{\alpha + 1} .$$

In the first case,

$$q_m = 1, \text{ and } q = \frac{\beta + \alpha}{\beta + 2\alpha + 1}.$$

In the second case,

$$q = \tfrac{1}{2}\left(\frac{1 + 3\alpha}{1 + 2\alpha}\right).$$

In both cases $q \geq \frac{1}{2}$. Only if there is no identification cost ($\alpha = 0$) or if sons and daughters are of equal cost ($\beta = 1$) does $q = \frac{1}{2}$. Figure 3.8 shows the ESS q for various costs for a son (β) and sex identification costs (α). It is somewhat surprising how little q departs from a half, even under relatively high α values. For example, the highest q possible for $\alpha = 0.3$ (i.e., identification costs are ~25% the total cost of a daughter) is $q = 0.59$, still fairly close to one-half.

These examples from Fisher and Maynard Smith illustrate how to use the product theorem to make testable biological predictions. I now consider data relative to Fisher's prediction of overinvestment in the cheaper sex.

33

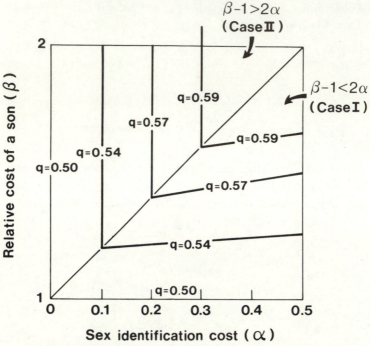

FIGURE 3.8. In Maynard Smith's sex ratio model, a certain quantity of resource (α) must be expended on an offspring before its sex can be identified. At that point the offspring can be destroyed or reared. Sex ratio at conception is equality. A son reared costs β additional units of resource, a daughter one unit. Total cost of a reared son is $\alpha + \beta$, a daughter $1 + \alpha$. In Case I, all sons are reared; in Case II, only some are. All daughters are reared. The symbol q represents the proportion of total resource given to sons (detailed discussion in text). If $\beta > 1$, $q > 0.5$, but q does not depart far from 0.5 even for fairly high sex identification costs (α).

ON TESTING SEX RATIO THEORY

This section discusses some aspects of testing sex ratio hypotheses, and uses data on free-living bees and wasps to test one prediction from Fisher's theory. For two reasons, I do not attempt an exhaustive review of sex ratios in nature. First, it would be impossible. Second, it would be mostly fruitless. Testing hypotheses about the sex ratio requires knowledge of population structure, forms of sex ratio control, differential mortality by sex, and so forth; few sex ratio studies provide these data and thus their results are mostly null. Wildish (1974) provides a bibliography of studies on invertebrate sex ratios. Most papers refer to adult sex ratios and question the extent of deviation from equality. While this reference, and the review by Anderson (1961) are useful as compilations of the literature, they provide little which will really help us test the theory. The exception is that, as predicted by Fisher's original hypothesis with sons and daughters of equal cost, primary (or near so) sex ratios are usually near equality. Strong deviations are most often associated with special population structure, or the implication of conflict situations (e.g., cytoplasm or sex-linked meiotic drive).

This chapter, and those to follow, provide theoretical tools for calculating, at least qualitatively, the ESS sex ratio under a wide variety of conditions. The key to testing the theory is now to ask if the special conditions do result in the appropriate sex ratio, and conversely, if observed sex ratios go along with the appropriate conditions. It is often the case that hypotheses are posed in terms of the direction of deviation from equality. I note here that rejection of the hypothesis of equality requires large samples, since the binomial variance is greatest near a half. My discussion will focus on systems well enough known to be used as tests, or provocative enough to warrant closer looks.

The simplest form of Fisher's hypothesis is that a son and daughter cost different amounts simply because each is given a different quantity of some limiting resource, such as energy. Then the ratio of sons to daughters is predicted to be the inverse ratio of their cost (equation 3.3). If a son costs 10 calories and a daughter 20, then two sons should be produced for each daughter. Organisms which approximate these simple assumptions are nonsocial bees and wasps where the mother excavates a hole (a cell) in the ground, puts an egg plus food (bees = nectar and pollen; wasps = insect prey) in the cell, seals it, and begins another cell. Often, sons are given smaller quantities of food than daughters. However, recall that the relative son/daughter cost (the substitution cost) is related to how many sons can be produced if one less daughter is

35

produced. Cell construction and the gathering of larval food both cost time. While differing food provisions for sons versus daughters most likely reflect differences in their cost to the mother, the amount of this difference is not likely to be simply related to the ratio of two provisions. Trivers and Hare (1976) examined data for 15 species of free-living bees and wasps. Male-biased sex ratios (at emergence) were found in 11, approximate equality in 3, and a female-biased ratio in 1. Of the 11, 10 had adult females larger in body size than males; 1 had the reverse. Of the 4 left, 3 had females larger than males. Probably the most useful comparison is among the 13 species with females larger than males. Ten of these had male-biased sex ratios (here taken to be proportion males > 0.52) while three had ratios not male biased. Of course, sample sizes varied between species, and the weight ratios were often based on small samples. However, the occurrence of male-biased sex ratios along with small males is still striking, particularly considering the rarity of male-biased sex ratios in haplodiploid organisms in general.

A ground nesting bee, *Osmia excavata* had the largest sample size (~ 3000 emerging individuals), a ratio of sons to daughters of 1.69, and a daughter to son weight ratio of 1.5. W. P. Stephen (per. comm.) has provided me with similar data for the ground nesting bee, *Nomia melanderi*. With adults of equal size, the sex ratio at emergence was equality. Trivers and Hare (1976) also showed sex ratio equality for this species, but their weight ratio had the females considerably larger than males ($\times$ 1.4). These data strongly support the prediction of overproduction of the cheaper sex.

CHAPTER FOUR

Sex Ratio
When Fitness Varies—Spatial and
Physiological Correlates

This chapter introduces the idea of facultative sex ratio, the alteration of son or daughter production in response to particular environmental conditions. The idea that the sex of the resulting offspring might be related to some aspect of the parents' condition, broadly defined, is an old notion (e.g., parents of high vigor will have daughters). I know of at least three books (in English) between 1880 and 1920 that discuss this idea (Dawson, 1917; Starkweather, 1883; Schenk, 1898). The problem they consider is the actual determination of the offspring's sex, rather than the sex of the offspring reared (a sex ratio shift). Thus, the egg was thought to develop into a male or a female depending upon the parents' physical vigor. Most of their discussion no longer makes sense (Parkes, 1971), but it might prove interesting to reexamine some of their claims, in light of the evolutionary theory discussed here.

Trivers and Willard (1973) initiated a natural selection approach to facultative sex ratios. They envisioned a mammal population where the females vary in physiological condition and where the mother's condition affects the reproductive abilities of the offspring; i.e., sons and daughters produced by females in poor condition will themselves be less than average reproducers. Offspring from mothers in good condition will be above-average reproducers. Thus, both sons and daughters gain by being reared by a mother in good condition. However, Trivers and Willard argued for polygynous mammals that a son should gain relatively more than a daughter by being in good condition because a male's reproductive success depends more on its condition relative to the other males. From this argument they concluded that *mothers in good condition should produce more sons, those in poorer condition should produce more daughters.*

Of course, the prediction requires that the mother have some measure of control over the sex she will rear. The degree of parental control will probably be of much importance. For example, if the sex ratio cannot be altered except by changing the clutch size, the predicted response will be different compared to when clutch size and sex ratio can be changed independently. Overinvestment in one sex could also involve the resource per individual with no alteration in the sex ratio itself. The key idea here is the relative gain through the production of males by healthy mothers. While the supporting data of Trivers and Willard (1973) have been challenged by Myers (1978), the basic idea is valid. This idea—that the allocation of resources to male versus female function (here, sons versus daughters) should be sensitive and respond *to the relative gains possible through either sex function*—can be generalized to hermaphrodites and many other sex ratio systems (Charnov and Bull, 1977; Charnov et al., 1978; Charnov, 1979a; Charnov et al., 1981; Bull, 1981a,b; Green, 1982).

This type of phenotypic plasticity will appear at several places in this book. To anticipate one of them, consider briefly sex reversal or sequential hermaphroditism, where an individual reproduces early in life as one sex and then later changes to the other. Young individuals are typically small, while older are larger. Suppose that females gain, in terms of reproductive success, relatively more than do males by being large. Selection then favors an individual who reproduces as a male when small and changes to a female when large (Ghiselin, 1969, 1974; Warner, 1975a,b; Warner et al., 1975; Leigh et al., 1976; Charnov, 1979a,b). This is known as the size advantage hypothesis for sex reversal.

These ideas can be developed in a more formal model that

reflects the Shaw-Mohler product theorem. In order to have a concrete example, the discussion will be in terms of a parasitic wasp (since this beast stimulated my modeling efforts: Charnov, 1979a). The model allows sex ratio to vary independently of clutch size, and is one of the simplest of its kind (some extensions are in Green, 1982; Bull, 1981a,b; a similar model is in Stubblefield, 1980). The wasp model assumes that the parent controls the sex ratio; Bull's (1981a,b) model vests control of sex ratio in the offspring. The answers are the same for both models.

Imagine an outcrossing parasitic wasp with discrete generations where the females attack insect hosts over a wide range of sizes. A single egg is laid on each host. The host is paralyzed or killed by a sting from the female wasp, so that all the food for her offspring's development is contained in the host at the moment of attack. If the host is small, the wasp larva will have relatively little food and will emerge as a small adult. If the host is large, the resulting wasp will be large. Suppose further that the reproductive consequences of being a large compared to a small adult wasp differ, depending on whether the individual is a male or a female. As an example, a large female may lay ten times the number of eggs over her lifetime as a small female, while a large male may only be three times as effective at inseminating females, compared to a small male. Because female wasps lay eggs in a variety of host sizes, the environment is patchy with respect to opportunities for production of sons versus daughters. The mother is assumed to control her sex ratio as a function of host size. Haplodiploid sex determination provides her with a physiological mechanism for this control. Our interest is in predicting what sex ratio she will produce in a given host size. To do this, we first specify the host size distribution and the expected reproductive success for an adult wasp of a given sex and size. At the time of mating, the adults from all the hosts form a random mating pool.

Let $g(x)$ be the proportion of attacked hosts which are size x (x a discrete variable). Let $W_1(x)$ be the relative fitness of a son derived from a host of size x. A male's fitness is measured relative to other males (Charnov, 1979a), so that $W_1(x)$ scales the ability of a male of size x to inseminate females over his lifetime. Let $W_2(x)$ be the lifetime egg production of a female derived from a host of size x. Both of these fitness measures include survivorship to adulthood, which may vary with host size (Assem, 1971). Finally, let $r(x)$ be the proportion of unfertilized or male eggs laid in host size x, with $r(x)$ controlled by the mother wasp. Using techniques from population genetics, it is possible to show that the ESS $r(x)$ satisfies the following product relation (Charnov, 1979a), namely, $r(x)$ is that function which maximizes the product of the fitness gained through the decisions to produce sons (m), times the fitness gained through the decisions to produce daughters (f). That is, it maximizes:

$$m \cdot f = [\Sigma_x g(x) \cdot W_1(x)$$
$$\cdot r(x)] \cdot [\Sigma_x g(x) \cdot W_2(x) \cdot (1 - r(x))],$$
$$0 \le r(x) \le 1. \quad (4.1)$$

If we impose the condition that a large daughter gains more in relative fitness than a large son ($W_2(x)/W_1(x)$ increases with x), the solution to this equation reduces to a very simple form. Only sons should be produced in small hosts and only daughters in large. There is a certain host size (τ) where the switch from sons to daughters occurs. To show this, we differentiate $\log(m \cdot f)$ with respect to some $r(y)$. We get:

$$\frac{\partial(\log(m \cdot f))}{\partial r(y)} \propto \frac{W_1(y)}{m} - \frac{W_2(y)}{f} \quad (y = \text{any host size}).$$

Since (m, f) will be the same for all host sizes, these derivatives will be either positive or negative. If $W_2(y)/W_1(y) > f/m$, they are negative and all daughters should be produced ($r(y) = 0$). The reverse means all sons ($r(y) = 1$). At one intermediate host size the inequality may really be an equality—here a mixed sex ratio should be produced. This general result is illustrated in Figure 4.1.

While the model predicts a threshold (τ) for the sex ratio change it is unlikely that biological data would show such an abrupt

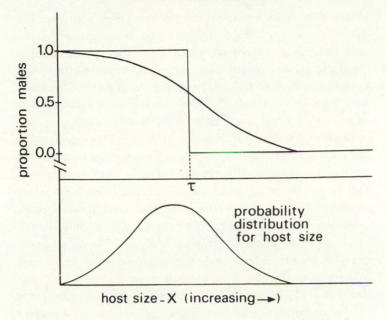

FIGURE 4.1. Sex ratio as a function of host size. Provided females gain more fitness by being larger than do males (that is, $W_2(x)/W_1(x)$ increases with x), the sex ratio is predicted to be female-biased in large hosts, male-biased in small. There is a threshold host size (τ) where a changeover occurs. Host size distributions are simply illustrative. For reasons discussed in the text, the expected pattern is not a threshold, but a more gradual sex ratio shift. (From Charnov et al., 1981.)

transition. A more likely pattern would consist of all sons in small hosts and daughters in large, with a gradual sex ratio transition in between (Fig. 4.1). We expect a gradual transition for several reasons. First, the model assumes fitness and host distribution values that do not vary in time. If these vary, then so does τ. The quality of a host may also depend somewhat on factors which cannot be known to the mother at the time she deposits an egg. Selection would then favor a more gradual shift in sex ratio. However, a third reason is that even if the mother wasp made perfect decisions, the biologist may not be able to classify the hosts perfectly with respect to criteria used by the wasps. For example, the hosts are theoretically to be classified by the ratio $W_2(x)/$

$W_1(x)$. Those with low ratios are son hosts, those with large are daughter hosts. Let k be the threshold ratio. Now, suppose that the wasp makes perfect decisions, with all hosts above k being given to daughters. If the biologist, however, uses a measure of host size ($\overline{x}$) which is imperfectly correlated with the $W_2(x)/W_1(x)$ ratio, we will not see the threshold. The data would show a gradual shift in sex ratio as a function of $\overline{x}$, *our measure of host quality*.

In addition to the sex ratio shift with host size, the model makes one other general type of prediction. The concepts of large and small host as discussed above have *no absolute meaning*. That is, a host is only large or small relative to the other hosts being attacked. To calculate theoretically whether a host is to be a son or a daughter host, we must first know the host size distribution. We expect to find an increasing fraction of daughters in larger hosts, but what constitutes larger may vary from place to place, or time to time. Consider the host marked z on Figure 4.2. If the distribution of host sizes is i, z is a large host. If the distribution is ii, z is a relatively small host. Host z should contain a greater proportion of daughters when large (case i), than when small (case ii). This relativity prediction is important for sex ratio theory, and will reappear often in the book. We now consider data on hymenoptera and nematodes.

SEX RATIO AND HOST SIZE: HYMENOPTERA AND NEMATODES

Nematodes

Environmental control of sex development (phenotypic plasticity for gender) is known or suspected in two groups of nematodes: plant parasitic nematodes in the genera *Meloidogyne* and *Heterodera*, and entomogenous nematodes of the family Mermithidae. These are of considerable economic importance, the first as serious crop pests, the second as agents for biological control of insects (Poinar, 1979). Christie (1929), working with two terrestrial Mermithids, first showed that sex was environmentally controlled. Individuals of the species *Mermis subnigrescens* develop to

42

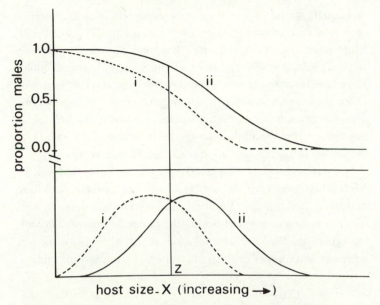

FIGURE 4.2. A relativity shift for the host size sex ratio. Whether a given host is to be a son host or a daughter host depends on the entire host size distribution. Host z is a relatively large host if the host distribution is i; it is a small host if the distribution is ii. It should contain more males when it is small. Host size distributions are simply illustrative. (From Charnov et al., 1981.)

adulthood in grasshoppers. They enter the host by being ingested as eggs. At maturity, adults leave the host, which is killed as a result, and mating plus egg deposition takes place externally, on vegetation. Males develop at a faster rate (emerge at 5 versus 9 weeks) and are significantly smaller than females (20–60 mm versus 50–160 mm). Christie showed that the proportion of males emerging from a host was related to infection number, as was the size of the emerging adult worms. With 1–3 worms/host only females emerged, while 14–23 worms gave rise to 80% males. Carefully controlled experiments eliminated sex-differential mortality as a cause of the sex ratio shift, and he rightly concluded that environmental control of sex development occurs. Apparently nothing is known about competition for resources within a host. For this species, given the mode of infection, the cohabiting individuals would be expected to be close relatives. Ingestion of eggs is a rare infection mode for Mermithids (Poinar, 1979). More often eggs hatch outside a host and an infective juvenile stage actively searches and burrows into a new host individual. Here, the cohabitants would be less likely to be close relatives. Often the insect attacked is in an immature stage and the worms also emerge from this stage. Some species attack immature insects but emerge from the adult, after the host has itself dispersed. Here the worms in a given host are quite unlikely to be relatives.

Sex development is also closely related to infection level for Mermithids attacking the larvae of aquatic insects (blackflies, mosquitos, and midges). Figure 4.3 shows a typical data set, here for *Hydromeris contorta* attacking the midge *Chironomus plumosus* (Johnson, 1955). Hominick and Welch (1971) present less extensive, but comparable, data for other species attacking midges.

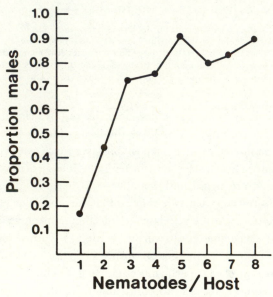

FIGURE 4.3. Emergent sex ratios in the nematode *Hydromeris* as a function of its infection level in the host midge (*Chironomus*). The nematodes grow up in the host and emerge to mate as adults. High infection levels mean small emerging worms. When constrained to be small, more worms "elect" to become male. (data from Johnson, 1955.)

44

Species attacking blackfly larvae show similar patterns, with 11% males at one worm/host rising to 87% males at three (Ezenwa and Carter, 1975). J. J. Petersen and colleagues have studied Mermithids attacking mosquito larvae, and have worked out mass rearing techniques. In *Romanomeris culicivorax*, Petersen et al. (1968) showed that it was not infection rate, per se, which affected sex ratio. In both a large (type 1) and a small (type 2) mosquito species, the sex ratio increased with the infection level (Fig. 4.4). At any given infection level, type 1 produced larger worms and more females. Petersen (1972) showed a similar pattern for the same nematode attacking six mosquito species—small hosts produced smaller adult worms and more males at any fixed infection level (see also Petersen, 1977). An ingenious feeding experiment, with *Culex pipiens* larvae as hosts, further strengthened the

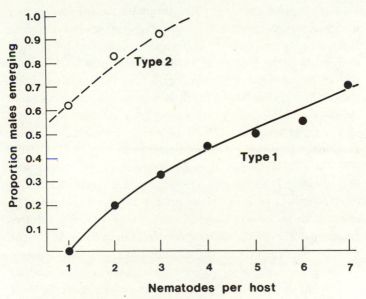

FIGURE 4.4. Sex ratio in the nematode *Romanomeris*, as a function of its infection level, in two types of hosts. Type 1 is a large host, Type 2 is small. At any given infection level, the emerging worms are larger in Type 1 hosts. Where emerging worms are larger, more of them are female. These data strongly suggest that size of emerging adult worm is closely tied to its "choice" of which sex to become. (data from Petersen et al., 1968.)

notion that the opportunity for a worm to grow to some threshold size was the critical factor in sex determination. Petersen (1972) infected at a rate of one to four worms per host, and after infection, divided the hosts into one group fed at normal levels, and one which got a minimal diet (0.33 × normal). With one worm per host the proportion of males emerging was 0.13 and 0.92, respectively! Obviously, host nutrition played a major role (emerging worms were much larger in the well-fed hosts), while sex differential mortality was completely ruled out. Harlos et al. (1980) showed a similar effect for a parasite of an *Aedes* species. In addition, their worm emerged from adult mosquitos and showed a host-sex effect. Male mosquitos (who would not have had a blood meal) produced small worms who were mostly male. Female mosquitos (with a blood meal) showed a more female-biased ratio, with larger worms emerging.

Assuming that there is a size threshold for sex choice, four questions present themselves. First, at what stage of development is sex actually determined? If intrahost competition forces some individuals in the host to be small, do they more often become males? Second, do female worms gain more reproductive success than males by being large? Third, is there geographic variation in the threshold, coincidental with geographic variation in the host species (large versus small) and/or average infection level? Such variation is predicted by the host size theory (Fig. 4.2). Finally, will the size threshold alter in response to an altered host environment? If the worms are reared (at a specified infection level) on only large hosts, theory predicts the threshold favored by selection to be larger. Since *R. culicivorax* is easily cultured (Petersen, 1972, 1973), such experiments can be done. At present, no data exist to answer these four questions.

The plant parasitic nematodes show patterns more puzzling than the Mermithids. I briefly discuss them here, since the work looks carefully at alternative hypotheses for a sex ratio shift, and because Charnov and Bull (1977) used them as positive support for environmental control of sex (in the sex allocation sense). This earlier conclusion now seems unwarranted.

Ellenby (1954) first suggested environmental control of sex in the potato root eelworm, *Heterodera rostochiensis*. The infective juveniles enter root tissue to feed. At adulthood, males leave the plant to find mates, while females remain within the plant tissue. Males are much smaller than females. Ellenby showed that the sex ratio (at adulthood) varies with intensity of attack (i.e., worms/cm of root). There were 55% males at low intensity, 80% at high. Den Ouden (1960) and Trudgill (1967) both worked with the same nematode species. Den Ouden (1960) inoculated 700 potato seedlings with one worm each, and four weeks later (at adulthood) recovered 270 females and 1 male. Trudgill (1967) got similar results, and showed sex ratio shifts similar to those of Ellenby (1954). One of his experiments is of particular interest. He inoculated tomato seedlings with 5000 worms each, and later cut the tops off half of the plants. Each treatment produced about 1500 adults per plant but the topped plants (with less food for the worms) produced 88% males, while the control (untopped) gave 59% males. Again, sexing was at adulthood. I mention these data since they present the strongest case for environmental control of sex. Workers on other species of *Heterodera* have either failed to show any dramatic sex ratio shift with infection level, and/or have concluded that genetically determined sex combined with sex differential mortality or penetration of the root system could account for the results (Johnson and Viglierchio, 1969; Koliopanos and Triantaphyllow, 1972). Triantaphyllow (1973) critically reviewed the early literature, and concluded that sex differential mortality was certainly not yet ruled out. However, he noted that mortality would not account for the results of Den Ouden (1960) and Trudgill (1967), particularly the experiments discussed above. More recent work (Bridgeman and Kerry, 1980, with several species, including *H. rostochiensis*) has failed to duplicate these earlier, provocative results. Trudgill's topping experiments remain unexplained. These new experiments show a sex ratio of equality even with one worm per host. In addition, various other experiments by the same workers have directly supported the hypothesis of sex differential mortality.

If the work on *Heterodera* is at present inconclusive, studies on the closely related genus *Meloidogyne* have conclusively shown environmental control of sex development (review in Triantaphyllow, 1973). Under poor growth conditions, a much greater proportion of individuals develop into small males. However, this presents a major puzzle since the genus has mostly polyploid, apomictic forms (including those studied above). That is, it would *appear* that these "males" have no direct reproductive function. It seems possible that selection at the level of the clone could favor the production of these sterile morphs since high population viscosity (little dispersal) would result in nearly all individuals in a neighborhood being clonally related. Triantaphyllow (1973) suggests a similar idea, but phrases it in terms of group, rather than clonal selection. It would be interesting to assay if "group" (clone) productivity increases because these small males use less resource. The males may play some sort of defensive role, benefiting their reproductive "sisters" still embedded in the plant tissue.

Hymenoptera

Most hymenoptera have haplodiploid sex determination. This provides a female with much control over the sex of an offspring, but it also means that males and females strongly disagree over the sex of "their" children (since the male passes no genes to his mate's sons). It also means that any environmental factor (e.g., temperature) which "interferes" with sperm viability (and use) affects sex ratio. Factors affecting sex ratio in parasitic hymenoptera have been repeatedly reviewed (Shiga and Nakanishi, 1968; Flanders, 1956, 1959, 1965; Bergard, 1972; Kochetova, 1977; Vinson and Iwantsch, 1980). Obviously, some of the "factors" constitute adaptive responses on the part of the female wasp, while others probably do not. I will not attempt a detailed review of these, but will concentrate here on evidence about the host size hypothesis.

It is very common for parasitoid emergence data to show a small female bias. For example, in a large study of the dynamics of spruce budworm, four years of emergence data for three larval parasitoids showed female proportions of 0.62, 0.58, and 0.52 (McGugan, 1955; sample sizes 375–1200). Similar female biases were noted by Legner (1969a, b) and MacKauer (1976). It has recently been suggested (Smith and Shaw, 1980) that emergence sex ratios for haplodiploid parasitoids might be slightly female biased due to increased male mortality caused by newly arisen (each generation) lethal mutations, which would express themselves in males. Since in many panmictic situations, sex differential mortality (egg → adult) does not alter the ESS primary sex ratio away from equality, this idea may explain small female biases. I note here that a small amount of Local Mate Competition (LMC, see Chapter Five) would also result in a slight overproduction of daughters. It may also be that the sex ratio is some sort of compromise between interests of the mother (for half and half) and the father (all daughters). However, this third hypothesis loses force when we realize that a female could begin to restore sex ratio equality among the zygotes by refusing to accept a mate, and thus produce all sons. The absence of widespread "acceptance of a mate" polymorphisms among the hymenoptera argues against much male participation in the sex ratio. The sex ratio shifts discussed here are much too large to be accounted for by the lethal mutation hypothesis. Indeed, sex differential mortality is eliminated as a major causal factor in several studies discussed below.

Clausen (1939) was the first to review the effect of host size on parasitoid sex ratios. Here, I review data relative to the host size model.

A general qualitative test of the model would consist of showing that sex ratio varied as a function of host size, and that the daughter/son fitness comparison likewise changed with host size. Both would have to change in the predicted directions. We would also have to show that sex differential mortality or LMC could not account for the results. (This does not mean that the alternatives cannot be involved in a sex ratio shift. Indeed, the host size model might well be extended to include the effects of some degree of LMC. This would tend to alter the overall sex ratio toward daughters.) For this discussion I will treat the outbreeding version of the host size hypothesis (equation 4.1). The predicted relative nature of the sex ratio shift itself provides a powerful, qualitative test of the hypothesis. There are at least three ways to test it.

(1) Geographic variation. If in different places the wasp species is associated with different host size distributions, this natural variation can be turned into a test. For instance, if the same host is present in both locations, but is a small host in one place and large in the other place, a sex ratio shift is expected in that host.

(2) Laboratory selection experiments. It should be possible to mimic the effects of geographical variation in the laboratory. If the parasitoids can be reared only on small hosts, or only on large hosts, sex ratio shifts through time (over several generations) are expected, if the sex ratio is a heritable character. The small hosts should shift from producing mostly males toward a more equal sex ratio. The large hosts should shift from mostly females toward a more equal ratio.

(3) Temporal variation. If the wasps naturally confront host size distributions which change from generation to generation, they might have the ability to alter their sex ratio on a short time scale, in response to the prevailing distribution. The most reasonable source for a shift in host size utilization would be a shift in host abundance. Since small hosts are poorer for offspring, a mother might be expected to ignore them when confronted with an abundance of larger hosts. This behavioral shift would require the wasps to pick up, store, and use information about the distribution. However, if the natural host size distribution was either constant through time, or continued to change *within* a wasp generation, we might expect the wasps not to respond to short-term shifts in the distribution. We would then require geographic variation or a laboratory selection experiment to test the relativity idea.

The sex ratio under discussion is the ratio at the egg stage. Data often show that survivorship declines in small hosts (Assem, 1971;

Sandlan, 1979; Fig. 4.10). If this decline is different for the two sexes, then the differential mortality as a function of host size would itself generate a sex ratio shift among emerging wasps, independent of a true sex ratio shift at the egg stage. However, such differential mortality would also contribute to natural selection favoring a shift by the mother wasp. Some evidence indicates that daughters may sometimes be unable to reach pupation size in very small hosts (a pupal parasite of Lepidoptera—Kishi, 1970), but even here a strong sex ratio shift at the egg stage with host size could be demonstrated. The relativity prediction discussed previously is a good control for this effect, since the shift is predicted within a single host size. The model also predicts that the overall sex ratio should be biased toward males. However, this is again sex ratio at the egg stage. If survivorship declines with host size, then at emergence the overall sex ratio may be female biased (since males are put in small hosts).

At present there are no data relative to geographic variation, nor are there any published selection experiments. However, Charnov et al. (1981) have studied short-term (within generation) shifts in sex ratio in two species.

Lariophagus distinguendus is a small (1–3 mm) parasitic wasp (family Pteromalidae) which attacks larvae of the common granary weevil, *Sitophilus granarius* (Assem, 1970, 1971, 1979). The weevils oviposit in grains of wheat, and a single larva develops inside the grain. The parasite stings the larva and deposits a single egg. An adult wasp emerges about 18 days later (at 25°C). The wasp will parasitize a variety of host sizes. The larva hollows out the grain as it develops. Size of weevil larvae is correlated with age, but the relationship is imprecise. The size of the weevil larva is strongly correlated with the diameter of its tunnel (Kirkpatrick and Wilbur, 1965) and tunnel diameter is easily measured by x-rays.

Heterospilis prosopoidis is a small (1–3 mm) parasitic wasp in the family Braconidae. It has a similar life history to that of *Lariophagus* in that it lays a single egg on the larvae of weevils, attacking a variety of host sizes. It was studied attacking the azuki

51

bean weevil, *Callosobruchus chinensis*. At 30° C, weevil development (egg to adult) takes about 21 days. Weevil larvae 11–19 days
old are accepted by the wasp. Experiments with this system used
weevil age as a measure of host size.

Assem (1971) showed, using weevil age as a measure of size,
that *Lariophagus* adjusts its sex ratio as a function of weevil size.
Mostly males were produced in young weevils, mostly females in
older weevils. His experiments were carried out by presenting
wasps with weevils of only one age class. The experiments were
also controlled to show that the observed sex ratio shift could not
be due to differential, sex-specific mortality (even though young
weevils produced a much higher death rate). The data also
suggested that the wasp used a relative measure of host size.

Charnov et al. (1981) repeated these earlier experiments, using
the more exact measure for host size—tunnel diameter. Figure
4.5*b* shows the results. As expected, sons are produced in small
hosts, daughters in large. A second experiment consisted of
presenting wasps with two host sizes, offered in equal abundance.
The hosts were always 0.4 mm different in size and the wasp was
presented with an alternating sequence (large, small . . .). The
data from these two experiments thus consist of a given host size in
three situations: alone, smaller of two sizes, and larger of two
sizes. For example, we have 1.4 mm hosts alone, and paired with
1.0 or with 1.8 mm hosts. If we consider some host size z, it is clear
that the three experiments (z small, z alone, z large) represent
successively more left-shifted host size distribution curves. This
corresponds to a shift from distribution ii to distribution i in
Figure 4.2. If the wasp is adapted to alter its sex ratio on a short
time scale, it should put relatively more daughters into host z as
we move across the three treatments.

Curve *a* in Figure 4.5 represents the sex ratio as a function of
host size, when the host represented was the larger of the two hosts
(for example, 1.0 was paired with 0.6). Note that every point lies
below (is more female biased) the curve for the hosts when they
were by themselves (curve *b*). Curve *c* (Fig. 4.5) shows the
corresponding relationship for hosts where they were the smaller

52

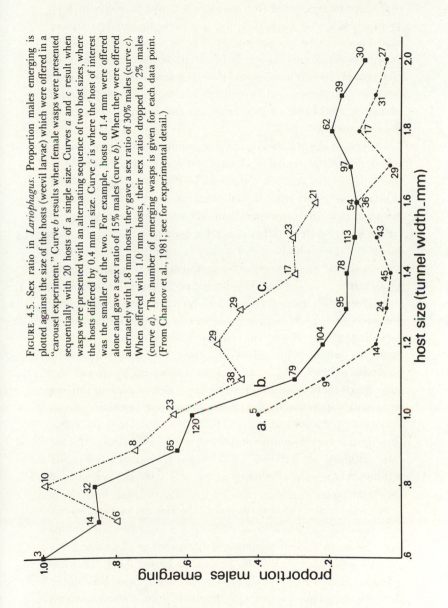

FIGURE 4.5. Sex ratio in *Lariophagus*. Proportion males emerging is plotted against the size of the hosts (weevil larvae) which were offered in a "carousel experiment." Curve *b* results when female wasps were presented sequentially with 20 hosts of a single size. Curves *a* and *c* result when wasps were presented with an alternating sequence of two host sizes, where the hosts differed by 0.4 mm in size. Curve *c* is where the host of interest was the smaller of the two. For example, hosts of 1.4 mm were offered alone and gave a sex ratio of 15% males (curve *b*). When they were offered alternately with 1.8 mm hosts, they gave a sex ratio of 30% males (curve *c*). When offered with 1.0 mm hosts, their sex ratio dropped to 2% males (curve *a*). The number of emerging wasps is given for each data point. (From Charnov et al., 1981; see for experimental detail.)

of the two being offered (for example, 1.0 was paired with 1.4). With a single exception, 0.7 mm, this curve lies above (is more male biased) the other two curves. The hypothesis relates to the general order of the curves. It is indeed remarkable that, even given small (10–30) to moderate (50–100) sample sizes, the curves preserve their theoretically predicted order over the entire range of host sizes. This is the strongest evidence for the shift predicted by sex ratio theory.

Using host age as a measure of size, a similar set of experiments was done with *Heterospilis*. Presenting wasps with a single host size produced the relationship shown in Figure 4.6A. Small hosts (11 days) were very male biased, whereas larger hosts were more female biased. Control experiments showed that this result could not be due to differential, sex-specific mortality. To see if these wasps could also adjust the sex ratio to a shifting host environment, a second set of experiments used just two host ages (11 and 15 days or 15 and 19 days), presented in equal numbers. In comparison with the experiments in which the wasp received only one host size, the 11- and 15-day hosts now showed no altered sex ratio. Indeed, the 15-day hosts showed the same sex ratio when alone, or when combined with either 11- or 19-day hosts. Moderate to large sample sizes (88–1024 emerging wasps per host size) make these results quite reliable. Only one predicted sex ratio shift was seen. When 19-day hosts were presented alone, they gave a proportion of males of 0.36 (n = 786). However, when they were presented with equal numbers of 15-day hosts, the sex ratio dropped to 0.25 (n = 88). Such a shift is statistically significant (one-sided, Fisher exact test: P = 0.03) in the predicted direction.

Charnov et al. (1981) carried out a further set of experiments with *Heterospilis*. These involved 11- and 15-day hosts, presented to the wasp in various proportions (proportions of 11-day hosts 0.1, 0.3, 0.5, 0.7, 0.9). As can be seen in Figure 4.6B, the wasp failed in eight out of ten cases to show any deviation (significant at the 0.05 level) from the sex ratio predicted from the experiments with only one host size. Clearly, there is no pattern of sex ratio

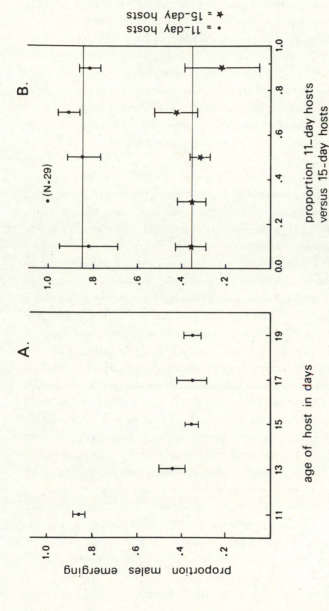

FIGURE 4.6. Sex ratio as a function of host age for the wasp *Heterospilis* attacking the weevil *Callosobruchus*. (A) Wasps presented with a single-aged host for a period of 24 h (30°C and 70% relative humidity, host density at ~20 hosts per female wasp). Data given are means ±2 s.e. (B) Wasps in an environment consisting of 11- and 15-day hosts presented simultaneously. In the five experiments, the proportion of 11-day hosts varied from 0.1 to 0.9. Data are the mean sex ratios within each host age (±2 s.e.). The lines in (B) refer to the proportion of males found in (A). (From Charnov et al., 1981.)

shift with changing host proportions (at least for 11- and 15-day hosts). Although *Heterospilis* does not immediately adjust its sex ratios to host size distributions, it is very possible that its offspring sex ratios are attuned to host distributions in a way predicted by the model. It may be that the host size distributions naturally encountered by *Heterospilis* do not vary greatly between wasp generations or that they vary within generations, and thus these wasps would not be expected to respond to short-term shifts in the distribution. At least for this species, a selection experiment or geographic comparison seems to be necessary to test the model further.

At least two other parasitic wasps which show a sex ratio shift with host size also show short-term adjustment of the sex ratio. Both species overproduce daughters in large hosts, sons in small. Chewyreuv (1913) studied parasitoid wasps of the genus *Pimpla* (family Ichneumonidae) which attack lepidopteran pupae. When he offered a female wasp a mixture of host pupae consisting of *Sphinx* (large) and *Pieris* (small), the wasp produced mostly females in the large, males in the small. However, when the *Pieris* pupae were alternated with those of *Vanessa* (still smaller), the same wasp produced female offspring in the former and males in the latter. Sandlan (1979) also studied a pupal parasite of Lepidoptera, the wasp *Coccygomimus turionella*. Here, individual wasps confronted with a single host size gradually altered the sex ratio through time. If the single size was large, the sex ratio declined from being female biased to being more male biased. A small size showed the opposite change, male biased toward more female biased. While these sex ratio shifts are in the theoretical direction (for our simple outbred model), unpublished work by Assem on *Anisopteromalus calandrae* shows the more puzzling pattern of the sex ratio changing within a wasp generation and converging to a uniform value of ~20% males, regardless of the host size presented. This is suggestive of LMC, but clearly we know very little as yet (especially in theory) of the within-generation dynamics of sex ratio.

As the sex ratio shift (Fig. 4.5) is toward daughters in larger hosts, a further test of the theory consists of determining whether a female gains more fitness by being large than does a male. Measuring individual fitness is very difficult, especially for males, where the value must reflect the relative ability to gain access to females. Using *Lariophagus,* a set of experiments was designed to investigate whether wasp size was correlated with the size of its host, and also whether increased wasp size translated into increased individual fitness. Figure 4.7 shows the result of rearing almost 2000 individuals. Clearly, larger weevils give rise to larger wasps. Two facts about Figure 4.7 are of particular interest. First, the relationship is different for males and females. From the same-sized host, males are on an average smaller than the corresponding females. This presumably reflects the fact that males show a shorter developmental time to adulthood on any given host size. Second, both curves show a steep linear increase over the weevil size range 0.7–1.3 mm. At 1.3 mm, both show an abrupt transition. Average male size no longer increases with weevil size, whereas average female size goes up at a much reduced rate (slope of curve here is about 12% the previous slope).

In both species (*Lariophagus* and *Heterospilis*), male and female lifespan increases with body size, as well as female fecundity and male mating ability. The present data are simply too imprecise to ask if one sex gains relatively more by being large (Charnov et al., 1981). However, Figure 4.7 suggests another type of data which bears on this fitness gain issue, at least for *Lariophagus.* If fitness within each sex is related to the size of the wasp, host sizes over the range 1.3–2.0 mm show very little change in relative female/male size, whereas relative female/male size is increasing over the host size range 0.6–1.3 mm. We might then expect that host sizes above 1.3 mm would be treated quite similarly with respect to sex ratio. As shown in Figure 4.5*b* (host size alone experiments), the proportion of sons drops rapidly with increasing host size until a host size of 1.3 mm. The sex ratio is about 0.17 males at this host size, but it does not become more female biased as we move to even larger hosts. The experiments

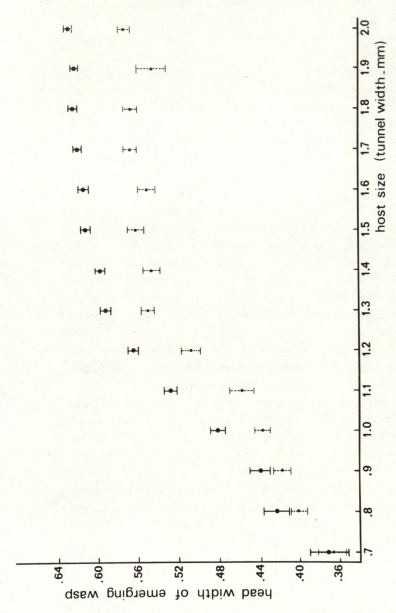

FIGURE 4.7. Size of *Lariophagus* related to its host size (tunnel width). Means (±1 s.e.) of head width of males (lower curve) and females (upper curve) are plotted against host weevil size. Hosts above 1.3 mm show little or no increase in average son or daughter size. Least squares regressions calculated on the means: (1) ♂, host sizes 0.7–1.3 mm, $y = 0.16 + 0.28x$, $r = 0.98$, $P < 0.001$. (2) ♂, host sizes 1.4–2.0 mm, correlation not significant at 0.05 level. (3) ♀, host sizes 0.7–1.3 mm, $y = 0.11 + 0.37x$, $r = 0.99$, $P < 0.001$. (4) ♀, host sizes 1.4–2.0 mm, $y = 0.54 + 0.044x$, $r = 0.92$, $P < 0.01$. (From Charnov et al., 1981.)

presented in Figure 4.3 show that the wasp can alter its sex ratio when a two-host environment consists of both hosts above 1.3 mm. However, these shifts are small relative to the alteration in sex ratio observed over a host size range of 0.6–1.3 mm.

There are many other solitary parasitoid systems where a range of host sizes is attacked, and where sex ratio alters with host size (Berry, 1939; Nozato, 1969; Ryan and Rudinsky, 1962; Brunson, 1934, 1937, 1939—only Brunson has eliminated sex differential mortality as a possible factor). The shift is always in the direction of more females from larger hosts. Larger may refer to various instars of a single (or more commonly several) host species. These include larval and pupal parasites, and almost all appear to immobilize the host at the time of attack.

Shiga and Nakanishi (1968) studied a gregarious, external parasite (of lepidopteran prepupae), so they could easily observe and manipulate the immature parasites. In field data, hosts with few (1–5) larvae produced virtually all (96%) females, while hosts with many larvae (11–20) produced mostly (75%) males. Lab experiments eliminated mortality as a factor and showed that adult parasite size was closely related to larval crowding. Nothing was known about how the large clutches were produced (superparasitism?), which makes this situation different from the more common solitary parasitoid system.

I have summarized data from four fairly well studied systems (solitary parasitoids) in Figures 4.8–4.11. Holdaway and Smith (1933, Fig. 4.8) studied a pupal parasite of blowflies (several species). Their field study eliminated mortality as a cause of the sex ratio shift. Arthur and Wylie (1959, Fig. 4.9) studied a lepidopteran pupal parasite and worked with nine host species. They provided no parasite mortality data. Kishi (1970, Fig. 4.11) also studied a pupal parasite (here of weevils). Adult parasite weight was linearly related to host weight and was fairly independent of host species. His experiments eliminated differential mortality and showed the most dramatic sex ratio shifts of all the species for which we have data, with a clear threshold for sex ratio change (Fig. 4.11). Sandlan (1979) has provided an excellent

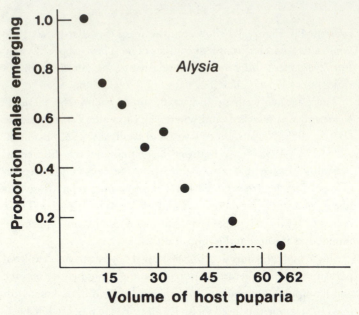

FIGURE 4.8. Emergent sex ratio as a function of host volume for a pupal parasitoid (*Alysia*) attacking several species of blowflies (data from Holdaway and Smith, 1933).

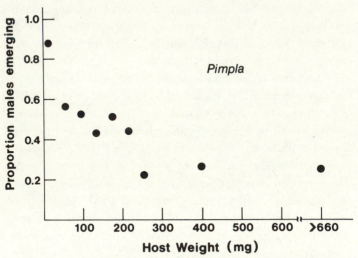

FIGURE 4.9. Emergent sex ratio as a function of host weight for a pupal parasitoid (*Pimpla*) attacking several species of Lepidoptera (data from Arthur and Wylie, 1959).

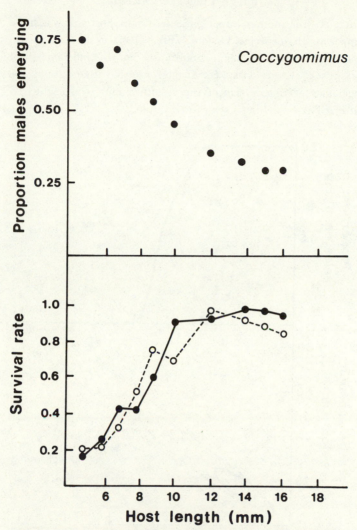

FIGURE 4.10. Emergent sex ratio as a function of host length for a pupal parasitoid (*Coccygomimus*) of Lepidoptera. Using virgin versus mated females, Sandlan (1979) also showed (lower graph) that while immature mortality was much higher in smaller hosts, it was not sex specific. Virgin females laid only son eggs, yet the immature survival of their offspring (●) was the same as the survival of offspring from inseminated females (○). (Data from Sandlan, 1979.)

study on still another pupal parasite. Again, host size was more important than species. His data (Fig. 4.10) also show that wasp mortality is much higher in small hosts, but it is independent of wasp sex. These data sets strongly suggest that, as in the nematodes, it is the size of the resulting adult wasp which is involved in the mother's sex ratio decision.

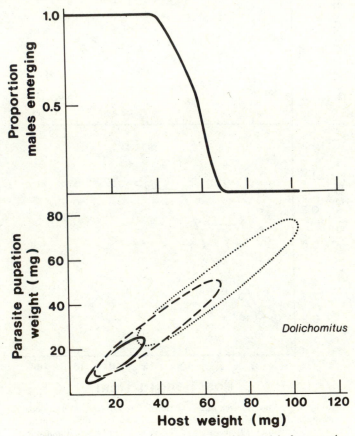

FIGURE 4.11. Emergent sex ratio as a function of host weight for a pupal parasitoid (*Dolichomitus*) of weevils. The data are numerous, so the figure is somewhat diagrammatic. The lower graph shows that parasite pupation weight was closely related to host weight, but independent of host species. Three host species are shown on this lower figure. (Original data in Kishi, 1970.)

It should be clear from these systems that we still have no observations on biogeographic variation in the sex ratio response, or lab experiments on the evolution of an altered response to altered host size distributions. Nor are there unequivocal data on male/female fitnesses versus host size. Such data are much needed.

There are other hymenopteran systems which show sex ratio shifts similar to the parasitoids. "Trap nesting" (Krombein, 1967) refers to free-living bees and wasps where the mother places food plus an egg in a cell constructed inside a crevice (e.g., hollowed-out twig). The size of the crevice places constraints on the cell size, the amount of food packed in, and consequently on the size of the resulting adult wasp. Trap nesters have been much studied because they will commonly nest in soda straws, holes drilled in wood blocks, or other human-made crevices. Given the importance of some trap-nesting bee species for agricultural pollination (Stephen and Osgood, 1965), a great deal of data now exist.

Figure 4.12 shows the sex ratio (proportion of males emerging) as a function of hole-diameter in artificial nesting material for eleven species of bees and wasps. These field data, uncorrected for mortality effects, are with one exception, from the excellent book by Krombein (1967). He lists no trap nester with a reverse sex ratio shift, although several species show evidence of no sex ratio shift for the hole sizes presented (several wasps of the genera *Stenodynerus* and *Ancistrocerus*). A reverse shift might be expected in species where the males show aggression and territorialty with respect to mating. Here, increased size could produce relatively greater male reproductive success. It would be very interesting to know if any trap-nesting species shows geographic variation in the hole-size distribution. Such variation should correlate with sex ratio shifts within a specified hole size, similar to those predicted for parasitoids. However, the situation for trap nesters is somewhat more complicated than the simple model discussed here. At least two other sex ratio effects co-occur with the hole-size shifts. There are often several cells placed in the same crevice; a straw will contain a sequence of offspring. Since males

63

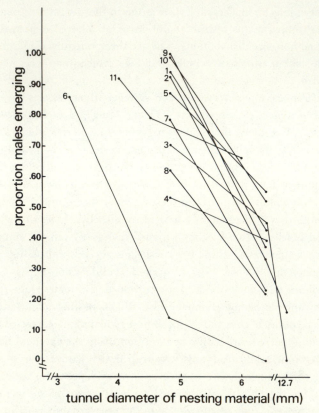

FIGURE 4.12. Sex ratio at emergence related to tunnel diameter of nesting material for trap-nesting Hymenoptera. Data points refer to diameter of nesting material used in sampling. Lines connecting points are simply to keep species distinct. All sex ratio shifts are statistically significant at the 0.05 level (one-tailed, Fisher exact test) or better. Species 1–10 are from Krombein (1968), species 11 from Stephen and Osgood (1965). Species as follows: 1. *Euodynerus foraminatus;* 2. *Euodynerus megaera;* 3. *Euodynerus schwarzi;* 4. *Pachodynerus erynnis;* 5. *Ancistrocerus antilope;* 6. *Ancistrocerus tigris;* 7. *Symmorphus canadensis;* 8. *Tryarpilum tridentatum* (North Carolina); 9. *Tryarpilum johannis;* 10. *Osmia lignaria;* 11. *Megachile rotundata.* Species 1–9 are wasps, 10 and 11 are bees. (Figure from Charnov et al., 1981.)

typically emerge before females, it is common for the mother to put more daughters in the deep cells, more sons near the opening. In this way the sons can get out first without having to destroy the wasp in front. Except where different mothers may supersede each other at a particular hole, the offspring in a given hole will be siblings. Some degree of cooperation may be expected (Hamilton, 1964) and the parent should benefit by using deep crevices for a mixture of sons and daughters. The other factor affecting sex ratio is that a son often costs (in the sense of Fisher, 1930) less than a daughter to produce. Sons require smaller cells (regardless of the diameter of the hole) and less food (Krombein, 1967). The equilibrium sex ratio should reflect this lowered cost through production of more males. There is strong evidence for this effect (Torchio and Tepedino, 1980; Stephen and Osgood, 1965). Even though these two factors complicate the situation, the hole-size effect, as illustrated in Figure 4.12, still appears to be a dominating factor.

All of our present insect data (host-size effect) are from haplodiploid organisms. Fewer data exist for Dipteran parasitoids. Here, the likely presence of sex chromosomes (White, 1973) would seem to a great extent to limit short-term sex ratio alterations. Likewise, many immature insects must inhabit an environment patchy with respect to growth opportunities (like the Mermithid nematodes). I know of no data which suggest similar environmental control of sex development in diploid insects (Bergard, 1972). The Tachnid fly, *Eucelatoria,* is a parasitoid of lepidopteran larvae (Ziser et al., 1977). In this study, most hosts had one parasite, but attack intensity ranged up to 17/host. Only small flies emerged from heavily parasitized hosts, and while we do not know if heavy parasitism is related to superparasitism, there was little or no sex ratio alteration with host infestation: equality at 1/host, rising to 0.58 males at 17/host, a statistically significant but biologically unimportant change. No immature mortality data were provided. Unless males and females do not gain differentially by being large, which seems unlikely, these data support the notion that sex determination mechanisms may often constitute a constraint on short-term alteration of the sex ratio. Interestingly, if we impose the condition that the sex ratio cannot vary with host size (a single ratio must be used all the time), the ESS result reduces to one-half (equation 4.1 with this constraint), even if offspring fitness varies with host size.

I can summarize this chapter with the suggestion that the nematodes and wasps provide useful and interesting data, and some very great possibilities for further testing of sex allocation theory. In Chapter Seven, we consider some of these "host-size" ideas applied to vertebrates.

CHAPTER FIVE

Sex Ratio in
Spatially Structured Populations

With the exception of the wasp host-size situation, all of the models discussed so far assume a large, homogeneous population of randomly mated individuals. In 1967 W. D. Hamilton realized that populations with spatial structure might well select for a sex ratio different from that selected for in a homogeneous population. Since 1967, a number of different kinds of spatial structure (and genetic control) have been studied (Hamilton, 1979; Werren, 1980a,b, 1982; Charnov, 1980; Hartl, 1971; Taylor and Bulmer, 1980; Bulmer and Taylor, 1980a,b; Taylor, 1981; Wilson and Colwell, 1981; Colwell, 1981; Clark, 1978; Maynard Smith, 1978). This chapter reviews these models and the data bearing on them. These models fall into three somewhat distinct classes: (1) local mate competition (LMC), (2) the haystack model, (3) local resource competition (LRC). I retain these names to be consistent with the literature.

LOCAL MATE COMPETITION (LMC)

Hamilton (1967, 1979) proposed the following population structure. The world consists of a large number of islands each of which in one generation is colonized by n fertilized females. These females produce sons and daughters, and mating takes place only within each island. The males die and the newly fertilized females (the next generation) then disperse to recolonize islands. Since generations are discrete, the islands are vacant at the end of each generation. Suppose that we introduce into a large population a mutant female who alters her sex ratio from a proportion r of sons to $\hat{r}$. While rare, this mutant will occur in a group with $n - 1$ normal females. Her fitness will be the number of migrants to which she contributes genes, through her production of daughters and the females inseminated by her sons. If each mother produces b offspring, the mutant's fitness will be $W_t =$ (her daughters) + (females fertilized by her sons);

$$W_t = b(1 - \hat{r}) + \left(\frac{\hat{r}b}{b\hat{r} + (n - 1)rb}\right)(b(1 - \hat{r})$$

$$+ (n - 1)(1 - r)b). \quad (5.1)$$

If $\hat{r} = r$, mutant's fitness equals the normal female's. By definition, an ESS is r^* such that the mutant cannot do better by setting $\hat{r} \neq r$. We require that $\partial W_t / \partial \hat{r} = 0$ when $\hat{r} = r$; if this is a maximum, then W_t will decrease for $\hat{r} \neq r$ (at least near r). Applying this rule to W_t, we find the unique ESS to be:

$$r^* = \frac{n - 1}{2n}. \quad (5.2)$$

If $n = 1$, we have strict sibmating and $r^* = 0$, which in practice means that a female should produce only enough sons to ensure the insemination of her daughters. We get the result that here $r^* = 0$ since the model implicitly assumes a very large family size. As n gets large, $r^* \rightarrow \frac{1}{2}$. This is the result Hamilton (1967) first derived and applied to a diploid population. It is possible to show that this ESS maximizes the following product relation:

$(m =$ sons produced, $f =$ daughters produced): $f \cdot m^{[(n-1)/(n+1)]}$.

The exponent $(n - 1)/(n + 1)$ shows how sons are devalued as a function of mating group size, relative to daughters. Using the same population structure, one may derive ESS sex ratios under a wide variety of genetic systems (haplodiploidy, autosomal control, sex linkage; see Appendix). Hamilton (1979) had done this for the random dispersal model (Fig. 5.1). This figure also illustrates the degree of conflict present within the genome with respect to sex ratio control. Note how close the autosomal and haplodiploid (♀

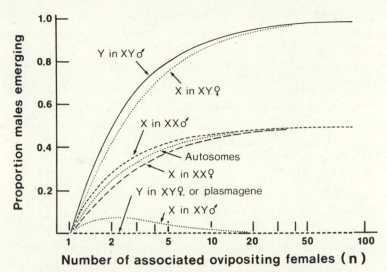

FIGURE 5.1. ESS sex ratios under local mate competition (LMC). Assuming Hamilton's (1967) original population structure, the graph shows the ESS as a function of the number of associated ovipositing (founding) females (n), and the particular part of the genome assumed to control the sex ratio. Note how close the answers are for autosomal and X, in XX♀ (= haplodiploidy), control. Also note the conflict of interest shown by various genomic components. Graph redrawn from Hamilton, 1979. See this reference for detailed discussion and method of derivation of results.

control = XX in XX♀) results are. Hamilton (1979) has also considered generalizations of the random dispersal model.

It has often been said (e.g., Alexander and Sherman, 1977; Maynard Smith, 1978) that local mate competition selects for a biased sex ratio because it involves mating between relatives (inbreeding; here, some degree of sibmating). Under diploidy, it is easy to show that this is not true (Taylor and Bulmer, 1980; Colwell, 1981; Taylor, 1981). Consider a slightly altered model where sibmating is not allowed (this requires that at least two mothers colonize an island). W_t now becomes:

$$W_t = b(1 - \hat{r}) + \left(\frac{\hat{r}(n - 1)(1 - r)b}{\hat{r} + (n - 2)r}\right). \tag{5.3}$$

69

Setting $\partial W_t / \partial \hat{r} = 0$ and $\hat{r} = r$, we obtain

$$r^* = \frac{n - 2}{2n - 3}. \qquad (5.4)$$

Here there is no sibmating, but there is still local mate competition and a biased sex ratio. There are several ways to describe why LMC selects for a sex ratio bias. The approach taken here shows that the bias can be considered due to group selection. In 1979 Hamilton first formulated LMC as a process of group selection. Following this work, several workers have likewise treated it in the group selection framework (Bulmer and Taylor, 1980a,b; Colwell, 1981; Wilson and Colwell, 1981, using the trait group model of Wilson, 1980). Later (in relation to local resource competition) I shall discuss an alternative way to view the force of selection (Taylor, 1981; Taylor and Bulmer, 1980). Now, in equation 5.1, the productivity of the group as a whole (in terms of fertilized, migrant females) is related to the sex ratios produced by the colonizers. An individual's fitness may be thought of as being made up of two parts: (1) What proportion of the migrants will carry the individual's genes? (2) How many migrants will there be? Suppose, for example, that regardless of the sex ratios produced, all groups will contribute c migrants. After the production of fertilized females, we simply draw c to migrate and destroy all the others. Our mutant's fitness will now depend only upon the proportion of c which carries its genes (called W_0), either in the migrant's genome or through the migrant's mate. This proportion will be W_t (equation 5.1) divided by the number of fertilized females just before we draw out the c migrants (or, from equation 5.1):

$W_0 = W_t / (b(1 - \hat{r}) + (n - 1)(1 - r)b)$, which gives

$$W_0 = \frac{1 - \hat{r}}{1 - \hat{r} + (n - 1)(1 - r)} + \frac{\hat{r}}{\hat{r} + (n - 1)r}. \qquad (5.5)$$

But this is simply the Shaw-Mohler equation for a population of size n. The ESS sex ratio is now again one-half, quite

70

independent of any sibmating. W_o shows that within each group, selection favors a sex ratio of one-half, the value which maximizes an individual's proportion of genes in the migrants. Selection for a biased sex ratio results because, in the original model, c is not a fixed value but varies with group composition. If all fertilized females become migrants, $c = b[1-\hat{r} + (n-1)(1-r)]$ for a group with one mutant. This is an explicit model of the process of group selection—the ESS r^* is the balance between selection within a group favoring a sex ratio of one-half, and selection between groups (for the production of migrants $= c$) favoring a female biased sex ratio (Colwell, 1981). In general, if c is taken to be a function of r and $\hat{r}$ in a group which contains one mutant and $n-1$ normals, the mutant's fitness (W_t) is $W_0 \cdot c$. The ESS sex ratio is then found by differentiating $\log(W_0 \cdot c)$ with respect to $\hat{r}$, setting $\hat{r} = r^*$, and solving for r^*. We get the following condition:

$$\overbrace{\frac{\partial \log c}{\partial \hat{r}}}^{\text{between-group productivity}} + \underbrace{\left(\frac{n-1}{2n}\right)\left(\frac{1}{r^*} - \frac{1}{1-r^*}\right)}_{\text{within-group}} = 0. \qquad (5.6)$$

This clearly shows the importance of a change in group productivity with sex ratio (i.e., $\partial \log c / \partial \hat{r}$) for selection to favor a shift from equality. In fact, since this model assumes that all males are equally likely to fertilize females and that all females are equally likely to be migrants, it also shows the possibility of selecting for male-biased sex ratio (i.e., if $\partial \log c / \partial \hat{r} > 0$) (Wilson and Colwell, 1981).

It is well known that the strength of group selection depends upon the variation between groups in gene frequencies. In the above models, sampling error is the source of this variation. This is why the sex ratio is more biased in smaller groups, where the sampling error is larger. Association among kin may also increase this variation (Hamilton, 1979). Hamilton noted that clutch-size variation among the foundresses would have similar effects. As an extreme example, if five foundresses are present but one produces

71

90% of the offspring, then the sex ratio behaves more like a single foundress. I have extended the basic diploid, autosomal model (equation 5.2) to the situation where variation in clutch size exists but where all females produce the same sex ratio. Later, we shall allow the various females to produce different sex ratios (Werren, 1980a,b, 1982). For the single sex ratio case, the ESS r^* takes a very simple form, given as follows.

$$r^* = \frac{n - 1 - \sigma^2/\mu^2}{2n}, \tag{5.7}$$

where

σ^2 = variance in clutch size among the foundresses within a group;

μ = mean clutch size.

If $n = 1$, $\sigma^2 = 0$. Otherwise, positive variance ($\sigma^2 > 0$) makes the group size effectively smaller.

THE HAYSTACK MODEL

Bulmer and Taylor (1980a) and Wilson and Colwell (1981) have considered generalizations of the basic LMC model. Bulmer and Taylor term their islands *haystacks* (after Maynard Smith's 1964 group selection model). Consider a hypothetical diploid mouse. At the beginning of each breeding season haystacks are colonized by a number (n) of fertilized females. Their offspring breed there for several generations (G) until the following year, when new stacks become available for colonization. Population growth within a stack is exponential. There are two possible mating structures: (1) dispersing females mate with males from their own stack prior to dispersal, and (2) females mate after dispersal with males chosen at random from the population. Wilson and Colwell (1981) considered very similar models but with haplodiploid sex determination, because the organisms which stimulated their efforts were haplodiploid mites. The qualitative results do not differ for the two modes of sex determination, so I shall discuss the diploid case.

If females mate prior to dispersal and one generation is spent in the haystack, the model reduces to LMC and r^* is $(n-1)/2n$. Surprisingly, r^* is quite insensitive to the number of generations in the stack, and $r^* \sim (n-1)/2n$ for up to eight generations in the stack. The error on r^* from using the formula is at most $\sim 3\%$. If mating is at random after dispersal, then r^* depends more strongly on the number of generations spent in the stack. I have graphed r^* as a function of n and G in Figure 5.2. Note that the sex ratio is one-half with one generation, as there is no group structure, only random mating in each generation.

It is clear that both these mating systems select for female-biased sex ratios because group productivity is related to population growth within a haystack, and thus is related to the females present. Within each stack, selection favors a sex ratio of a half. Again, if there is population regulation within each stack so that the groups do not differ in productivity, the ESS sex ratio returns to a half. In some extreme situations, group productivity may even be enhanced by a male-biased sex ratio (Wilson and Colwell, 1981).

LOCAL RESOURCE COMPETITION (LRC)

In the examples discussed so far, dispersal was at random at some phase of the life history; we could define a colonizer. Clark (1978) considered a more complicated situation. Suppose that a female occupies a territory. She produces both sons and daughters. Her daughters remain in the natal area and inherit her territory, while her sons disperse widely in search of mates. Her daughter's mates will come from elsewhere in the population. Clearly, if only one female will inherit the territory, the mother should produce one successor and make the rest of her brood males. There is local competition for resources among her daughters but not her sons. A son's reproductive success is not related to what his brothers are doing, but if the natal space is limited, the daughters do compete with each other. Clark proposed that selection would favor a sex ratio biased toward the sex where there is relatively less competi-

73

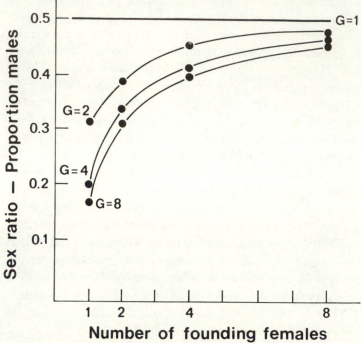

FIGURE 5.2. ESS sex ratios (autosomal control) under the haystack model. At time zero haystacks are colonized by founding females (and their mates) drawn at random from a large population. The founders mate, produce offspring, and die. Their offspring do likewise until G generations have been spent in the haystack. The descendants of the founders then leave the haystack and form a random mating pool. New founders are drawn from this pool. This process is like LMC, except that mating takes place after dispersal. Population growth within the haystack is exponential, and the result is an ESS female-biased sex ratio. This is a process of group selection (original values from Bulmer and Taylor, 1980a.)

tion among close relatives (here siblings). She also noted that there could exist local resource enhancement if cooperation among same-sexed siblings enhanced their reproductive success.

W. D. Hamilton (unpublished) has modeled LRC as follows. Consider an insect with winged males and wingless females. Let n adult females occupy an island that can support precisely n adults. Each adult female produces a large clutch. The males disperse and the daughters remain behind to compete with each other for the island. The daughters from the n broods are now reduced to n adult females and they are inseminated by migrant males. For such a situation the ESS sex ratio is $1 - r^* = (n - 1)/(2n - 1)$. If $n = 1, 1 - r^* = 0$, which effectively means that a mother produces a single daughter to replace herself. Bulmer and Taylor (1980a) and Taylor (1981) have also proposed this general principle: the sex ratio will be biased in favor of the sex with the smaller degree of competition between sibs. Relative dispersal of the two sexes will often mediate the potential for competition, with the sex showing less dispersal also showing more competition. They considered this for some special models and showed that qualitatively the principle works well.

The LRC principle is not really different from the previous models. The sex ratio is to be biased toward the "more productive sex." In the LMC model without sib mating (equation 5.3), reproductive gains to the mutant mother are linear through daughters ($\propto 1 - \hat{r}$) but show diminishing returns through sons, or,

$$\propto \left(\frac{\hat{r}}{\hat{r} + (n - 2)r} \right),$$

i.e., daughters do not compete with each other, while sons do. The same holds for the basic LMC model of Hamilton (1967). The effect of forcing all groups to produce the same number of migrants (c) was to force daughters to compete with each other to the same degree that sons did. Thus, the sex ratio moved from a female bias back to equality.

The next section examines the evidence for the structured population hypotheses.

HAPLODIPLOIDY AND SPATIALLY STRUCTURED POPULATIONS

In the original formulation of local resource competition, Clark (1978) applied the principle to a prosimian primate, where daughters compete (perhaps even with their mother) for the natal area, while sons disperse widely. Sex ratio among the young animals was biased toward sons, consistent with the model. However, the strongest evidence for LRC comes from social hymenoptera which reproduce by fission of existing colonies. In honeybees, a new queen inherits the nest and a good fraction of the workers; the old queen departs (to found a new nest) with the rest of the workers. Disregarding the question of the division of workers between queens (and possible conflict of interest—Chapter eight), Stubblefield (1980) noted that this is extreme LRC, as there is only one nest to inherit. Consistent with this is the fact that honeybees produce few new queens, but many drones. Hamilton (1972) had earlier suggested that the overproduction of drones might be considered due to the fact that the "workers invested" in the new queen are similar to resource invested in daughters; Fisher's principle of equal allocation would then insure the production of many sons. Stubblefield (1980) suggested that the biology is more consistent with LRC.

Since local mate competition (LMC) and the haystack model are founded upon almost identical principles, I will discuss the evidence for both of them in this section, again using haplodiploid organisms. Both models predict an extremely female-biased sex ratio with few foundresses (small local breeding population), and an equal sex ratio with many foundresses. If sons and daughters are of unequal cost, this latter situation equilibrates the resource in each sex, rather than the sex ratio itself. Different population structures alter the expected shape of the relation between group size and the sex ratio, but a steady rise from female biased to equality is shown in most if not all models.

In his original formulation of the LMC hypothesis, Hamilton (1967) listed twenty-six insect and mite species which were haplodiploid and typically had sib mating. All had a strong female bias in the sex ratio. Scolytid bark beetles were of particular interest since they could be divided into two general life histories. In the first, a female and her brood occupy a gallery under bark, and mating takes place before dispersal from the larval host. In the second type mating takes place after dispersal, upon arrival at the

76

new host. In the first, there is typically sib mating, the sex ratio is strongly female biased, and males are often flightless (reviewed in Beaver, 1977). In the second, sex ratio at emergence from the larval host is near equality (data in Bartels and Lanier, 1974; Bakke, 1968). Hopping (1962, 1964) discussed a situation in the genus *Ips* in which mating takes place after dispersal but where the population sex ratio is nonetheless female biased. Here two kinds of females were observed. One produced all-female broods, the other a sex ratio of equality. Both needed to be fertilized, and Hopping proposed that the single "species" actually consisted of a normal bisexual plus a strain with gynogenetic females (sperm not used in fertilization). Bakke (1968) found the same pattern in another *Ips* species. Sex ratios were very female biased overall, but within the mixed broods there was equality (total for 4 study areas = 48% males, N = 843). He also proposed that the all-female type was a parthenogenetic race. While more data are needed, it is clear that this female-biased sex ratio is quite unlike that predicted by an LMC model, where *each* mother should have a female bias among her children.

In a later paper on fig wasps, Hamilton (1979) showed a general positive relationship between the presence of winged males (an indicator of how much mating takes place after dispersal from the host fig) and the proportion of males. Waage (1982) studied LMC in the hymenopteran family Scelionidae. The large majority of species parasitize the eggs of Lepidoptera and Hemiptera. A single wasp egg is laid per host egg, but Waage argued that the degree of LMC was probably related to the dispersion of host eggs. The hosts ranged from those depositing eggs singly to those with masses of up to ~ 1000 eggs. Wasp species attacking eggs deposited singly should show little LMC, as should those attacking large masses. Here, the mass exceeds the egg-laying capacity of a single female, and the mass would most likely attract several wasp females. Excluding species attacking singly deposited eggs, LMC should generally decline with increasing size of the egg mass attacked. Waage examined field data (his own and from the literature), and assigned each species to an egg mass of typical size. Data for nearly thirty species showed the expected trend, with the sex ratio increasing from female biased to near equality, as a function of increasing egg mass size (shown in Fig. 5.3).

Probably the strongest evidence for the LMC model comes from wasps and mites in which the degree of LMC varies dramatically through space and time, and where theory predicts a facultative, short-term alteration in the sex ratio. LMC is more likely in a gregarious parasitoid, in which several eggs are laid on a single host and where most mating takes place among the children emerging from the host. This effectively provided the material for Hamilton's 1967 list. Here, LMC declines if superparasitism

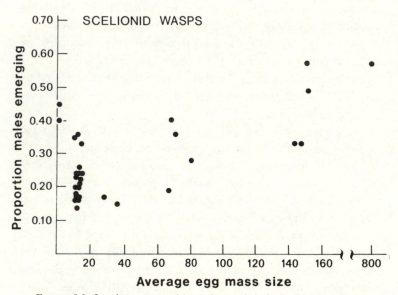

FIGURE 5.3. Local mate competition and sex ratio in Scelionid wasps. The wasps are solitary egg parasites. Host eggs show various degrees of dispersion, from just a few eggs in a clump to several hundred. Wasp species attacking hosts with few eggs per clump show much LMC; those attacking hosts with many eggs per clump show little LMC, since here several female wasps oviposit on each mass of eggs. Data for nearly 30 species of wasps (each species assigned to its typical egg mass size) show the expected trend. At low egg mass size, the sex ratio is very female-biased. As egg mass size increases, the sex ratio increases to near equality. (Figure redrawn from Waage, 1982.)

occurs because mating then takes place among the broods of two or more females. LMC may occur in solitary parasitoids if the hosts are clumped so that mating mostly takes place among the offspring emerging from a single clump, as just discussed for the Scelionidae (Waage, 1981). LMC declines for both gregarious and solitary species if the hosts are clumped with several mothers ovipositing on a clump. One wasp species (*Nasonia*) has been well studied with respect to these effects.

Nasonia vitripennis is a small (1-3mm), gregarious, parasitoid wasp (family Pteromalidae) which attacks the pupae of cyclorrhaphous flies (blowflies). It has been much studied (particularly its genetics) and the general biology is well known (reviews in Whiting, 1967; Cassidy, 1975). Edwards (1954) and Wylie (1958) describe the host-finding and oviposition behavior. *Nasonia* females parasitize pupae from one to several days old (Wylie, 1963; Chabora and Pimentel, 1966). Upon locating a host puparium, a female climbs on and searches its surface, tapping rapidly with her antennae. She drills through the puparium wall with her ovipositor which then is plunged deep within the pupa. At this time, she presumably assesses host suitability for oviposition and also injects a venom which kills and preserves the pupa (Beard, 1964; Wylie, 1958). Eggs are laid in a circle around the sting site in the space between the pupa and the puparium. Following oviposition, females feed on host fluids, which are necessary to mature additional eggs (Edwards, 1954; King and Hopkins, 1963). Multiple attacks are made upon a single host before oviposition is complete (Wylie, 1965). During the interval between attacks, while new eggs are maturing, a female may rest quietly or move about the immediate vicinity of the host, possibly assessing the presence of nearby hosts. After several batches of eggs are laid, a female leaves in search of new hosts. The final clutch size ranges from 10 to 50 eggs. The sex ratio of the primary parasite is 10–15% males. Superparasitism occurs when a female oviposits on a previously parasitized host.

Nasonia was of particular interest to Hamilton (1967) since the superparasite increased the proportion of males among her brood,

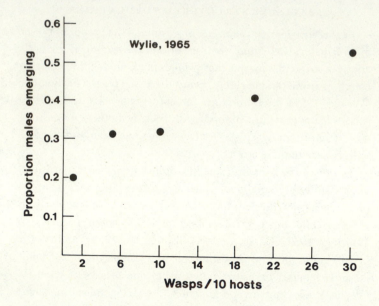

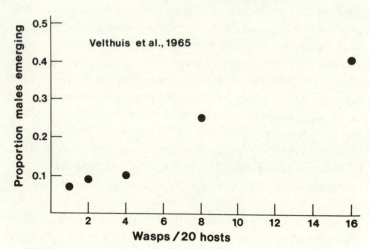

FIGURE 5.4. Sex ratio as a function of number of associated ovipositing females for the wasp *Nasonia* attacking fly pupae. Experimental details (e.g., blowfly versus housefly hosts, container size, etc.) varied widely among workers, yet the results are quite comparable. As predicted by LMC, sex ratio rises from few males to near equality. Walker's 1967 data show a clear asymptote.

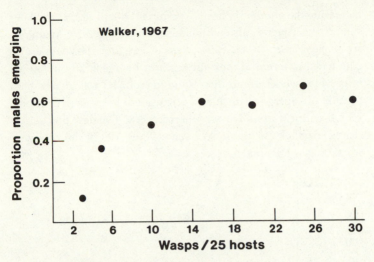

FIGURE 5.4. continued

as is predicted by LMC theory (Wylie, 1966; Holmes, 1970, 1972, Werren, 1980a, 1982). Males have short wings and cannot fly, so that mating takes place on the host or, if hosts are clumped, in the immediate vicinity. There are several lab studies of sex ratio alteration related to the degree of crowding of females. Wylie (1965, 1966) studied *Nasonia* on a house-fly host (*Musca*). *Musca* is not a natural host for *Nasonia* and mortality was rather high compared to studies on blowfly hosts. When he confined increasing numbers of wasps with ten hosts, the sex ratios clearly increased from female biased to near equality (Fig. 5.4). Walker (1967) and Velthuis et al. (1965) carried out similar experiments (using blowfly hosts) with similar results (Fig. 5.4). Walker's (1967) data are of particular interest since they show an asymptote at about 60% males. In addition, data from another of her experiments, which varied both host and parasite number, show that the proportion of males increases (for a fixed number of wasps) as the number of hosts increase, or (for a fixed number of hosts) as the number of wasps increase. This shift is predicted by theory since LMC delines with increased spacing of the broods, brought about by either decreasing the number of wasps or

81

increasing the number of hosts. Werren (1980b, 1982) carried out similar experiments, also with blowfly hosts (Fig. 5.5). Again, we see a clear rise in sex ratio to near equality. His work also eliminated differential mortality as a factor (generally unknown in previous work). In all these situations, LMC was altered both because of superparasitism and because the hosts were clumped. In lab cultures of *Nasonia,* where several females' broods are reared together (details in Werren, 1980b, 1982), the emergent sex ratio is ~ 50% males.

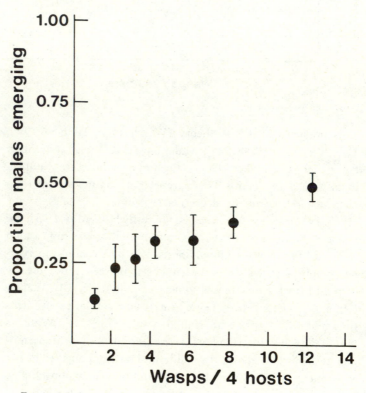

FIGURE 5.5. Sex ratio from patches containing 1 to 12 associated ovipositing females for the wasp *Nasonia* attacking blowfly pupae. Mean values ±2 standard errors are represented (at least 8 replicates per density). The mean values are rather close to those predicted by haplodiploid LMC theory (Fig. 5.1). These experiments eliminated sex-specific mortality as a causal factor (its effect is generally unknown for the data in Fig. 5.4). (Redrawn from Werren, 1982.)

In nature, *Nasonia* attacks a wide range of blowfly species (Whiting, 1967). Werren (1980b, 1982) has shown that the host situations utilized range from single pupae to thousands of pupae in a patch (i.e., under a large carcass). In general, more females are attracted to larger carcasses. While it is not possible to know the number of females (foundresses) at a given patch, it is possible to estimate the number of wasps emerging from a patch. This should generally be correlated with number of foundresses. Figure 5.6 is such a sex ratio plot for *Nasonia* (Werren, 1980b, 1982; unpublished data of S. W. Skinner). These field data show a clear rise to a sex ratio near equality. Since fewer than one-third of the hosts in these patches were attacked, these data eliminate superpa-

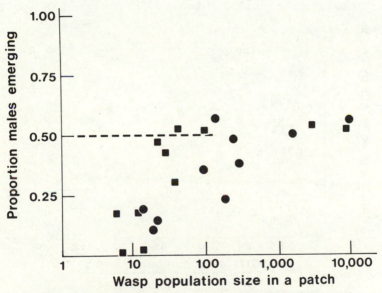

FIGURE 5.6. Field sex ratios among emerging *Nasonia,* for various sized patches of hosts. While the number of associated ovipositing females could not be determined, the number of emerging wasps (*X* axis) could. These two variables are positively related, so that LMC declines in larger patches. As predicted by LMC theory, the proportion of males increases to 0.5. Since fewer than a third of the hosts were attacked in these patches, the data eliminate superparasitism and sex differential mortality as factors in the sex ratio shift. (Redrawn from Werren, 1982 [●], with additional unpublished data of S. W. Skinner [■].

rasitism and sex differential mortality as factors in the sex ratio shift. The data must be treated with some caution, however, since at least two extrachromosomal factors affecting the sex ratio are known to occur in the populations studied (Werren, Skinner, and Charnov, 1981; Skinner, 1982). These are further discussed in Chapter Eight.

Holmes (1970, 1972) and Werren (1980a,b, 1982) analyzed in detail the sex ratio response for *Nasonia* under superparasitism. In the original Hamilton (1967) formalism, two females ovipositing on a host were assumed to be aware of each other's presence and to be identical in all respects (e.g., same clutch size). Werren and Holmes both realized that with *Nasonia*, the second female (superparasite) usually lays a smaller clutch than the first. Both authors (see also Suzuki and Iwasa, 1980) developed ESS type

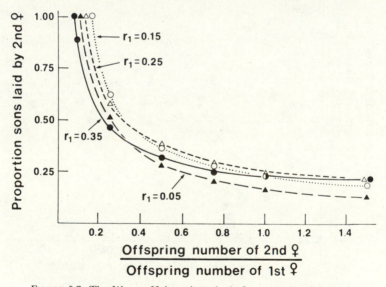

FIGURE 5.7. The Werren-Holmes hypothesis for sex ratio adjustment under LMC and superparasitism. Two females oviposit on a host, the second (the superparasite) producing a smaller clutch size than the first. An ESS argument shows the sex ratio of the second female (proportion of sons) as a function of her relative clutch size (x axis) and the sex ratio of the first female (r_1). The second female's predicted sex ratio is fairly independent of the first's, but very dependent on the relative clutch size. (From Werren, 1980a,b. 1982.)

models for the superparasite similar to Hamilton's (1967), but allowing for differential clutch size. Werren's theoretical results are shown in Figure 5.7. The second female's ESS sex ratio is rather insensitive to the first female's sex ratio, but changes dramatically with the relative clutch sizes. Likewise, the primary parasite's sex ratio is very insensitive to what the second female does. Holmes (1970) obtained similar theoretical results. Werren (1980a,b, 1982) used genetic markers to identify the offspring of the two females, and carried out many experiments to test this model. His 1980a and 1982 papers provide experimental detail (and consideration of alternative hypotheses), and Figure 5.8 is the final result. There is a striking correspondence between theory and data.

Data on other parasitoids also support the prediction that females kept in groups may shift the sex ratio from female biased

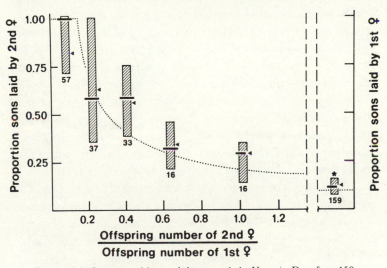

FIGURE 5.8. Superparasitism and the sex ratio in *Nasonia*. Data from 159 superparasitized hosts show the second female's (the superparasite) sex ratio as a function of her relative brood size. The data are divided into five *X*-axis categories. Bars present median values, stippled areas the first quartile. Small arrows present mean values. The dotted line shows the theoretical expected relation, using the first female's sex ratio as shown at the right. (From Werren, 1980a, 1982.)

85

toward equality. Some of these are reviewed by Kochetova (1977). *Trissolcus grandis* is a solitary egg parasite. Viktorov and Kochetova (1973a) showed that females kept alone produced about 13% sons. Females simply kept in tubes which contained traces of other females (previous occupancy) altered their sex ratio to 37% sons. In this same species, females kept in groups also produced more sons (Viktorov, 1968). Viktorov and Kochetova (1973b) showed a similar result for *Dahlbominus fuscipennis*, a gregarious ectoparasite of sawfly pupae. They also eliminated differential mortality as a cause of the sex ratio shift.

Wilkes (1963), working with *D. fuliginosus,* showed a similar sex ratio shift under crowding, but different strains of wasp showed different shifts. These differences may be genetic. If so, they provide material for experiments on natural selection for the sex ratio. Wilkes (1963) explained the data by a differential mortality hypothesis and produced some direct evidence for this effect. By mixing up several broods and placing them on hosts at clutch sizes of 5 to 175/host, he produced a shift in males from 14% in the low to 28% in the high. Mortality rose from 25% to 43%. This sex ratio shift must have been due to differential mortality, since the starting sex ratio was on average the same in all treatments. However, in other experiments, he observed sex ratio shifts which were in the direction predicted by the LMC theory and were simply too large to be accounted for by these mortality levels. The implication is that both mortality and a shift in the primary sex ratio are required to explain the pattern.

Differential mortality has also been suggested as the cause of a well-known sex ratio shift in the egg parasite *Trichogramma evanescens* (Salt, 1936). The species is facultatively gregarious since large eggs will allow the development of several individuals. In his classic experiments, Salt varied the number of wasps/100 hosts (Fig. 5.9). There is a clear rise in the sex ratio from below 25% males to just over a half. Mortality increased dramatically with crowding, and Salt suggested that females fared relatively worse than males. I know of no direct evidence for this differential mortality, and suggest (based on the form of Fig. 5.9) that the sex

86

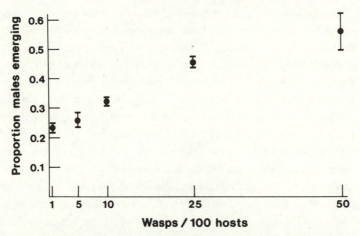

FIGURE 5.9. Sex ratio versus crowding of females (in lab experiments) for the egg parasite *Trichogramma*. Immature mortality was much higher under crowded conditions, and Salt (1936) proposed that this caused the sex ratio shift. However, the pattern is very suggestive of a shift in the primary sex ratio due to decreased LMC under crowded conditions. Data are means ±2 s.e. (averaged over several replicates). (Original data from Salt, 1936.)

ratio shift represents the theoretically expected LMC response. Even if differential mortality is eventually implicated, the strong female bias at low densities (very common in *Trichogramma* species) remains unexplained and is very suggestive of LMC.

To summarize, the evidence from parasitic wasps strongly supports the LMC-Haystack predictions. Since group productivity is almost always a positive function of the females present, we expect the sex ratio to be female biased with small mating group size, moving to near equality as group size increases. Many species show the female bias associated with small group size. Many also show the predicted sex ratio shift with increasing group size. I now turn to sex ratio in mites.

Wilson and Colwell (1981) applied the haystack model to two genera of hummingbird flower mites, *Rhinoseius* and *Proctolaelaps* (11 spp.). They showed a positive correlation of group size with adult sex ratio (proportion males), and convincingly argued for a haystack interpretation.

87

Predacious mites in the family Phytoseiidae have been widely studied with respect to sex ratio, since they are used in biological control of phytophagous spider mites. They have a form of haplodiploidy, although females must mate to produce offspring. Several studies have shown sex ratios to be female biased at maturity (Dyer, 1975; Schulton et al., 1978; Amano and Chant, 1978). In the last two studies, the three species employed gave female proportions of 0.89 to 0.73, and the work eliminated sex differential mortality as a major factor. In an experiment with poor versus good food conditions, female proportion decreased from 0.89 (good) to 0.76 (poor); again, mortality was not a major factor. Poor food conditions may well be an indicator of crowding. Dyer (1975, with Swift, 1979) studied adult sex ratios in field collections of 15 species of Phytoseiid mites. Female proportion ranged from 0.52 to 0.97, although most were between 0.75 and 0.90. Literature data for 19 species showed a mean female proportion of 0.73 (range 0.63–0.85). Analysis of field data for 8 abundant species showed no seasonal sex ratio trends, and field data for all 15 showed no relation to crowding. Since the data are for adult sex ratios, critical interpretation is difficult and it is hard to know what the lack of relation to crowding really means. This form of haplodiploidy *may* also limit short-term alteration of the sex ratio (but recall the work cited above). However, Bull (1983) offers an interesting alternative to the LMC hypothesis. Under random mating and maternal control, the ESS sex ratio is ½ males. However, with this form of haplodiploidy, called "paternal genome loss" by Bull (1983), *and zygotic* (as opposed to maternal) *control* of sex ratio, the sex ratio evolves to an equilibrium of only ⅓ males under random mating.

Probably the ultimate haystack organisms are quill mites who inhabit the shafts of bird fathers and feed on tissue fluids by piercing the wall of the quill. Kethley (1971) studied *Syringophiloidus minor*, attacking the house sparrow. During the fall molt, one finds one or more fertilized, nongravid females in a new quill. The females, mated before they left their brood quill, enter the umbilicus of the developing feather. As the feather develops, the umbilicus closes, and no new foundresses can enter. Most infected feathers had one foundress, but a few had two or more. It is not known if more than one foundress reproduces in a single quill, although the sex ratio strongly suggests that only one does. The foundress produces ~12 eggs, and she dies before the progeny mature. Usually there is only one male, and he inseminates his sisters, who then each produce ~12 eggs. Again, each brood contains a single male. By spring the second generation is mature, and fills the feather shaft. Some individuals disperse at this time to the nestling birds, but many wait and leave their quill just before the fall molt. Hamilton (1979) lists several other genera of mites with similar life histories, and notes a strong tendency for the sex ratio to be female biased. Situations with multiple foundresses should show a sex ratio shift toward sons, but at present there are no data. As a final mite example, I will discuss spider mites, a very common pest of house and agricultural plants.

Spider mites are small, haplodiploid creatures (~0.5mm length) that suck out the contents of leaf cells. They are of immense economic importance (Welch, 1979; Wrensch, 1979). I will discuss their life history in some detail because they seem almost ideal for testing aspects of sex ratio theory; they are very simple to rear. The general life history (with reference to the genus *Tetranychus*) has been reviewed by Mitchell (1973), from which most of this discussion is drawn. A post-dispersal, fertilized female mite feeds in a restricted area, which she marks out with silk. All of her eggs are laid in this area, and the young feed and develop within the territory. At the end of immature development, the young enter a quiescent deutonymph stage, and most are still in the original territory or very near it (McEnroe, 1969, 1970). Adult males actively guard female deutonymphs, and mate with them upon emergence as adults (Potter et al., 1976a,b). Since sperm competition favors the first male to mate (Helle, 1967), such guarding is of much importance to male reproductive success. Since only this female stage is available for mating, males often greatly outnumber available females, and actively fight for possession of the quiescent deutonymphs, particularly at high population densities (Potter, 1978, 1979). At low population densities, sibmating is probably the rule (Mitchell, 1973; McEnroe, 1969). However, at high densities, the territories are more closely packed and much of the mating is among non-relatives. After mating, on the first day of adult life, females become restless and disperse. This response is strong in crowded conditions but weak when resources are abundant. After dispersal, females settle down to begin a new cycle. Males do not disperse. They are much smaller than females (15–30% a female's weight), and stop growing at maturity. Females continue growing as adults. The sex ratio at maturity is often very female biased (Mitchell, 1972), and McEnroe (1969) suggested that this was due to LMC. If we consider the territory a feeding resource which a mother allocates to sons and daughters (under low population density), a sex ratio of 20% males translates into a resource allocation of 5% into males.

Two published studies have considered the impact of crowding on the sex ratio at maturity (Wrensch and Young, 1978; Zaher et al., 1979). Both confined various numbers of fertilized females to leaf discs and looked at the sex ratio produced among the progeny. Since leaf areas were very similar in the two studies, I have graphed the data in Figure 5.10 as sex ratio versus female mite density. As LMC predicts, the sex ratio increases with density to almost equality. At high population densities, the size difference in sons versus daughters may not represent a differential cost to the mother. Provided broods of several females compete for the same food resources, the "home" territory is no longer a resource the female allocates to *her* sons and daughters. Zaher et al. (1979) provided no mortality data for the immatures, while Wrensch and Young (1978) concluded that the sex ratio shift was due both to sex differential mortality *and* a shift in the primary sex ratio. Neither study discussed LMC.

Since male spider mites guard and fight over emerging females, an interesting situation presents itself. This paragraph is a short digression into the theory of kin-selection (Hamilton, 1964). At low population density, the contenders would most often be sibs. At high density they would often not be. We might expect

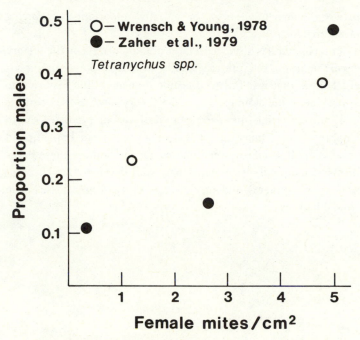

FIGURE 5.10. Crowding of females versus the sex ratio in spider mites (*Tetranychus*). The experiments confined females to leaf discs and looked at the sex ratio among the progeny produced. Leaf discs were ~3 cm^2 in both studies, so data are represented as female (associated ovipositing females) mite density. Data show a clear rise in the sex ratio from few males to near equality. (Data from Zaher et al., 1979; Wrensch and Young, 1978.)

aggression to be low when siblings interact, and much accentuated when the males are non-relatives (see Hamilton, 1964, 1979 for a discussion of fighting males in insects). Under crowded conditions and low resource availability, female spider mites emerge at much smaller sizes than in uncrowded conditions. However, under the same crowded conditions, newly emerged adult males are significantly larger compared to males in uncrowded populations (Mitchell, 1973). This may be due to the greater numbers of males per female at high densities (the sex ratio shift) and the fact that larger males are better able to win contests over females (Potter et al., 1976a,b). However, that the male-male competition is here

91

between non-relatives may be equally important in favoring larger male size.

This chapter has discussed a large amount of data on life history versus sex ratio, relevant to spatially structured population models. I think that it is fair to conclude that many life histories do approximate the assumptions of the theory, and the sex ratio is qualitatively (sometimes even quantitatively) as predicted. As in Chapter Four, almost all of the data come from haplodiploid organisms. It would be very interesting to compare these organisms with diploid species which have well-developed sex chromosomes (e.g., Diptera), and may lack the ability to alter the sex ratio from a half.

CHAPTER SIX

Sex Ratio in
Age-Structured Populations

Thus far all of our models have assumed discrete generations (e.g., Chapter Three). In this chapter I alter these models to look at age-structured populations. Age structure adds at least three new factors.

(1) The offspring may interact to affect the survival of the parent. For example, a son (compared to a daughter) may demand more maternal resource and increase maternal mortality.

(2) Time itself becomes an important resource since reproduction early in a generation is worth more than later in the generation. This is because the mother is less likely to be alive at an older age (Williams, 1957).

(3) Most age-structured population genetic models assume the population to be in a stable age distribution (we call this the SAD assumption). Studies of both short-lived insects (F. Taylor, 1980) and long-lived vertebrates (deer—McCullough, 1979) show that this assumption is often violated in nature. This may have interesting consequences for sex ratio evolution.

I would like to consider two special cases, which represent the end points of a continuum. In the first, many small offspring are produced in each breeding season; in the second a single large offspring is produced.

For the first situation, survivorship of the mother should be more closely related to the total resource (R) she allocates to reproduction and not to how that resource is divided each year among her numerous sons and daughters. Selection determines the tradeoff between R and her survivorship, but the division of R

93

among the sexes will be independent of that survivorship. Under the SAD assumption, all of the models from Chapter Three will apply here also. Age structure adds almost nothing new (see Leigh, 1970; Charnov, 1975, 1978; Charlesworth, 1977).

The second case is quite different. The mother invests in each offspring as an individual, and a son (for example) may well pose a different cost to the mother than a daughter. Consider the simple life history represented in Figure 6.1. Sons cost more than daughters because they impose a higher yearly mortality rate on their mother. How many sons should be born? If we require that all maternal age classes have the same sex ratio, the population genetics of the Appendix says that the ESS sex ratio from the mother's viewpoint is

$$r = \frac{1}{2}\left(\frac{S_f}{S_f + P_2 - P_1}\right) \qquad (r = \text{proportion sons produced}).$$

For a stationary (non-growing) population, this reduces to

$$r = \frac{1 - P_2}{(1 - P_2) + (1 - P_1)},$$

or (in words),

$$\frac{r}{1 - r} = \frac{\text{mom's mortality for rearing a daughter}}{\text{mom's mortality for rearing a son}}. \qquad (6.1)$$

As expected, the sex ratio is biased toward the cheaper sex and the expense is now measured in the mother's mortality. This equation (6.1) may be contrasted to equation (3.3). In (6.1) the cost of a son is the mortality imposed on the mother, and the ESS ratio of sons to daughters is the inverse ratio of the offsprings' costs. This is analogous to the discrete generation model (equation 3.3). It is of interest to note that the father's ESS sex ratio is one-half, since the decrements to maternal fitness do not affect his fitness. To complete the record, the offspring has an ESS sex ratio of

$$r = \frac{1}{2}\left(\frac{S_f}{S_f + \dfrac{P_2 - P_1}{2}}\right),$$

which is less biased than the mother's.

94

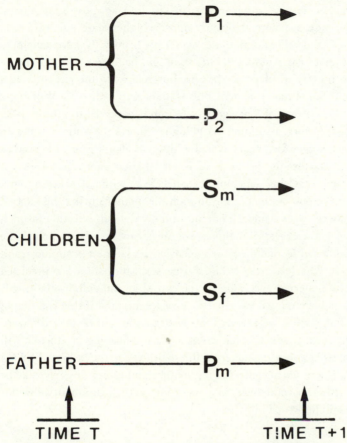

FIGURE 6.1. A simple life history with age structure. Breeding is at yearly intervals, and the young are first reproductive at age one year. Adult males have yearly survival of P_m. A single offspring is born each year. A son survives to age 1 at rate S_m, a daughter at rate S_f. A mother rearing a son has survival P_1; rearing a daughter, P_2. If $P_1 \neq P_2$, sons and daughters are of unequal cost to the mother. The mother's ESS sex ratio (equation 6.1) is biased toward the cheaper sex. However, the father's ESS sex ratio is equality.

The derivation of these results made no reference to a Shaw-Mohler equation or to the product theorem. However, they may be put in this form (Charnov, 1979a).

Hidden in these results is the assumption that one sex ratio must be used by all maternal age classes. When the cost to the mother is her survivorship, an interesting possibility arises. Suppose, as before, that sons impose a higher maternal death rate. Now, mortality accumulates over a life history. If more daughters are born early in life, the life span will be longer than if sons are born early in life. *Life-span* is thus related to the sex ratio as a function of maternal age. This is an example of G. C. Williams's (1957) theory of senescence; selection is expected to push to later ages factors associated with higher mortality and to bring to earlier ages factors associated with lower death rates. In this case the "factor" is the birth of a son (higher mortality) versus a daughter. Using some simple models (e.g., with two breeding ages, sons impose a higher mortality on the mother during the interval between ages 1 and 2), our intuition is upheld; selection favors a form of sex reversal with more of the cheaper sex born early in the mother's life, and the more expensive sex later on (a similar result is in Charlesworth, 1977). Large sex ratio shifts are predicted with maternal age. Thus, if the cost of an individual offspring is negatively related to maternal survivorship and if this is different for the sexes, we predict that the sex ratio will be biased toward the cheaper sex and that sex reversal in offspring production will take place over the maternal life span. Again, the father's ESS is a half, with no age effect. That mother and father disagree may be quite important here, and we know very little about how this might be settled in nature.

ON VIOLATION OF THE STABLE AGE DISTRIBUTION ASSUMPTION

The models thus far discussed assume a stable age distribution. Werren and Charnov (1978) investigated (both analytically and through computer simulation) what happens if the SAD assumption is violated. Assuming equal son-daughter cost, adult survivorship independent of sex ratio, and panmixia, the answer was very simple; the ESS sex ratio was still one-half. However, these models assumed that a single sex ratio was used all the time. If we allow a female to produce an altered sex ratio at some particular time, the situation becomes more complex and more interesting.

To investigate sex ratio selection under these conditions, two models were developed, a cyclical model and a perturbation model. In the cyclical model, life history expectations for males and females vary cyclically over time, perhaps because of seasonality. Consider the following simple example. Let individuals be born in the spring and the autumn. Males and females born in the spring survive until the autumn. They then reproduce and die. Of those born in the autumn, the females survive to reproduce in the spring (and then die), while the males survive to reproduce in the spring and some survive to reproduce again the following autumn. Life history expectations differ for individuals born in the spring versus the autumn, and some overlap exists in generations (Fig. 6.2). This example is extreme in that only one sex (δ) reproduces twice (so that spring-born males face reproductive competition from males born the previous autumn, while spring-born females face no such competiton).

If r_f and r_s are the offspring sex ratios (proportion males) in the autumn and spring respectively, the ESS results predict that $r_f >$ ½ while $r_s < $ ½. As the amount of competition for mates faced by spring-born males in the autumn increases due to the presence of autumn-born males of the previous year, the deviations in sex

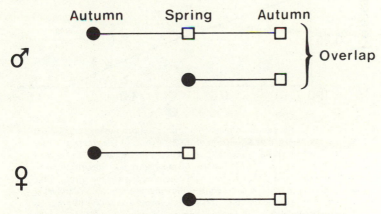

FIGURE 6.2. Representation of the hypothetical set of life histories in a seasonal environment. ●, born; □, mating period. Autumn-born males and females both live to breed in the spring *but,* of these two, only some males are still alive the next autumn. (From Werren and Charnov, 1978.)

ratios increase from ½. Figure 6.3 shows this effect of increasing overlap upon the ESS sex ratios among spring-born and autumn-born, as derived from an analytical population genetics treatment of the life history outlined above (Werren, 1980b). This simple model captures the basic points. Selection can favor seasonal shifts in sex ratio if males and females experience different life histories which vary seasonally, and, because of overlapping generations, if those born at different times compete with each other for relative reproductive success. This creates a situation where a parent may "derive" more fitness by shifting the sex ratio toward offspring of the sex with improved reproductive success relative to the other sex. Seger (1982) has extended this idea of a seasonal shift in sex ratio (for bivoltine life histories) to include partial overlap among one or both sexes, and haplodiploid, as well as diploid genetic

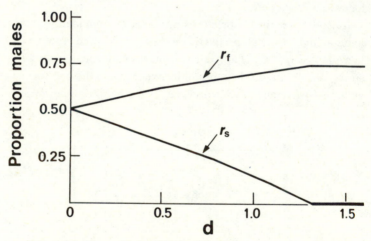

FIGURE 6.3. The equilibrium (ESS) solutions for autumn sex ratio (r_f) and spring sex ratio (r_s) as a function of d, a measure of the competition for mates faced by spring-born males in the autumn due to the presence of autumn-born males. The life history is from Figure 6.2. Specifically, if N_f is the number born in the autumn, N_s the number born in the spring, S_f the survival of autumn-born males to the following autumn, S_s the survival of spring-born males to autumn, and C the competitive ability of autumn-born males relative to spring-born males in gaining mates during the autumn, then $d = C(N_f S_f / N_s S_s)$. As d increases, the reproductive success of spring-born males decreases. (From Werren and Charnov, 1978.)

98

control. His results are similar, but more general than those given here.

The model just presented assumed that life history characteristics vary seasonally. Now consider a perturbation model. Assume that a population with overlapping generations has a stable age distribution, and suppose that the population is occasionally perturbed by a period of exceptional mortality or survival, followed by a return to "normal conditions." These sorts of perturbations may be common in nature; they can be caused by dramatic weather changes such as cold or heat spells and floods. Further suppose that one sex can be affected considerably more than the other by such events, due to behavioral or physiological differences. Males are known to be more vulnerable to environmental stress than females in many species. The perturbations must be dramatic and fairly frequent if they are to select for facultative sex ratios. The question follows: does selection favor genes which allow an individual (mother or father) to respond to the change from stable age distribution conditions by producing more of the sex which suffered the greater mortality (in terms of deviation from normal survival)? We (Werren and Charnov, 1978) investigated this question using computer simulation.

Let us suppose, for example, that the perturbation caused young males to suffer twice their normal rate of mortality between birth and age one. A gene which biases sex ratio toward males in the next generation would be favored because of the reduced competition faced by those males relative to their own expected mortality. On the other hand, if females suffered twice their normal rate of mortality, selection would favor biasing sex ratio toward females in the next generation. Again, if the facultative response is not possible (a single sex ratio is used all the time), the computer results indicate that one-half is the equilibrium value, and that the violation of stable age distribution does not itself alter the value from that predicted under Fisher's theory (i.e., Chapter Three).

I have discussed both models in terms of varying ability to survive; however, the results should also hold for other fitness components which vary over time (such as fecundity or competition for territories; do early spring-born males procure the best territories?). The basic difference between these two models is that the life history changes are predictable in the cyclical model and unpredictable in the perturbation model. Therefore, in the latter case the sex ratio response can occur only after the life history change. Both models predict that selection will favor a shift in offspring sex ratio toward the sex with improved reproductive success relative to the other sex. McCullough (1979) has made similar suggestions, particularly in reference to deer. I now consider data relative to these non-SAD models.

This facultative sex ratio response requires that the parent be able to control the sex ratio among its offspring (or the offspring control its sex development) at the appropriate time. This suggests that we begin by looking for cues which may be used in this time assessment. It is important to note two factors. First, the cues used for response to a perturbation in the sex ratio are likely to be very different from those involved in seasonal shifts in the sex ratio. The first situation involves a response to an event that has just happened, while the second entails a prediction of an event in the future. The second factor is that, just as in the case of the host-size model (Chapter Four), the responses to altered conditions are relative. For example, whether or not mortality falling on the young males is unusual depends upon what the usual mortality is. This means that the sex ratio response should vary from place to place, scaled to the normal conditions in a location.

Seger (1982) examined sex ratio data for twelve species of bivoltine solitary Hymenoptera. The general prediction was that the spring generation should be female-biased, the second (summer, or fall) generation male-biased (Fig. 6.3, or Fig. 2 of Seger, 1982). Eleven of the twelve species showed the *expected direction* of sex ratio shift, while seven (of the twelve) showed statistical significance at the 0.06 level, or better. See Seger (1982) for qualifications on the data sets. Aside from these I know of no other data which are complete enough to permit a definitive test of this temporal or facultative shift model. However, I discuss here some

100

case histories of particular interest in the hope of stimulating further work. For much of the older literature I have found it very difficult to evaluate the data critically. Clearly, replication of the work is needed. (This discussion is from Werren and Charnov, 1978.)

There is evidence for temporal shifts of sex ratio in some parasitic Hymenoptera (Clausen, 1939; Flanders, 1946). Photoperiod (a seasonal cue) affects progeny sex ratio in several parasitoid wasps. In *Pteromalus puparum,* LD10:14 results in two to three times as many female progeny as are produced under LD14:10, although fertility is unaffected (Bouletreau, 1976). In another parasitic wasp, *Campoletis perdistinctus,* the greatest percentage of females is produced under LD12:12 (Hoelscher and Vinson, 1971). In the Brachonid wasp *Chelonus inanitus,* LD14:10 produced 61% emerging males while LD12:12 showed a slight excess of females (Rechav, 1978).

Life history expectations vary during the population cycle of multi-voltine rodents, and these changes may differ for males and females (Evans, 1949; Petrusewicz, 1960; Krebs et al., 1973). Juvenile sex ratios have been found to change with the population cycle in several species (Kalela, 1971; Canham, 1970; Fordham, 1971); however, this is difficult to interpret because of potential bias. The effect could be due to changes in behavior, mortality after weaning, or rates of maturation, none of which are sex ratio adaptations. In one case, litter sex ratios of field populations of the bank vole (*Clethrionomys glariolus*) were examined by bringing pregnant females into the laboratory. The sex ratios of the resulting litters were found to vary significantly with the population cycle (Nanmov et al., 1967).

There are several phenomena consistent with the prediction of the perturbation model that a scarcity of one sex leads to its overproduction in the next generation. Among mites of the genus *Macrocheles,* offspring sex ratio varies inversely with the adult sex ratio (Filipponi et al., 1972; Filipponi and Petrelli, 1975). In the plants *Silene dioca* (Correns, 1928) and *Rumex acetosa* (Rychlewski and Zarzycki, 1975), the sex ratio of seedlings varies inversely with density of pollen on the stigma. The physiological mechanism may be slow pollen tube grown of Y-bearing pollen. When pollen densities are low (a male perturbation?) the Y-bearing pollen has an improved chance of fertilizing ova. In a small population, random sampling on the adult sex ratio would have the same effect as a perturbation, therefore favoring a facultative response (see also Williams, 1966). Snyder (1962, 1976) manipulated populations of the woodchuck, *Marmota monax*, by removing adult females. While the sex ratio among young adults in natural, control populations was close to equality, the sex ratio among young adults in the experimental group (in the *next year*) was very female biased. This example was first discussed by Maynard Smith (1978).

Another line of evidence for the perturbation model is the effect of delayed fertilization on sex ratio. In some organisms a delay in mating or fertilization causes a dramatic increase in the proportion of males in the progeny. This is predicted if the mating delay reflects an abnormal scarcity of males. Hertwig (1912) showed in the anuran *Rana exculenta* that the sex ratio resulting from eggs with late fertilization gave a greater proportion males. Kuschakewitch (1910) demonstrated that the result was not due to differential mortality (according to Huxley, 1920, and James, 1937). Delayed fertilization leads to a predominance of males in several species of mealy bugs (James, 1937; Nelson-Rees, 1960), a butterfly (*Talaeproia tubulosa*) (Seiler, 1920), and three species of copepod (*Tisbe*) (Volkmann-Rocco, 1972). In the mealy bug (*Planococcus citri*), mating 0, 6, 8, and 10 weeks after emergence resulted in 102, 181, 327, and 991 males per 100 females, respectively. Sex ratio was ascertained at the prepupal stage; however, James (1937) showed that the changes in sex ratio were not due to differential mortality between conception and the prepupal stage. Nelson-Rees (1960) showed similar shifts in another species but also documented some other rather complex sex ratio shifts (which at present remain unexplained).

I summarize this chapter by noting that age structure provides some interesting additions to basic sex ratio theory, particularly under non-stable age conditions. The extension of LMC models to include age structure is yet to be done and will not be attempted here. Some of the age-structure predictions will be considered in the next chapter, which deals with vertebrate sex ratios.

CHAPTER SEVEN

Sex Ratio
in Vertebrates

This chapter will discuss vertebrate sex ratios and the extent to which we may use them to test aspects of sex allocation theory. It will focus on systems or data of particular interest for testing sex allocation hypotheses.

Many higher vertebrates (e.g., birds, mammals) have well-developed sex chromosomes. Under Mendelian segregation, this alone insures a sex ratio near equality at conception. The data (discussed later in the chapter) would also suggest that: (1) there is virtually no genetic variability for the early (near fertilization) sex ratio; (2) alteration of the sex ratio requires the parent to make decisions after fertilization. These decisions (e.g., abortion) may be costly to the parent, and this cost must be considered in any theory of sex ratio adjustment (either a population-wide adjustment toward overproduction of the cheaper sex or short-term adjustments in the sense of Trivers-Willard or Werren-Charnov).

Williams (1979) discussed sex ratio in vertebrates (particularly mammals and birds) and concluded that virtually all the data supported the simple notion that the sex ratio was an automatic result of segregation of the sex chromosomes. He concluded that this evidence said that the sex ratio is not really adaptive (i.e., it is *just* a result of segregation). I strongly disagree with this position, for two reasons. First, it begs the issue of why there are sex chromosomes in the first place. What are the selective forces involved in the establishment of sex chromosomes? Bull (1983) has shown that sex ratio selection plays an important part in the evolution of sex-determining mechanisms. A sex ratio of equality

104

near conception is selected for under such a wide variety of circumstances (see Chapter Three) that we should feel compelled to ask why the mechanism produces equality. Second, the existence of sex chromosomes may facilitate other processes (Charlesworth, 1978; Lucchesi, 1978), resulting, for example, in degeneration of the Y chromosome (i.e., the YY individuals die). This makes it difficult to evolve out of the system to a more flexible system of sex determination (Bull, 1981b). That is, the system may bring forth constraints on its own alteration. Thus, I disagree with Williams's position because it does not make full use of selection thinking. Selection on and resulting from sex chromosomes (or any other proximate mechanism) is an important and interesting question. Constraints (costs) to alteration of the sex ratio or the sex-determining mechanism are an integral part of the process and simply must be included in the theory, even if at present we have few guidelines as to how to do it. See Bull (1983) for a beginning.

The discussion in this chapter will be largely taxonomic (fish, herps, birds, mammals).

FISH

Sex ratio has been less studied in fish than in other vertebrate groups. Two classic studies on the viviparous top minnow, *Gambusia*, showed the juvenile sex ratio (microscopical examination of embryonic gonads) to be equality, with large sample sizes (Hildebrand, 1927; Geiser, 1924). Adult sex ratios were always considerably female biased. M. J. Holden (per. comm.) has provided data for embryonic sex ratios in the spiny dog-fish shark (sampled from a Scottish-Norwegian fishery). One-thousand-and-five pups (223 litters) showed 49% males. Since neither the sharks nor *Gambusia* have sex differences in cost of an offspring (measured by size), these data support the equality prediction, even though the adult sex ratios may depart from equality.

The strongest evidence for selection on sex ratio in fish comes from studies of species where the "two sexes" consist of a protogynous hermaphrodite morph and a male morph. Such species sometimes occur in situations in which the hermaphrodite is effectively a female (i.e., sex reversal is very rare). Here, the sex ratio at the time sex is determined is predicted to be equality. Data from two tropical wrasses (*Thalassoma* spp.) strongly support this prediction (Warner, 1982; Warner and Hoffman, 1980a). These species are discussed in detail in Chapter Eleven.

With respect to sex determination, the platyfish, *Xiphophorus maculatus,* is of much interest. Many populations are polymorphic for three sex chromosomes (females are WX, WY, or XX and males XY, YY [Kallman, 1973]). Obviously, if the X is absent we have female heterogamety (WY females, YY males), and with the W missing we have male heterogamety (XY males, XX females). The sex chromosomes have not been identified cytologically but are linked with visible (often color) marker genes. Bull and Charnov (1977) studied the theoretical population genetics of this system, and found that if all genotypes within a sex had equal fitness, there were an infinite number of possible equilibria, and the resulting genotype frequencies depended upon the starting conditions. To put it another way, there was a ridge in genotype frequency space which connected male to female heterogamety. If the population was moved off the top of the ridge, selection pushed it back, but not necessarily to the same spot. As one might expect, the primary sex ratio was a half all along the ridge, and sex ratio selection played a major role in forcing the population back to the ridge after displacement. With equal fitnesses the ridge was flat, so that we might expect genetic drift to lose the X or W allele. However, if the fitnesses of the genotypes are not equal, the ridge can become a peak and selection may favor all three sex chromosomes to be present (Bull and Charnov, 1977).

Since the sex chromosomes are linked to color genes, and since color plays different roles in male versus female fitness (sexual selection favors brighter males), all genotypes are probably not of equal fitness. Orzack et al. (1980) provide a general solution of the fitness conditions for all three chromosomes to be present in

106

equilibrium and experimental evidence that the conditions are indeed met in nature. With fitness differences with respect to sex genotype (and W, X, Y all present in equilibrium), the population primary sex ratio departs from equality. However, the departure is not very great unless the fitness differences are extreme (Charnov and Bull, 1977). This example is useful since a primary sex ratio near equality is probably present in natural populations, even though two of the mating combinations (WX:XY, YY:XX) produce very biased sex ratios. Sex ratio selection clearly plays a part in the equilibrium. This raises one interesting issue. For the polymorphism, XX females must suffer reduced fitness relative to WX or WY females and there is evidence that this is the case (Orzack et al., 1980). We might then expect XX females, when mated to XY males, to bias their sex ratio toward sons, substituting XY sons for the XX daughters. Another possibility would be for XX females to mate only with YY males. These patterns do not appear to occur (Kallman, 1973, 1975; Orzack et al., 1980).

REPTILES

Shine and Bull (1977) have reviewed sex ratio theory and data for several species of snakes. They sexed embryos for three species of Australian Elapid snakes. Two showed equality while the third showed a female bias (59% females, prob. < 0.05). Since sons and daughters apparently cost the same (based on size of embryos), this bias remains unexplained. They reviewed data on natal sex ratios for nineteen other species. Seventeen showed equality while two showed biased ratios. Unfortunately, the sexing technique for these two may have been incorrect, and Shine and Bull (1977) suggest that the data are suspect. An unpublished study by McKinley (1980) gives the most complete data for a snake. He studied the live bearer *Nerodia sipedon,* the northern water snake, and sexed and sized (dry wgt.) over 600 embryos from 28 gravid females from a single location. Male embryo size was equal to female embryo size, and the sex ratio did not vary with clutch size or mother's size. In all, there were 48% males, not different from equality.

Bull (1980) has reviewed sex determination in reptiles, and discussed what must be the most spectacular example of sex ratio shift for a vertebrate, that of temperature control of sex development. Bull and Vogt (1979) conclusively demonstrated that in nature sex determination is temperature dependent in several species of turtles. In lab studies, one of five species showed a sex ratio of equality regardless of incubation temperature, while the other four showed dramatic shifts. At a high temperature (30.5°C) almost all the eggs became females, while at a low temperature (25°C) almost all became males. Sex differential mortality was ruled out as a cause. Field experiments showed the same results for eggs buried in the sun versus the shade. Natural nests for map turtles (*Graptemys*) showed a bimodal sex ratio distribution with nests mostly male or female. Hatchlings from shaded nests were nearly always male.

Temperature-dependent sex determination (TSD) is now known from five families of turtles and two families of lizards (Bull, 1980). I have reproduced the data reviewed by Bull (1980) in Figure 7.1. Some reptiles show no temperature effect, those with a temperature shift show a threshold response at 28–30°C, while the snapping turtle shows two thresholds with all males at both high and low temperatures. Interestingly, the direction of sex ratio shift is the reverse in lizards; high temperature results in mostly males.

Bull et al. (1982a) studied the threshold in several turtle species, in both northern (Wisconsin) and southern (Alabama) locations. The mean June temperature varied by about 2–3°C between these locations; however, the temperature threshold varied by no more than one degree, if at all, between locations. It seems that female turtles must be selecting very particular habitats for their nests, and the sex ratio control follows from the distribution of nest temperature in the population as a whole. Bull et al. (1982b) conducted some elegant experiments on the sex ratio produced in

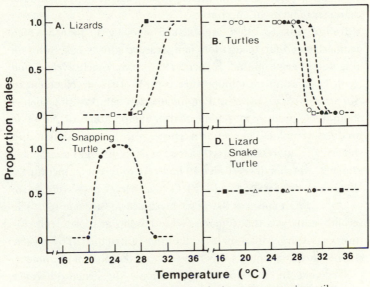

FIGURE 7.1. Responses in sex ratio to incubation temperature in reptiles. Dashed lines indicate hypothetical responses based on the data points shown. A. Lizards; B. Turtles; C. Snapping Turtle: *Chelydra serpentina* (Chelydridae); D. Lizard, Snake, Turtle. The sex ratios of a half in (D) are based on totals of males and females which do not differ significantly from a half.

Species and Symbols	Family
A. □ *Eublepharis macularius*	Gekkonidae
■ *Agama agama*	Agamidae
B. ● *Caretta caretta*	Cheloniidae
○ *Emys oribularis*	Emydidae
▲ *Testudo graeca*	Testudinidae
□ *Graptemys* (3 spp.) and	
Chrysemys picta	Emydidae
D. ■ *Lacerta viridis* (lizard)	Lacertidae
△ *Natrix fasciata* (snake)	Colubridae
○ *Trionyx spiniferus* (turtle)	Trionychidae

(Redrawn from Bull, 1980; see for original references.)

the threshold (28–30°C) range. From these, they estimated a heritability for the sex ratio threshold, and surprisingly, found the character to be highly heritable.

Bull (1980) also cited unpublished work by T. Joanen which demonstrates that incubation temperature affects sex ratios in alligators. Ferguson and Joanen (1982) have conclusively found (with large samples) temperature control of sex development in *Alligator mississippiensis*. Egg incubation temperatures below about 30°C produce all females, while temperatures above 34°C produce all males. They studied temperature in natural nests and showed two interesting effects. First, nests in different microhabitats (e.g., wet marsh versus levee) had very different temperatures. Wet marsh nests were cool (∼ 30°C) while levee nests were warm (∼ 35°C). As expected, the nests produced mostly one sex. The second result was that females, who develop at cooler temperatures, were larger than males at the time of hatching. The greater size of hatchling females was due to a greater amount of unmetabolized yolk. In laboratory-reared animals, the sexual difference in weight was maintained (at least) during the first year of life. The authors propose that size at hatching differentially benefits females (see their paper for detailed discussion), and that this is a possible selective advantage of individuals developing into females at low temperatures. They also note that adult male and female alligators occupy different microhabitats; males in open-water canals beside levees and females in the marsh. It is intriguing that marsh nests produce mostly females, levee nests mostly males. These are the first attempts to look seriously for fitness-related sex differences associated with incubation temperature. Nichols and Chabreck (1980) suggested that sex may be environmentally determined in alligators after hatching. However, Fergusen and Joanen (1982) show that sex is determined before hatching.

Bull (1980, 1981a,b) and Bulmer and Bull (1982) have considered other selective forces which may be involved in the origin and/or maintenance of these temperature systems, and the possibility that such systems are not adaptive. At present, such questions remain the largest puzzle in vertebrate sex ratios.

BIRDS

When thinking about sex allocation in birds and mammals, which have well-developed sex chromosomes, it is particularly useful to consider the mechanisms by which allocation to sons versus daughters can possibly be controlled. In birds (which have female heterogamety) the mother (that is, *her autosomal genes*) "may be able" to control segregation of the sex chromosomes, altering the primary sex ratio, although there is no evidence that this is possible. Otherwise, she can control three factors (if the species is altricial). First, one sex might be given more food. Second, one sex might be selectively destroyed at a young stage. If the clutch size at the egg stage were much larger than could actually be reared, this destruction would alter the sex ratio without lowering the effective clutch size. However, this would still be fairly expensive to the female since egg production is often a major energetic cost for female birds. Third, if one sex dies at a higher rate during the nesting stage, the parents may compensate by giving more food to the survivors. Note here that (2) posits the sex differential mortality itself to be an adaptive response, while (3) considers it a constraint, with the adaptation being the shunting of resources to the survivors. Clearly this dichotomy will not always be justified, nor easy to apply.

Precocial species (where the offspring are active and effectively feed themselves) have fewer options since post-hatching investment and control are much weaker. Altricial birds would, at first sight, seem good candidates for non-equal sex ratios, particularly since in some species adults would appear to invest differentially in the sexes. At fledging one sex is sometimes larger than the other, and their resource demands during the nestling period would often seem to differ.

Sex ratio in domestic poultry has been studied for many years. Some data exist on the primary sex ratio but most pertain to hatching (Hutt, 1949; Taylor, 1949). Some studies show a slight excess of females at hatching (e.g., 68,000 chicks, proportion males = 0.488; Taylor, 1949), but most published data fall

111

between 0.485 and 0.524 with no consistent tendency in either direction (Taylor, 1949; Hutt, 1949). The search for genetic variation in sex ratio at hatching has shown that there is none (Foster and McSherry, 1980). Studies have also searched for correlations between sex ratio and various egg characters—no relations have been found (Hutt, 1949). Indeed, sexing chicks at hatching (to cull males) is an economically important business and the techniques are well developed (Stromberg, 1977). According to Hutt (1949), experienced sexers can examine 800 chicks per hour and determine sex with an accuracy of 98% (mistakes take the form of labeling females as males). Since poultry typically do not feed their offspring post-hatching, they seem unlikely candidates for biased ESS sex ratios. The mother invests in the chicks, but probably not differentially by sex of offspring. Waterfowl are similar in this respect. Bellrose et al. (1961) have summarized our knowledge of duck sex ratios. Adult ratios are usually male biased, but data from several species (with sample sizes of several hundred each) show the sex ratio during the egg stage or at hatching to be equality.

Raptors often show extreme sex dimorphism in size at fledging. In the European sparrowhawk (*Accipiter nisu*), females are twice the weight of males at fledging. Newton and Marquiss (1979) examined 2163 offspring (651 broods) at fledging and found 51% males. However, in spite of the size difference, the males and females were fed the same amount of food during the nestling period and thus probably did not differ in energy cost to the parents (Maynard Smith, 1978).

Dhondt (1968) studied nestling sex ratios (15 days old) for the great tit (*Parus major*) in several habitats. The sexing technique (feather morphology) was slightly biased toward females, so that equality would show up as a slight female bias. In this species male offspring are larger than female. The nesting areas fell into two categories: urban and rural. Urban areas had greater nestling (egg to 15-day) mortality (43% versus 33%, prob. < 0.05) and a more male-biased sex ratio (55% versus 47% prob. < 0.05). Within the rural areas, the months of May and July showed 30%

112

nestling mortality (for broods fledging during those months) and a sex ratio of 46% males; June showed 40% mortality and 54% males. These percentages are remarkably close to the urban-rural comparison. Dhondt (1968) provided direct evidence that female offspring died at a faster rate. It is hard to arrive at an explanation for these data couched in terms of sex ratio adaptations. Dhondt proposed that the larger sons simply fare better in competition with their smaller sisters for food.

A great deal of sex ratio work has been done on blackbirds (Icteridae). Howe (1977) studied the common grackle, *Quiscalus quiscula,* nesting in southern Michigan. Male weight at fledging is about 1.2 times female weight, and fledging sex ratios were female biased (63% females). Embryonic sex ratios showed a small seasonal trend but overall were at equality. Thus, sons died at a faster rate and Howe argued that this was part of a brood reduction strategy under food stress. This pattern appears to be the opposite of the great tit where food stress favors the larger nestlings.

Several studies have considered sex ratio in the red-winged blackbird (*Agelaius phoeniceus*) (summary in Fiala, 1979, 1981). Most studies sexed the birds at about 8 days of age by which time the males are considerably larger than the females. Fiala used both this and surgery to sex younger birds. Using several definitions of cost of an offspring, he showed that the larger males were more costly to the parents. Five previous red-wing studies showed female-biased sex ratios at day 8, although none of the shifts was significant at the 0.05 level. Pooling his data with these (over 2000 offspring), Fiala showed a sex ratio of 47.4% males, different (prob. < 0.02) from equality in the direction of overproduction of the smaller sex. He suggested that the shift seemed too small to support the Fisher hypothesis of overproduction of the cheaper sex. I suggest that another problem was that nests taken by predators could not be sexed. Of the hatched eggs, better than 25% were lost to predation. If differential begging by one or the other sex makes nest predation more likely, such predation affects the ESS sex allocation. Fiala also considered the relation of sex ratio to other parental life history variables (egg size, laying sequence, hatching dates, clutch size, male harem size). He found no significant correlations.

The data on bird sex ratios suggest that the sex ratio is typically very near equality at the egg or nestling stage. Even though some data says that one sex may sometimes be more costly to the parents, there is really no evidence for the overproduction of the cheaper sex (*but* even less evidence suggesting that sons and daughters are of unequal cost). In addition, there is virtually no evidence supporting the notion of short-term adaptive alterations in the sex ratio. A major problem is that even when deviations from equality are observed, they are typically very small (say 10% or less). Changes of this order of magnitude are almost impossible to study.

MAMMALS

Sex ratios in mammals, usually at birth, have been reviewed several times in the last hundred years, particularly relative to domestic animals and humans (Darwin, 1871; Parkes, 1926; Lawrence, 1941; Edwards, 1962, 1970; Kiddy and Hafs, 1971; Teitelbaum, 1972; Pop. Report, 1975; Nishida et al., 1977; Hohenboken, 1981). More recently, they have been reviewed from the viewpoint of selection theory (Williams, 1979; Clutton-Brock and Albon, 1982; Edwards, 1962; Charlesworth, 1977). These reviews also consider factors, such as mother's age, thought to influence the sex of the offspring (Shuster and Shuster, 1972; books cited in introduction of Chapter Four). In his summary of a symposium on the prospects for control of sex ratio at birth in mammals, Casida (1971) stated, "One of the most impressive things about studies on control of sex ratio thus far has been the extreme variability and difficulty of repeating results, whether by a different investigator or the same investigator." To this one might add that even when the birth sex ratio has been shown to alter with some variable, the shifts are usually very small. For example, the proportion of males declines with birth order in humans, but the shift is about 3% (Teitelbaum, 1972).

A recent book on breeding farm animals (Warwick and Legates, 1979; also review by Hohenboken, 1981) reaches three general conclusions on sex ratio: (1) the sex ratio at birth is almost always near equality, and most, if not all, variation around this is binomial; (2) while it is economically advantageous to alter sex ratios, none of the *hundreds* of proposed methods (e.g., separation of X and Y sperm) has proven satisfactory; (3) there is essentially no genetic variability for the birth sex ratio. Let me briefly consider these three conclusions.

It is telling that these authors cite, as do many other reviews, the two mammalian sex ratio selection experiments which have shown changes (King, 1918, for the Albino Norwegian rat; Weir, 1971, for laboratory mice—both of these studies produced high and low lines of approximately 0.55 and 0.45 males at birth), as well as D. S. Falconer's (1954) failure to alter sex ratio in the house mouse. Attempts to alter the sex ratio physiologically have shown small shifts ($< 10\%$) (papers in Kiddy and Hafs, 1971), but the failure to alter it very far is striking.

James (1975) showed some evidence for less-than-binomial distribution of sexes in pigs, rabbits, and mice, but other mammal data show a binomial distribution (see Williams, 1979, for brief review; also above-cited data on livestock) with the mean near a half. For example, Venge (1953) found about 51% males in birth sex ratios for $\sim 10^4$ farm mink cubs. Other typical agricultural data are those of Nishida et al. (1977) on pigs. They examined $\sim 10^4$ pigs at birth from five research stations. The proportions of males were 0.514, 0.496, 0.52, 0.508, 0.508. In another study, Nishida et al. (1974) showed male-biased sex ratios (0.54–0.59), related to time of year and to aspects of the father. They noted that other research stations did not find similar sex ratio shifts. A study of sex ratio in sheep examined birth and weaning ratios (Napier and Mullaney, 1974). Fewer males were produced at birth with twins (e.g., in one breed: 0.489 versus 0.516). Survival rate to weaning was different for the sexes in single births (males 83%, females 86%), but not for twins (66%). The distribution of young/litter was binomial. The sex ratio of blastocysts, approximately the primary sex ratio, has been studied in pigs, rabbits, and lab mice; the sex ratio was equality (reviewed in Fechheimer and Beatty, 1974; Beatty et al., 1975).

This background of agricultural and lab experience says that the birth sex ratio is usually near equality (or slightly biased) and difficult to alter. The first question one might ask is—is there anything special about domestic or lab animals? Might the domesticated species just happen to be those where sex ratio modification would not be favored under natural conditions? Or does domestication itself select against the ability to alter sex ratio? The search for correlates to altered sex ratios (e.g., physiological condition of the mother) is part of the process of agricultural attempts to alter the ratio—that is, letting the animal tell us how to do it. And these, too, have failed. Given the wide variety of domesticated animals studied (e.g., pigs, mice, cows, rabbits), I doubt that the first suggestion can in general be true.

Clutton-Brock and Albon (1982) have reviewed data and sex ratio theory applied mostly to wild mammals. They are well aware of the lessons from agriculture, and provide a very careful review. Their approach is to consider two basic sex allocation theories—the Fisher hypothesis for equal allocation of resources to sons versus daughters (or at least overproduction of the "cheaper" sex), and the Trivers-Willard (1973) hypothesis for overproduction of sons or daughters by particular females. They also consider non-adaptive explanations for sex ratio shifts (for example, that maternal stress simply causes higher death rates for sons, the heterogametic sex).

Clutton-Brock and Albon (1982) and Clutton-Brock (per. comm.) note one generalization for sex ratios near birth in wild mammals; male biases (of the order of 10–15%) are much more common than the reverse (probably also true for domestic mammals). They also note that males commonly die at a faster rate earlier in life (e.g., during the period of parental care). The data are thus consistent with the idea that the high early mortality makes males the less expensive sex (see Table 3.1). Males may also be less costly because of LRC among a mother and her daughters, since males are typically the sex which disperses

116

(Clark, 1978). If the male biases in birth sex ratio are adaptive in this sense, the mechanism of adjustment is as yet unknown.

Clutton-Brock et al. (1981) have shown in red deer (*Cervus elaphus*) that males who survive to weaning are more costly to the mother (in contrast to the above suggestions). Several measures were used, the most conclusive being that a mother rearing a son (compared to a daughter) was less likely to breed the following year. They noted that a daughter remains on the mother's home range post-weaning while the son disperses, but argued that the retention of a daughter in red deer is unlikely to be an added cost to the mother, since the home ranges of unrelated hinds much overlap. They also showed no correlation of sex ratio with age, reproductive status of the mother in the previous year, or quality of the home range. The proportion of males at birth was 0.57. This biased sex ratio is at present unexplained.

Clutton-Brock and Albon (1982) also review the patterns of alteration of birth sex ratio as a function of various environmental conditions. The burden of their review is that the results go in both directions in different species (it is not immediately obvious which of the sex ratio shifts are indeed real, let alone what their meaning is). I refer the reader to their paper for a detailed review; here I will discuss a few particular systems. Maternal nutrition stress is implicated for several species. Lane and Hyde (1973) stressed albino rats during pregnancy. Eleven stressed females gave birth to 38 sons and 68 daughters, while 11 control females produced 72 sons and 70 daughters. Clearly, more sons died in utero, so both the sex ratio and clutch size altered. Two studies with lab mice have shown similar results (Geiringer, 1961; Rivers and Crawford, 1974). Without other data (e.g., cross-fostering experiments to examine the consequences to the offspring of non-reduction of brood size), it is impossible to know whether this effect is an adaptation or whether male offspring simply die faster under stress.

Verme (1965) carried out similar experiments with white-tailed deer. Prior to the deer mating, he shifted one group to a low level of nutrition; after mating all females were fed an adequate diet. The low nutrition group produced 68% sons, while the normal group produced 34% sons. However, most of the normal group produced twins, while the low group had singles. In 1969 Verme published another set of experiments with comparable results. Robinette et al. (1973) found that the proportion of males increased with litter size in mule deer (singles 40%, twins 46%, trips 55%), although they note that other mule deer studies have not shown similar results. Again, interpretation in terms of sex ratio theory is difficult.

An example which more strongly supports adaptive modification of the sex ratio/clutch size (in the sense of Trivers-Willard) is provided in McClure's (1981) work with the wood rat, *Neotoma floridana*. Lab-reared females, with newborn litters, were assigned either a restricted diet (~80% the maintenance requirement of an equal-sized, non-reproductive female) or free access to food (control). Over the 20-day period until weaning, the sex ratio among the offspring of restricted-diet mothers became increas-

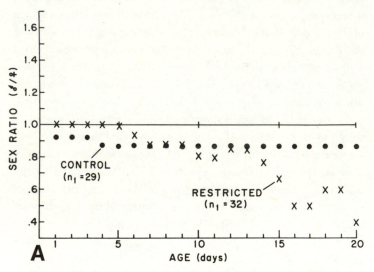

FIGURE 7.2. Sex ratio control in food-restricted woodrats (*Neotoma floridana*). (A) Changing sex ratio (male/female) in control litters and litters in which the mother's food was restricted during lactation. n_1 = total number of young at birth.

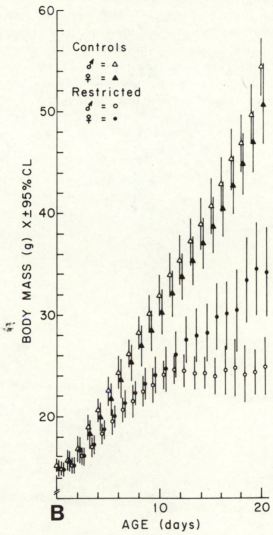

(B) Average body mass of male and female nestlings in control litters and litters in which the mother's food was restricted during lactation. (Figures from McClure, 1981.)

ingly female biased (Fig. 7.2a), while the control group did not show this effect. McClure stated that males died because they were actively discriminated against by the mother. Prior to death, these sons stopped growing, while their sisters continued to grow (Fig. 7.2b). The key point is whether or not the sons were actively discriminated against by the mother. McClure's unpublished observations strongly suggested that they were.

CHAPTER EIGHT

Conflict Situations
for the Sex Ratio

In this chapter I briefly discuss three situations where conflict exists over the sex ratio: cytoplasmic DNA elements (or virus particles), sex-linked genes, and worker-queen conflict in the haplodiploid eusocial insects. The word conflict is used since the sex ratio preferred by these elements (their ESS) usually differs dramatically from that favored by the autosomes (Fig. 5.1). In the case of haplodiploid eusocial insects, the ESS sex ratio differs between workers and queen (Trivers and Hare, 1976; Charnov, 1978). Thus, we expect to find a complex interaction between the respective parties. My purpose here is simply to point toward relevant literature, as theoretical development of the interaction would take us far from the general theme of this book.

A cytoplasmic DNA (or virus) particle, which is maternally transmitted, by definition does not pass through the male line. From the view point of this "gene," males do not exist. If it has any control over the sex ratio, perhaps via influence on segregation of sex chromosomes under female heterogamety (i.e., the Y always ending up in the egg, the X in a polar body), selection favors forms that shift the sex ratio toward daughters. Such non-chromosomal agents are known from several insects (including *Drosophila*) and terrestrial isopods (Johnson, 1977). In *D. bifasciata* (Ikeda, 1970) and members of the *D. willistoni* group (Williamson and Poulson, 1979), they cause reduced male production by killing XY (= male) zygotes. However, some studies suggest that brood size may still be about equal for carrier and non-carrier females. Poulson (1963; also above) and Preer (1971) have reviewed this literature and noted the complex interactions which exist between the host genotype and the expression of the trait. Uyenoyama and Feldman (1978) also review the literature and develop a simple population genetics model for host-particle interaction.

Recently, two forms of extrachromosomal inheritance (of factors affecting sex ratio) have been discovered in the wasp *Nasonia* (Werren, Skinner, and Charnov, 1981; Skinner, 1982). One trait (Werren et al., 1981) is very unusual in that it is transferred paternally and causes the mates of carrier males to produce only sons. In lab experiments where the trait was introduced into populations at low frequency, the trait increased to predominance in only a few generations. The second trait (Skinner, 1982) has the converse effect; it is maternally inherited and causes its carriers to produce only or mostly daughters. For both these traits, the overproduction of one sex is not caused by differential mortality of the young (contrasted to *Drosophila*). At present we know almost nothing about these traits in nature, or about their interaction with the host nuclear genome.

The genus *Drosophila* has male heterogamety. Several species have a condition known as "Sex Ratio" (SR). Males with an X chromosome carrying the SR gene produce mostly daughters. In SR males of *D. pseudoobscura,* the Y-bearing spermatids degenerate, leaving only X-bearing sperm (Policansky and Ellison, 1970). This condition is apparently widespread in various *Drosophila* populations (reviewed in Curtsinger and Feldman, 1980); in southwestern U.S. populations of *D. pseudoobscura* it occurs at a frequency of 5–15% (Dobzhansky and Epling, 1944). Several hypotheses have been advanced to explain why the gene is maintained in equilibrium. In a detailed lab study of fitness values for the various sex genotypes, Curtsinger and Feldman (1980) showed that there was reduced viability in SR males and females, and that females heterozygous for SR showed the highest female fertility. When inserted into a population genetics model, their fitness estimates for the sex genotypes predicted very well the SR frequency trajectories through time in a series of experimental populations. The fitness values predicted a stable polymorphism with the SR frequencies in males and females of 11% and 14%, respectively. These were slightly higher than the values (three-year average: 4% and 8%) found in the population which had provided the original flies. This work, and similar work by Wallace (1948), suggests that the SR polymorphism *may be* maintained by a balance between meiotic drive and counteracting viability and fertility selection (Curtsinger and Feldman, 1980). There is no evidence for the existence of autosomal suppressors of SR in this species (Policansky and Dempsey, 1978), although there is such evidence for other *Drosophila* species.

In the mosquito *Aedes aegypti*, sex is determined by a single pair of alleles (or a small chromosome segment). Males are the heterogametic sex. In many lab populations, the sex ratio at adulthood is slightly male biased (Christophers, 1960; Hickey, 1970). The sex ratio distortion is caused by a locus (called Distorter) at or closely linked to the sex determiner (Hickey and Craig, 1966a,b; Hickey, 1970). Distorter functions only in hetero-zygous males, and then only in genotype YD, Xd. These males produce mostly male offspring. The other male heterozygote shows a normal sex ratio. The degree of distortion varies greatly from male to male (and strain to strain), and Hickey (1970) produced evidence that there were several forms of Xd, with different levels of sensitivity to Distorter (YD). Apparently nothing is known about the dynamics of Distorter in nature. Interest in the distorter has focused on its possible use in biological control.

Acraea encedon is a butterfly very common in tropical Africa south to the Cape (Owen, 1966; Owen and Chanter, 1969; Chanter and Owen, 1972). It is a weak flier and occurs in semi-isolated, local populations. Some localities showed adult sex ratios near equality, while others were heavily female biased (average for nine localities ~3% males—Owen 1966). The species is not parthenogenetic. In the low male populations many females were not mated and laid only infertile eggs. A conspicuous feature of the low male populations was intense aggregating behavior; in the afternoon individuals settled in groups on vegetation. Males were present and mating often took place then. In populations with a normal sex ratio this behavior did not occur. Rearing experiments showed the existence of two types of females. One group produced an equal sex ratio, the other all daughters. The all-female trait is inherited from the female parent. Since butterflies have female heterogamety, this strongly suggests Y-linked meiotic drive. Cytoplasmic inheritance could not be ruled out, but Chanter and Owen (1972) noted that the trait could be cytoplasmic control of meiotic drive for the Y chromosome. Field studies showed that while the proportion of females remained low there was no directional trend in the sex ratio. That is, the populations did not appear to be going extinct, as simple Y-linked meiotic drive theory would predict (Shaw, 1958; Hamilton, 1967). The authors considered the possibility that suppressor genes (X or autosomally linked) might exist, but the evidence was negative. The maintenance of these all-female broods is at present unexplained, although Heuch (1978) has discussed a model of group selection, where a balance is struck between local extinction and the recolonization of open habitats. He applied it to the *Acraea* case and showed that such a balance was possible. There is a problem here in that his model has extinction as a usual course of events, while the work of Chanter and Owen shows no such directional trend in populations with low sex ratio.

An unusual sex-determining system occurs in wood lemmings (*Myopus schisticolor*) (Kalela and Oksala, 1966; Fredga et al., 1976, 1977) and varying lemmings (*Dicrostonyx torquatus* and *D. groenlandicus*) which leads to a female-biased sex ratio (reviewed by Bull and Bulmer, 1981). There are two types of X chromosome in the populations, X^0 and X^*, which differ in that X^0Y is male but X^*Y is female. There are thus four genotypes, as follows,

Female	Male
X^0X^0	X^0Y
X^0X^*	
X^*Y	

In wood lemmings, X^*Y females are of normal fertility and produce only X^* ova, due to a non-disjunction in fetal oocytes. In varying lemmings, X*Y females produce both X* and Y ova with equal frequency, and consequently a quarter of the progeny are YY and die. The fecundity of these females is closer to 90% of the other females' fecundity, suggesting compensation of lost embryos.

The population genetics of these systems is straightforward and has been worked out by Bengtsson (1977) and Bull and Bulmer (1981). In the wood lemming system, the expected equilibrium sex ratio (proportion of males) is 0.25; in the varying lemmings it is 0.42. The greater female bias in the wood lemming system is due to the segregation distortion of X*. Sex ratios in laboratory colonies and wild populations (wood lemmings only) are indeed female biased, but the observed sex ratios are in some cases more female biased than expected. There is also an excess of X*Y females relative to the proportion predicted (Bull and Bulmer, 1982). Thus, there is qualitative agreement with the models, but quantitative disagreement, suggesting that other effects are present.

The evolutionary stability of these systems (i.e., why don't the autosomes return the sex ratio to equality?) has been considered by Stenseth (1978), Maynard Smith and Stenseth (1978), Bulmer and Taylor (1980a), Carothers (1980), and Bull and Bulmer (1981). All studies consider the evolution of autosomal or Y-linked genes which suppress X* so that X*Y is male. These studies have concluded that extreme inbreeding or LMC is required to prevent the suppressor from invading the population, though Bull and Bulmer show that a suppressor can be maintained polymorphic (in the varying lemming system) with low levels of inbreeding. Owing to the fact that there is a wide variance in family sex ratios in these systems, since X^0X^0 females produce 50% sons but X*Y females produce an excess of daughters, the equilibrium sex ratio under LMC in the presence of an autosomal suppressor is not expected to coincide with the equilibrium under the ESS model, and they do not (Bull and Bulmer, 1981). The question of autosomal intervention is thus still very much open.

As the final example of conflict situations for the sex ratio, consider the haplodiploid eusocial insects. The ESS sex ratio from the queen's viewpoint is that of a usual haplodiploid female; i.e., under the common Fisher assumptions, half the resources should go to sons, half to daughters. The workers' perspective is quite different. With a single insemination of the queen (and no worker-laid male eggs), the workers are three times as related to their sisters as to their brothers. Thus, their ESS is for three-quarters of the resource to go to the colony's female reproductives, their sisters; and one-quarter to go to the drones, their brothers. In the Appendix, I show that the workers' allocation satisfies a particular product theorem, namely, $m \cdot f^3$. Here, the exponent 3 displays the thrice greater value of sisters compared to brothers.

In their original paper, Trivers and Hare (1976) showed data from several ant species which appeared to support the three-quarters prediction of worker control of sex ratio. Alexander and Sherman (1977) attacked both the data and the theoretical interpretation. They proposed that at best the data indicated an overinvestment in female reproductives (with no close correspondence to three-quarters) and suggested that queen control with LMC could well explain the data. While the issue is clearly still open, the evidence that the ants have a population structure conducive to LMC is not strong. In some cases, known breeding structures do not seem at all like the breeding structures of species with LMC. Furthermore, even if the LMC population structure does often exist for these eusocial species, this tells us nothing about worker versus queen control of sex ratio. There is an LMC model with worker control, just as there is one with queen control. Recent theoretical work (reviewed and extended in Stubblefield, 1980) has focused on the worker-queen conflict and its possible resolution. These models are well beyond the scope of this book.

In conclusion, the three conflict systems (cytoplasmic versus nuclear, sex chromosomes versus autosomes, worker versus queen) provide some very interesting material for testing aspects of sex allocation theory. However, if the complex interactions known to exist between cytoplasmic particles and the host genome

126

in *Drosophila* (or comparable systems of extrachromosomal male sterility in plants) are typical, unraveling and understanding the systems may be very difficult. Selection thinking (but not simplistic notions of well-designed organisms) should play a major role in this research.

Sequential Hermaphroditism
(Sex Reversal)

A sequential hermaphrodite reproduces as one sex early in life, then changes to the other for the rest of its life. The condition is widespread among invertebrates and fish (Giese and Pearse, 1974–1979; Bacci, 1965; Ghiselin, 1969, 1974; Reinboth, 1975; Atz, 1964) and known for a few plants (Heslop-Harrison, 1972). In addition, in a number of plant species gender expression is closely related to size or physiological condition (Freeman, Harper, and Charnov, 1980). Since individuals grow as they age, they tend to show sex reversal.

There are five questions which are of general interest about sex reversal.

(1) When is sex reversal favored over dioecy or simultaneous hermaphroditism?
(2) When should an individual be male (or female) first?
(3) When should an individual change sex?
(4) If the time of sex change is facultative, how is this labile response used?
(5) What meaning can be attached to the adult sex ratio?

Answers to these questions can be given at two levels. First, we can derive the conditions for selection to favor genes affecting the sexual pattern. For example, we can consider mutants which alter the age of sex change. In general, answers at this level will be in terms of the reproductive tradeoffs inherent in spending more or less time in (say) male phase. Given a certain shape for the male versus female tradeoff, we then solve for the ESS age of sex change. A second approach makes use of the first. We may inquire as to what biological factors give rise to a particular tradeoff relation. Here we look for answers in the ecological relations. An

129

example would be the habitat conditions which allow large individuals (as males) to monopolize spawning sites. This would make it disadvantageous for small individuals to be males, and selection may then favor small, younger individuals to be females.

This section of the book consists of five chapters. First (Chapter Nine), I briefly review the biological factors which are thought to select for or against sex change. This includes discussion of the population genetic formalism, which will reduce to a Shaw-Mohler equation. This chapter also discusses the breeding sex ratio for sex reversers (i.e., ESS age of sex change) and proposes a theoretical generalization for protandry contrasted to protogyny. The next two chapters (Ten and Eleven) apply the theory to Pandalid shrimp and Labroid fishes. These organisms provide a quantitative test of theory. Chapter Twelve discusses sex change for some selected animal groups (fish, marine molluscs, and one annelid worm). While these animals provide some valuable data, they are more important as systems potentially useful for further tests of sex change hypotheses. Here the emphasis is on natural history and some yet unsolved puzzles raised by these animals. The last chapter (Thirteen) looks at labile sexuality in plants. It draws on both the sex change theory of this section, and the patchy environment sex ratio models of previous chapters (e.g., Chapter Five).

CHAPTER NINE

Basic Stable Age Theory
for Sex Reversal

Ghiselin (1969) has suggested that natural selection should favor sex change over dioecy when an individual's reproductive success (RS) as a male or a female is closely related to age or size, and where the relationship is different for each sex. For example, if large size increases the egg output of a female, but does not aid a male in competition to fertilize eggs, selection favors genes which cause an individual to operate as a male when small, then switch to a female at a later age (or larger size). The reverse order of sex change would be favored if larger size or older age were relatively more important for male RS. This is called the "size advantage model." Note its close similarity to the sex ratio model developed earlier for parasitoid wasps attacking a range of host sizes. In its original form, the hypothesis says nothing about the importance of the *cost of changing sex*. However, recent authors have repeatedly raised the issue (Leigh, Charnov, and Warner, 1976; Warner, 1975a, 1978). For example, RS within a sex may not be simply related to size or age, if experience or developmental history play important roles. Likewise, the act of changing sex may itself entail a cost in terms of energy or time unavailable for breeding. Clearly, these costs act to decrease the selective advantage of sex change; they tend to favor dioecy.

A series of papers employing population genetic techniques have in general supported Ghiselin's suggestion (Warner, 1975a,b; Warner et al., 1975; Leigh, Charnov, and Warner, 1976; Charnov, 1979a,b). The models can also be used to suggest life history constraints, in addition to size advantage, which influence selection for sex change. The formal models have the added value

131

that they allow us to make quantitative (or semi-quantitative) predictions on the nature of sex change. For example, the genetical models can be used to predict the age of sex change favored by natural selection. In a general way, two factors greatly influence the ESS age of sex change. These are (1) how quickly reproductive success in each sex increases with size or age, and (2) the length of adult life. Suppose that selection favors being a male first. If there are on average ten breeding years, more years will be spent as a male than if there are (say) five years. In addition, for a fixed length of life, any factor which causes a greater proportion of the population to be in the younger age groups selects for a lower age of sex change. Since a growing population has relatively more young animals, such populations should show lowered ages of sex change (when compared with populations with similar adult mortality and fertility schedules). A species colonizing a new area may have only a few (mostly young) age groups present initially. If sex change is facultative, such a population should show a lower age of sex change, compared to older, established populations where older individuals are present. This result is analogous to the host size sex ratio model where we shift the size distribution toward smaller hosts. If reproductive success goes up very slowly with size in one sex, but rapidly in the other, selection favors an older age of change, compared with the situations where RS increases at about equivalent rates in both sexes. I now turn to a genetical treatment of these ideas.

A GENETICAL THEORY OF SEX REVERSAL

Sex change theory makes use of the following ideas. Consider a large, randomly mated population with overlapping generations, stable in numbers and with a stable age distribution. The species is a protandrous hermaphrodite (male first) with the various life history parameters (fertility as a male or female, survival rate) assumed to be age specific. Protandry is used here simply for illustrative purposes. Let t be the age at which an individual changes sex. Define as follows (in continuous time):

$b(x)$ = birth rate of an age x female *relative* to the birth rate of an age y female. y is an arbitrary age, chosen simply to make female fertility a relative measure.

$Q(x)$ = fertility of an age x male *relative* to the fertility of an age y male. This age y is the same as used above, so that an individual operating as a male or a female at age y has a relative fertility of one. $Q(x)$ is the relative ability of an age x male to fertilize eggs (e.g., compete for females).

Finally, let

$l(x)$ = probability an individual is alive at age x. This is the usual life table definition from demography.

It should be noted here that these three functions could also be related to t (e.g., $b(x,t)$), with $l(x)$ both sex and age specific. In this way, they may represent some assumed cost of sex change, or the assumption that mortality is different for the two sexes.

With these definitions, we may designate the *genetic contribution of an individual through male function, $M(t)$*, as:

$$M(t) = \int_0^t l(x)\, Q(x)\, dx. \tag{9.1}$$

The genetic contribution of an individual through female function is defined in a similar way:

$$F(t) = \int_t^\infty l(x)\, b(x)\, dx. \tag{9.2}$$

Note in (9.1) that if $t \rightarrow \infty$, the individual is a male all of its life; thus $M(\infty)$ is the fitness or genetic contribution of a pure male. In (9.2), if $t \rightarrow 0$, the individual is a female for life; thus $F(0)$ is the fitness of a pure female.

Suppose now that this population consists entirely of individuals changing sex at time t. Introduce into this group a rare mutant gene which causes its bearers to change sex at some other time $(\hat{t})$.

133

Elsewhere (Leigh et al., 1976; Charnov, 1979a,b) it is proven that this mutant is selected against, provided

$$\frac{M(\hat{t})}{M(t)} + \frac{F(\hat{t})}{F(t)} < 2, \qquad (9.3)$$

where $M(\hat{t})$ and $F(\hat{t})$ refer to equations (9.1) and (9.2) for the mutant. Equation (9.3) provides a rule for finding the ESS age of sex change. If we can find a t such that (9.3) is satisfied for all $\hat{t}$, then the t will be the ESS (which will be denoted as t^*).

Of course, equation (9.3) is simply a Shaw-Mohler equation. By reference to our sex ratio derivations of Chapter Three, some of its consequences are fairly straightforward.

(1) If the $Q(x)$ are not frequency dependent, the ESS t^* maximizes the product of $M(t^*) \cdot F(t^*)$.

(2) If $\hat{t}$ goes to zero (or infinity), the mutant under consideration is a pure female or male. Such mutants are selected against, provided $2 \cdot M(t^*) > M(\infty)$ and $2 \cdot F(t^*) > F(0)$; sex change is stable to dioecy provided the sex changer has more than half the male RS of a pure male (and the same for female RS). If either of these two conditions is not met, sex change will not be stable. Either selection will push the populations to dioecy or a mixture of sex reversers and a pure sex will be stable.

(3) As in the case of sex ratio (Fig. 3.6), it is easy to ask about the selective advantage of mutants which create a mixture of sex types (for example, a mutant which creates half males, half females, introduced into a sex-changing population). The appropriate Shaw-Mohler equations will be of the form:

$$\frac{\text{fitness of mutant through male function}}{\substack{\text{fitness of typical individual through} \\ \text{male function}}} + \frac{\text{fitness of mutant through female function}}{\substack{\text{fitness of typical individual through} \\ \text{female function}}} < 2.$$

For example, if we have a dioecious population (with a primary sex ratio of a half) and introduce a mutant sex changer (protandrous with reversal time $\hat{t}$), the mutant is selected against, provided that:

$$\frac{F(\hat{t})}{\frac{1}{2} \cdot F(0)} + \frac{M(\hat{t})}{\frac{1}{2} \cdot M(\infty)} < 2 \text{ or } \frac{F(\hat{t})}{F(0)} + \frac{M(\hat{t})}{M(\infty)} < 1. \quad (9.4)$$

Thus, equation (9.4) is the condition for dioecy to be stable to invasion by a sex changer. It is clearly possible for *neither* equation (9.3) (applied to a pure sex) nor (9.4) to be satisfied, in which case selection favors a mixture of sex changers and a pure sex.

These stability conditions may be easier to see if we resort to a fitness set analysis, as in Chapter Three. For every value of t, we find a pair of fitnesses $= M(t), F(t)$. If these pairs are plotted on Cartesian coordinates, a curve such as Figure 9.1 results. Each point on the curve is associated with a t value, and the endpoints are the fitnesses for the pure males and females.

As in the previous sex ratio analysis, we guess some pair $M(t)$, $F(t)$ to be the ESS and construct through that point a line of slope minus $F(t)/M(t)$ (line B). As before (Chapter Three), all points on the line (denoted $M(\hat{t}), F(\hat{t})$) satisfy the relation

$$\frac{M(\hat{t})}{M(t)} + \frac{F(\hat{t})}{F(t)} = 2;$$

while all points above the line make the equation > 2. Contrast this to equation (9.3). In Figure 9.2, we have found the point on the fitness set where the B line is just tangent. It is clear that the fitness set must be *convex* (Fig. 9.2) for both pure males and females to be selected against (i.e., $F(0)$ and $M(\infty)$ must both be to the inside of the tangent B line). *A convex fitness set favors sex change.* Likewise, Charnov (1979b) shows that a concave fitness set favors dioecy. Figure 9.3 shows how a cost of sex change also acts to favor dioecy.

Consider now *three* situations which will force the fitness set (zero cost of sex change) to the convex. First, suppose that fecundity is size dependent but equivalently so for the two sexes. If growth rates are the same but mortality is sex dependent, selection

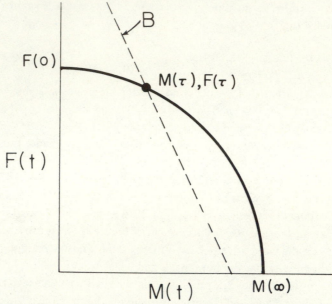

FIGURE 9.1. A fitness set for sex change (protandry). The curved surface plots $F(t)$, $M(t)$ for various t. $F(0)$ and $M(\infty)$ refer to pure female and male respectively. The B line is a line through $M(\tau)$, $F(\tau)$ with slope of minus $F(\tau)/M(\tau)$. All points to the outside of the line are of life histories which would be selected *for* in a population of mostly $M(\tau)$, $F(\tau)$. In this figure, individuals spending more time in male phase are selected for. (From Charnov, 1979b.)

may favor sex change, with the early years being spent in the sex with the lowest mortality rate (Policansky and Charnov, unpublished). This is analogous to age reversal of the sex ratio, when the birth of one sex imposes a greater mortality on the mother (Chapter Six). Second, if mortality rates and fecundity versus size are the same for each sex but growth rates differ, selection again favors sex change, with the early years spent in the sex with the highest growth rates (Freeman et al., 1980a; Bierzychudek, 1981b). These "mortality or growth advantage" hypotheses have yet to be tested in nature (but see Chapter Thirteen, particularly the discussion of Jack-in-the-Pulpit). It seems likely that they would interact with the third hypothesis, Ghiselin's size advan-

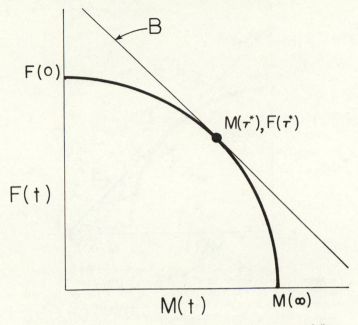

FIGURE 9.2. A convex (bowed out) fitness set favors sex reversal (here, protandry). The *B* line is as in Figure 9.1. Since no points on the fitness set fall to the outside of this line (it is tangent), no life histories (on or in the fitness set) are selected for in a population made up of $M(t^*)$, $F(t^*)$ individuals. The ESS t^* is the value which *maximizes the product of $M(t^*)$ · $F(t^*)$*. (From Charnov, 1979b.)

tage model. The fitness set is convex provided $dF(t)/dM(t)$ and $d^2F(t)/dM(t)^2$ are both < 0. Suppose that mortality and growth are the same for each sex, then from (9.1) and (9.2) we have $dF(t)/dM(t) = -b(t)/Q(t)$. Thus, if $b(t)/Q(t)$ increases with t, the fitness set is convex. To put it another way, if female RS, $b(t)$, increases with age *relative* to male RS, $Q(t)$, selection favors sex change. An individual should be a male when young, changing to a female at a later age. I invite the reader to contrast this condition with the wasp host-size model, Chapter Four. They are the same.

Sex change is widely distributed, but rare in animals (Ghiselin, 1969; Giese and Pearse, 1974–1979). As discussed here (and in

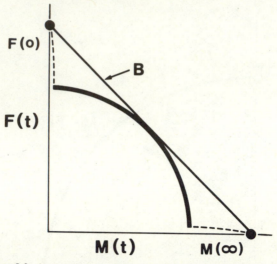

FIGURE 9.3. A cost to changing sex tends to favor dioecy. The dark curve is the fitness set for an individual who changes sex. Pure males, $M(\infty)$, and pure females, $F(0)$, omit the cost, so we represent this by putting them further out on the axes, away from the sex changer. The ESS age of sex change is where the B line is just tangent (as in Fig. 9.2), *but* the end points of the B line tell us if a rare pure male or female can invade such a sex-changing population. If the $M(\infty)$, $F(0)$ values fall to the outside of the B line intercept, a mutant pure sex is favored. In this figure, the B line just touches the $F(0)$, $M(\infty)$ values, so that pure males or females have the same fitness as a sex changer. If $F(0)$ and/or $M(\infty)$ were just a bit larger, dioecy would be favored.

the chapters to follow), sex change theory allows us to pose and test (sometimes quantitatively) several hypotheses within species which do change sex. While the theory also predicts when this condition is favored over dioecy, the data bearing on such questions are much less available. In a brief review, Policansky (1982) notes that theory predicts sex reversal under some *seemingly* easy-to-meet conditions, and suggests that it should be much more common than it seems to be. Its rarity is a puzzle which at present has no particularly good answer. Here I would like to pose four hypotheses to explain the rarity of sex reversal (see also Warner, 1978). I do this with the realization that meaningful tests of these ideas may often be very difficult. First, there may be added costs to

138

changing sex (Fig. 9.3), either in the form of increased mortality or time out from breeding. Second, any *apparent* correlation of reproductive success with size or age (suggesting the size advantage hypothesis) may be spurious in that the real correlation may well be with experience (or time in a particular sex). Thus, the fitness of a male of age x or size x may depend not upon x alone but x combined with the previous time spent in the male sex. Third, the factors of growth, mortality by sex, and fertility as a function of size may combine to make the fitness set concave. For example, if mortality were higher in the sex which under the size advantage hypothesis would be the first sex, mortality and size advantage would tend to cancel each other out (since the mortality advantage notion would have this sex the second sex). Finally (fourth), developmental or anatomical constraints may make it very difficult to evolve from dioecy to sex reversal. It may be hard to alter developmental pathways to change sex in the middle of the lifetime. Note that this last hypothesis is asymmetrical. It is the transition from dioecy to sex change which may be difficult. The reverse change should be simple, since all an individual need do is to not change sex (or change at once). It would immediately be a pure male or female. With appropriate choice of organism, tests of these hypotheses may be possible.

ON THE MEANING OF THE BREEDING SEX RATIO

In my review of the life history data on sex changing species, one general pattern emerged. The breeding, adult sex ratio was almost always *biased toward the first sex*, but the degree of bias differed between protandry and protogyny. In protandry, males (first sex) made up from 50% to 75% of the breeders. Hoagland's (1978) data on *Crepidula* spans this range, although there were sometimes < 50% males. The various data sets on *Patella* show ratios typically higher than *Crepidula,* with closer to 75% males (Chapter Twelve). In contrast, fully protogynous fish had the ratio of adult females (first sex) always above 75%. Realizing potential problems of such wide taxonomic comparisons (fish

139

versus molluscs), it would appear that the first sex always makes up a larger share of the breeders under protogyny.

This raises the question of the meaning of the breeding sex ratio. To suggest an answer, I will assume the size advantage model, and let males and females experience the same growth and death rates. Suppose we have protandry, and consider an individual just at the ESS age (size) of sex change (t^*). Let $b(t^*)$ be the female fecundity of this individual, $\overline{b}$ the fecundity of an average female, and let $z(t^*)$ be the fertility of this individual as a male, contrasted to an average male. Thus, as a male, our individual is $z(t^*)$ times as good at inseminating females as is the average male. I will call $z(t^*)$ the *marginal relative fitness* of a male. As a male this individual will fertilize

$$N(1 - r)\overline{b}\left(\frac{z(t^*)}{Nr}\right) \text{ eggs,}$$

where r = proportion of the breeders who are male, and N is the size of the breeding population. At the ESS age of sex change (t^*), an individual should fertilize (or produce) the same number of eggs regardless of whether it is a male or a female (Policansky, 1981), or this expression should equal $b(t^*)$. Hence,

$$\frac{r}{1 - r} = \frac{z(t^*)}{b(t^*)/\overline{b}}. \tag{9.5}$$

Equation (9.5) relates the breeding sex ratio (r) to the marginal fitnesses through being male, $z(t^*)$, or female, $b(t^*)/\overline{b}$. The ratio $b(t^*)/\overline{b}$ is the female counterpart to the male $z(t^*)$. It is our female fecundity at age t^*, contrasted to an average female. We can obtain a similar equation under protogyny. In words, both results may be written as:

$$\frac{\text{number of 1st sex breeders}}{\text{number of 2nd sex breeders}}$$

$$= \frac{\text{marginal relative fitness of sex 1}}{\text{marginal relative fitness of sex 2}}. \tag{9.6}$$

Suppose that females gain by being large, while males do not.

140

Selection then favors protandry. Male fertility $z(t^*) = 1$ while $b(t^*)/\bar{b}$ must be < 1, since the average female has more eggs $(\bar{b})$ than a female who has just changed sex $(b(t^*))$. This makes $r/(1 - r) > 1$. If we now allow males to gain some added fertility by being larger, then $z(t^*) > 1$, and the proportion of males (the first sex) goes up even more. Under sex reversal with neither sex losing fertility by growing larger, the breeding sex ratio should be biased toward the first sex (equation 9.6).

In invertebrates and fish, female fecundity almost always goes up with size. I suggest that the proportion of the first sex is higher under protogyny because both sexes gain fitness by being larger, while protandry is favored where males gain little or nothing by being larger $(z(t^*) \sim 1)$. Equation 9.6 suggests that the breeding sex ratio contains interesting information about rates of fitness gain for the two sexes. Chapter Twelve discusses a situation where the breeding sex ratio (for molluscs of the genus *Crepidula*) alters with population density. Equation 9.6 suggests hypotheses which may explain these shifts.

CHAPTER TEN

Sex Reversal in Shrimp

Sex reversal is rare in Crustaceans, being almost confined to a few free-living decapods and some parasitic forms (Bacci, 1965; Charniaux-Cotton, 1960). Carpenter (1978) provides a list of known sex-changing decapods; the list has thirty species in nine families. Crustacean sex reversal is almost always from male to female, except perhaps for some isopods of the family Anthuridae and some Tanaidacea which are said to be protogynous (Lang, 1958). All the decapods have close relatives who are dioecious. Protandry may be more common in long-lived shrimp (most *Pandalus* species live three to seven years), but many long-lived decapods are dioecious, and there are some short-lived protandrous species (Carpenter, 1978). Since in female shrimp egg production increases with body size (Jensen, 1958), it may be that protandry is favored by a combination of long life and little or no male size advantage in reproduction. At present there are few data which bear on this issue. My discussion will focus on the life histories of shrimp who do change sex.

Shrimp in the family Pandalidae are of major commercial importance in temperate to sub-arctic waters. They have been the subject of two major symposia (*F.A.O. Fish. Rep.*, 1968–1970; Marine Biol. Assn. India, 1967), numerous life history monographs and reviews (Allen, 1963, 1959; Gotshall, 1972; Appolonio and Dunton, 1969; Hjort and Rudd, 1938; Palenichko, 1941; Ivanov, 1969; Mistakidis, 1957; Kubo, 1951; Aoto, 1952; Fox, 1972; Butler, 1964; Horsted and Smidt, 1956; Haynes and Wigley, 1969) and some sophisticated population modeling (Fox, 1972; Abramson and Tomlinson, 1972; Geibel and Heinmann, 1976). Much of the data discussed here are from these references

(Charnov, 1979b). A bibliography of this literature also exists (Scrivener and Butler, 1971).

Most commercial species are protandrous hermaphrodites. This was first established by Berkeley (1930). They tend to be found at higher temperate and boreal latitudes, associated with mud (or mud plus sand) bottoms at depths ranging from tens to hundreds of meters. Several species show inshore-offshore migrations, as well as vertical movement (upward at night) in the water column. Breeding takes place in the autumn. After copulation, females carry the eggs until they hatch in the spring. The larvae are planktonic, settling to the bottom in mid to late summer. Individuals breed for the first time at 1.5, 2.5, or 3.5 years after hatching. Age of first breeding is often related to the attainment of a certain size (Rasmussen, 1953) and varies accordingly with growth rates. After a variable time as a male, individuals reverse sex and reproduce as females for the rest of their lives.

This chapter considers four pieces of evidence bearing on sex change theory. In order of consideration, they are (1) the presence in some populations of individuals who reproduce as females for their entire lives; (2) biogeographic patterns in the length of time spent as a male; (3) alteration in the age of sex change in response to strong fishing pressure, which greatly alters the lifespan; (4) temporal alteration in the age of sex change in response to temporal fluctuations in the age (or size) distribution of the population.

Shrimp breeding is typically at yearly intervals, except perhaps in very cold water (Rasmussen, 1953) where it may be less frequent. Seasonal breeding means that an individual can spend only an integral number of years as a male, and that the appropriate mathematics replaces integration with summation in equations (9.1) and (9.2). Likewise the fitness set will be discrete points, rather than the continuous curve of Figure 9.1. A hypothetical example is shown in Figure 10.1. Each point (numbered 0 to 5) represents the fitness through male and female function for spending 0, 1, 2, 3, 4, or 5 years as a male. The example shows a

143

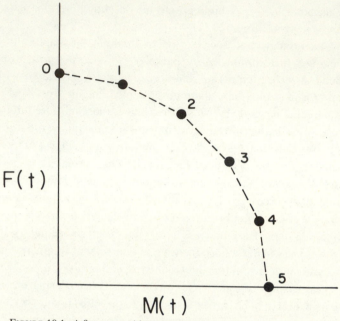

FIGURE 10.1. A fitness set with seasonal reproduction (i.e., breeding takes place once each year). The set consists of points, each referring to the fitnesses associated with spending an integral number (0–5) years as a male. If the points are connected in succession by lines, a continuous curve results. This may be treated in the same way as the curves in Figures 9.1 and 9.2. If t^* falls on the line segment connecting two points, the population may average t^* by having a proportion of the cohort change sex at each of the two ages. (From Charnov, 1979b.)

life span of five years. Note, however, that the points can be connected successively with lines (as in the figure) to form a continuous curve. This curve will be convex provided $b(x)/Q(x)$ increases with x (with $l(x)$ not sex specific).

This curve can be treated just like the continuous fitness set in Figure 9.1. The only alteration is that if the ESS age of sex change (t^*) falls on the line segment connecting two points, it implies that the average member of a cohort spends t^* as a male (Warner, 1975a). For example, suppose t^* falls between ages 1 and 2. For a cohort to average t^*, one fraction of the cohort should change sex at age 1, the rest at age 2. If the fitness set is convex, t^* will be either a single age, or two successive ages with a fraction of the cohort changing at each.

This splitting of a cohort into two parts with respect to age of sex change is well known for Pandalid shrimp (e.g., Rasmussen, 1953). Probably the most common situation is the occurrence of "early maturing females" (EMF) (Fox, 1972). These are individuals who mature or breed for the first time as females, never having reproduced as males. At the age of first reproduction (α), the cohort splits into two parts. Some fraction of breeders are males (and typically will turn into females by age $\alpha + 1$); the rest are females. This is shown in Figure 10.2. In reference to Figure 10.1, this case would result if the product maximization fell between ages 0 and 1.

The presence or absence of EMF, and their frequency when present, provides a good test for sex change theory, for the following reason. Theoretical presence or absence does not depend upon knowledge about the male fertility function, which would be very difficult to measure. Since only one breeding male age group is present (all males are predicted to change to females by age $\alpha +$

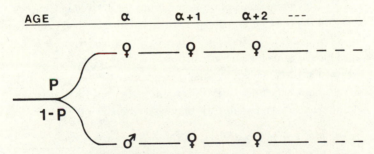

FIGURE 10.2. In many Pandalid shrimp populations, there are two life history pathways. At the age of first reproduction (α), the cohort splits into two parts. Some proportion (P) of the individuals mature as females and remain as females for their entire lives. These females are called "early maturing females" (EMF). The other fraction ($1 - P$) mature as males, and typically sex reverse one year later. In reference to Figure 10.1, this situation would result if the $M \cdot F$ product were maximized along the line segment between zero and one year as a male. The ESS P may also be calculated by equalizing the reproductive gains for the two pathways. Recall the gynodioecy sex ratio example from Chapter Two. The ESS P here is the same as equation 2.1.

145

1), the potential fertility of older males is unimportant. Suppose t^* is less than one year; t^* then maximizes $M \cdot F$ where the product takes the form,

$$[P \cdot F(\alpha) + (1 - P) F(\alpha + 1)] [(1 - P) M(\alpha)] = M \cdot F,$$

where P is the fraction of a cohort acting as early maturing females.

Setting $\partial(M \cdot F)/\partial P = 0$ and letting $W = F(\alpha + 1)/F(\alpha)$ (the relative female fitness of a hermaphrodite compared to an early maturing female), we find that the ESS P is of the form:

$$P/(1 - P) = 1 - 2W; \qquad W < \tfrac{1}{2};$$
$$P/(1 - P) = 0, \qquad\qquad W > \tfrac{1}{2}. \qquad (10.1)$$

This relationship provides a rather unusual hypothesis. If $W > \frac{1}{2}$, all individuals should spawn at least once as males (thus we predict there to be no EMF). If $W < \frac{1}{2}$, we expect a negative, linear relationship between W and the ratio of females to males at the age of first reproduction (with a limiting value of 1:1). Note that the relationship is the same as the predicted frequency of females in gynodioecious plant populations (as derived in Chapter Two). In reference to Figure 10.2, an alternative method to derive the ESS is to solve for the value of P which equalizes the reproductive gains for each life history pathway.

Provided EMF and sex changers experience the same mortality and fecundity schedules (they differ only in that an EMF gets one additional year as a female), W may be written as follows:

$$W = \frac{l(\alpha + 1) \cdot b(\alpha + 1) + l(\alpha + 2) \cdot b(\alpha + 2) + \ldots}{b(\alpha) + l(\alpha + 1) \cdot b(\alpha + 1) + l(\alpha + 2) \cdot b(\alpha + 2) + \ldots}$$

This assumption is essentially that of the size advantage hypothesis. To estimate W requires knowledge of (1) age of first reproduction, α; (2) age-fertility relations (in terms of egg production, $b(x)$); (3) mortality rates, $l(x)$. Charnov (1979b) has shown how these may be estimated for shrimp. Briefly, female fecundity (egg count) increases with the third power of body length (e.g., Jensen, 1958), while linear growth is well described by the

146

Bertalanffy growth equation (Beverton and Holt, 1957);

$$\ell(x) = \ell\infty[1 - \exp(-K \cdot x)],$$

where $\ell(x)$ = length at age x, $\ell\infty$ = maximum length, and K = growth coefficient. Finally, adult mortality rates have been shown to be highly correlated with the growth coefficient K. This is illustrated in Figure 10.3a for twenty-seven shrimp populations. Data for this plot came from various locations in the northern hemisphere, ranging in latitude from northern California to the sub-arctic. Figure 10.3b schematically shows the study locations (plus one additional California location)—the details are in Charnov, 1979b. In general, populations show increasing lifespan and decreasing growth rates at higher latitudes. Using a regression technique developed by Beverton and Holt (1959) and Beverton (1963), the relationship from Figure 10.3a was used to provide an estimate of the yearly adult survivorship. Twenty-seven shrimp populations provided the necessary life-history data plus estimates of P, the proportion of EMF. Figure 10.4 shows the result of plotting $P/(1 - P)$ versus W (original data sources in Charnov, 1979b). More than half of the P values plotted in this figure are means of three or more years. The theoretical expected relation is also shown on the figure. With the exception of one population, the correspondence between theory and data is rather good. P for this single population is based on only one year's data. Since the figure represents (for the estimates of P) over eighty-five years of data, this single exception is at present of little consequence.

In one sense, Figure 10.4 is not an explanation of the geographic variation in time of sex reversal (here, proportion of EMF) in shrimp, because no explanation has been put forth for variation in W (except the broad correlation with latitude—see below). Also, for those populations which have $P = 0$, we would like to predict how many years will be spent as a male. On the assumption that male fertility does not increase with age, Figure 10.5 shows the ESS age of sex change as a function of the instantaneous adult mortality rate (Z) and the growth coefficient

147

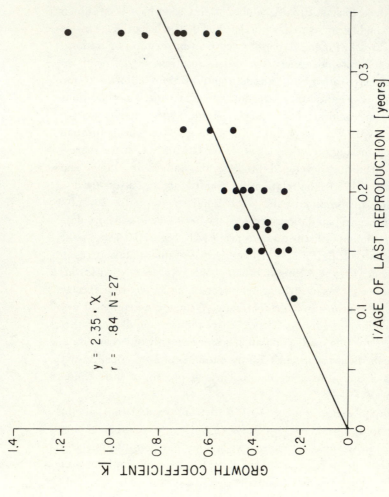

FIGURE 10.3a. Twenty-seven shrimp populations show that adult mortality rates (here the inverse of the age of last reproduction) and relative growth rates (the growth coefficient K from the Bertalanffy growth equation) are correlated. Line is the least squares fit through the origin. (From Charnov, 1979b; see for original data and further discussion.)

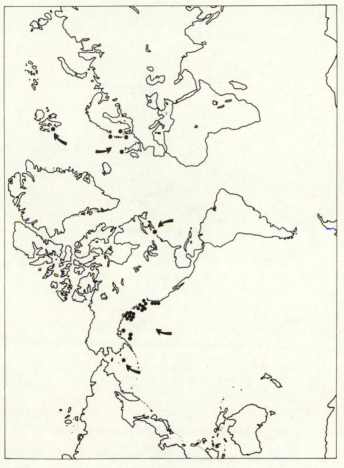

FIGURE 10.3b. The study populations range in latitude from California to the sub-arctic. This figure shows only general locations.

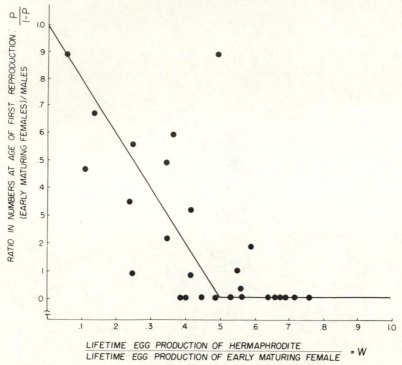

FIGURE 10.4. Occurrence of "early maturing females" (EMF) in Pandalid shrimp. Data are (proportion EMF):(proportion males) plotted against relative hermaphrodite fitness (W) for 27 shrimp populations. Theoretical relationship (equation 10.1) is shown by the heavy line. Each $P/(1 - P)$ data point is the average of from one to eleven years of data, depending upon population. See Figure 11.6 for another plot of these data. (From Charnov, 1979b; see for original data.)

(K). Recall that $l(x) = \exp(-Z \cdot x)$. This is a three-dimensional diagram, so the contours or regions refer to parameter (Z, K) combinations which favor equal time spent in male phase. The region marked 1 contains Z, K values where the ESS is for each individual to spend one year as a male. To the right of this region selection favors a mixed strategy. Some proportion of a cohort should mature as females when they first breed (EMF), and the rest should spend one year as a male and change to females one

150

year later. For example, the contour marked 0.3 is where 30% of a cohort should mature as females, 70% as males; the 70% would then change to females by the next year. The region marked 2 is where all individuals are expected to spend two reproductive seasons as males. Between the 1 and 2 regions, the cohort is again predicted to show a mixed strategy. Here some proportion of the

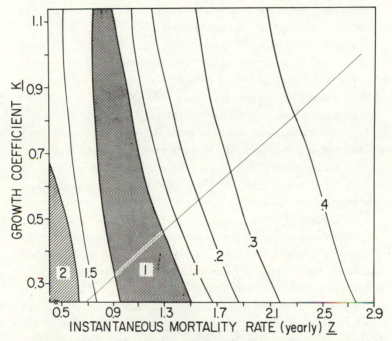

FIGURE 10.5. A times of equal sex change diagram. As a function of growth (*K*) and death (*Z*) rates, the graph plots the ESS time as a male, assuming an age of first breeding of 1.5 years. *K* refers to the growth parameter of the Bertalanffy growth equation. Zones 1 and 2 refer to 1 and 2 years in the male phase. The fractions to the right of zone 1 denote the fraction of a cohort which breeds as females at 1.5 years (see text for further discussion). The line in zone 1 represents what might happen to a population which is heavily fished. Individual growth may or may not increase, but higher adult death rates move the population toward the edge of zone 1. As the population moves to the right of this zone, some shrimp are predicted to mature as females at the age of first breeding. (From Charnov, 1979b.)

151

cohort should spend one year as males, the rest two years. The 1.5 contour is where half the cohort should spend one year as males, half two years.

It is clear in this figure that the predicted age of sex reversal is most sensitive to the adult mortality rate (Z) and not to growth rates. Higher adult death rates select for shorter time as a male. However, since an individual must spend an integral number of years (0, 1, 2, etc.) as a male, this shorter male phase can only be expressed in what the average individual does.

Rasmussen (1953, 1969) was the first to point out that various life history parameters varied with latitude in *P. borealis* in northern Europe. Table 10.1 summarizes his data for five locations, ranked by increasing latitude (58° to 78° N). Age of first reproduction increased with latitude from 1 to 3 years, but size at first reproduction was almost constant. Life span increased (4 to 8 years) while growth rate declined (indexed by the growth parameter K). The length of time spent in male phase likewise increased, from <1 to a full 2 years. This is the pattern predicted by sex change theory (Warner, 1975a). Many physical variables alter with latitude, the most conspicuous being temperature. With invertebrates, lower temperatures typically mean slower growth rates and a longer life span. The most interesting aspect of these data is the tendency for the mean size at sex change to be a constant (~119 mm). Fox (1972) noted that this was very close to the size at sex change for *P. borealis* off Kodiak Island, Alaska. Rasmussen drew the obvious conclusion that sex reversal was closely related to a critical size, regardless of age. However, while this is approximately true, some data suggests that it may be the life span (and its *correlation* with growth rates, Fig. 10.3) which really governs the age of sex change.

The first piece of evidence comes from asking what would happen to the ESS age of sex change if adult mortality rates increased while growth rates remained constant. Of course (Fig. 10.5), t^* would decline. This change in life history may happen under heavy fishing exploitation. Consider Figure 10.5. Suppose that growth and death rates are such that every individual is

152

TABLE 10.1. *Pandalus borealis* in Northern Europe. (From Rasmussen, 1953, 1969, as discussed in Fox, 1972.)

Location	Latitude	Years in male phase	Length and age at male maturity	Average total length at sex change (when first female)	Approx. age at last breeding (yrs)	K (from Charnov, 1979b)
Oslo Fjord	58° N	≤1	1.5 yrs (90 mm)	120 mm	4	0.7
Sogndals Fjord	61° N	1	2.5 yrs (83 mm)	106 mm	—	—
Mist Fjord	67° N	2	2.5 yrs (74 mm)	119 mm	6	0.27
Jan Mayen	71° N	1 to 2 (mixed)	3.5 yrs (94 mm)	119 mm	—	—
Spitzbergen	78° N	2	3.5 yrs (85 mm)	119 mm	>7.5	0.23

predicted to spend one year as a male (stippled area 1). If we start in this area and slowly increase the death rate, at first nothing happens to the age of sex change. However, continued increase will eventually move the population to the boundary of the 1 zone. As we move to even higher death rates, selection begins to favor some first breeders to become females. That is, there will appear in the population a new size class of females who correspond to first-breeding shrimp.

This alteration in sex development appears to have happened at least once in *P. borealis*. The data are from Jensen (1965, 1967), as analyzed by Charnov (1981). A Danish/Swedish fishery began in the Skagerrak before 1930. A large change in the length distribution of shrimp was found in the eastern Skagerrak in the 1950's. For summer samples, the average proportion of shrimp over 80 mm in length declined from 44% in 1949–1950, to 25% in 1954–1957, to 14% in 1961–1962 (Jensen, 1965). Numerous other data are cited which also support this observation. To quote Jensen: "The most likely explanation of the change in length is that it is due to the intensive fishery—the same effect that we have seen in so many other heavily fished stocks." The growth rate of an individual shrimp either did not change or slightly decreased (but surely did not increase) over this time period (data in Jensen, 1965, 1967). Finally, the most interesting observation: prior to 1954, no female shrimp were found less than 75 mm in length. In June 1954 an average of 8% of the females were 55–74 mm. For summer samples over the years 1955–1962 (no data for 1958), the following proportion of females were 55–74 mm in length: 18, 6, 4, 15, 22, 30. These form a special female length group of nearly the normal length of the one-year-old males (Jensen, 1965). These females were clearly one-year-old shrimp.

The second type of data, which bear on whether size is directly related to the time of sex change, come from violation of the stable age assumption. Temporal fluctuation in age or size composition of the population would mean that sometimes the breeders would be mostly small, at other times mostly large. The ESS approach predicts that individuals may respond to this temporal variation

154

by altering their age of sex change. However, if growth rates do not alter, we predict no alteration in the time of change under the hypothesis of a size threshold for sex change.

The basic model developed in this chapter assumed the population to be stationary (i.e., constant in size with a stable age distribution). This assumption is of course often violated in nature. This may be particularly true for an organism with planktonic larvae, where wide variation in recruitment may be expected from year to year. Sometimes many immatures survive to the age of first breeding, sometimes few. Consider, for example, a shrimp population with only two breeding ages. If P_1 is the survival from the first to the second breeding, then a stationary population will have P_1 older breeders for every younger breeder, and P proportion of the first breeders are predicted to be female (equation 10.1). Variation in recruitment will alter this ratio. If recruitment to the first breeders is unusually high in a given year, then the value of being a male has decreased, because there is now an abundance of small shrimp. In this situation selection favors a greater proportion ($>P$ discussed above) of the little shrimp to be females. In the extreme case where all the shrimp are first breeders, half of them should be female. In this situation it is as if we had a dioecious species with a single breeding age group. If the recruitment is very small, so that most of the breeding shrimp are larger, selection favors some of these older shrimp to remain males a second year. This is a model for alteration in the time of sex change (t^*) in the face of changes in the age distribution within a single population. Earlier (Charnov et al., 1978) an exact model was developed to predict the degree of these shifts. Figure 10.6 shows what the theory predicts. Here, I omit the algebra and only note that the product theorem in equation 4.1 is appropriate. The shrimp sex ratios are treated in the same way as the host-size shifts in wasps' sex ratios, and the ESS is as if only two sizes of hosts are present. First breeders are equivalent to small hosts, older breeders to large hosts. To describe the hypothesis in words: (1) if the proportion of first breeders acting as females is plotted against the ratio of older to first breeders, we expect a negative relation for

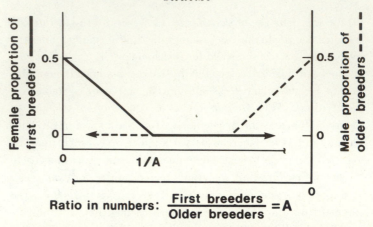

FIGURE 10.6. Alteration in the time of sex reversal in response to fluctuating age distributions. Illustrated is a population with only two breeding age groups (first breeders, older breeders). Their ratio gives the age distribution, which is assumed to vary from year to year. If there are few older breeders ($1/A$ small), all the older breeders should be female, and some fraction of the first breeders should also be female (the rest male). If there are few first breeders ($1/A$ large, or A small), all the first breeders should be male, while some of the older breeders should also be male (the rest female). As the age distribution varies from year to year, the cohorts are predicted to alter their sex ratios accordingly. Note that >50% of first breeders are male, while <50% of older breeders are male—thus the theory *never* requires an individual to sex reverse from female to male. (Original derivation and equations in Charnov et al., 1978. The reason for graphing one sex ratio versus A, and the other versus $1/A$ is to make the theoretical relations linear.)

small abscissa values and zero for large ones; (2) if the proportion of older breeders acting as males is plotted against the ratio of first to older breeders, we expect the same shape of relation as given in (1).

Charnov et al. (1978) analyzed data from three populations of *Pandalus jordoni* off the west coast of the United States. For each of several years, we estimated for each population: proportion of the breeders who were first breeders; proportion of the first breeders who were female; proportion of the older (mostly second) breeders who were still male. In all, thirty-six years of data were available. These data are shown in Figures. 10.7–10.9 and the statistical analysis in Table 10.2.

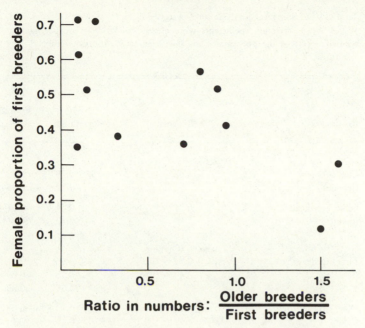

FIGURE 10.7. *Pandalus jordani* in Northern California for twelve years. The female proportion of first breeders is negatively related to the ratio of older to first breeders, as predicted by theory (Fig. 10.6). Data analysis is given in Table 10.2. Note that all years had a positive proportion of females among the first breeders. Theory thus predicts that all older breeders should be female. They were. (Redrawn from Charnov et al., 1978.)

For California, the proportion of first breeders acting as females is negatively correlated with the ratio of older breeders to first breeders (Fig. 10.7, Table 10.2). Here the theory also predicts that no older breeding shrimp should be males; none were found. Contrary to the critical size hypothesis, growth rates do not correlate with changes in P. The two Oregon populations (Figs. 10.8 and 10.9) differ from California in that both show years in which some older individuals reproduced as males. The data support the ESS hypothesis of Figure 10.6. I find these data very surprising since they support the idea that the shrimp are altering the time of sex reversal (here, the proportion of a cohort acting as male or female) in response to fluctuations in the population's age

TABLE 10.2. Statistical analysis for sex reversal in *P. jordani* (data in Figs. 10.7–10.9). Correlation coefficients were either the Pearson product moment coefficient (r_1) or the Spearman rank coefficient (r_s). Abbreviation: N.S., not significant.

Relation	Sample size (yrs)	Regression	Correlation	Prob. level
		Areas 82–84 (Oregon)		
First breeders	8	$y = 0.62 - 0.54x$	$r_1 = -0.75$	<0.05
(female)			$r_s = -0.72$	<0.05
Older breeders	13	$y = 0.31 - 0.20x$	$r_1 = -0.84$	<0.01
(male)			$r_s = -0.78$	<0.01
		Area 86 (Oregon)		
First breeders	8*	$y = 0.57 - 0.29x$	$r_1 = -0.96$	<0.01
(female)	9†	$y = 0.44 - 0.16x$	$r_1 = -0.75$	<0.05
	8*		$r_s = -0.64$	<0.05
Older breeders	7	$y = 0.4 - 0.51x$	$r_1 = -0.73$	<0.06
(male)	7		$r_s = -0.38$	N.S.
		(California)		
First breeder	12	$y = 0.6 - 0.20x$	$r_1 = -0.67$	<0.05
(female)			$r_s = -0.51$	<0.05

*Fit without the point $x = 3.4$, $y = 0.14$. †Fit with the point $x = 3.4$, $y = 0.14$. From Charnov et al., 1978.

or size distribution. We can only wonder at what cues the animals may be using.

The data on Pandalid shrimp clearly support sex change theory. The biogeographic patterns (proportion of EMF and age of sex change) are close to those theoretically predicted, as are the temporal patterns within a single population. Here, the reader will no doubt wonder how it is possible for a model which assumes a stable age distribution to be applicable (Fig. 10.4), while at the same time the data show fluctuations in age distribution (Figs.

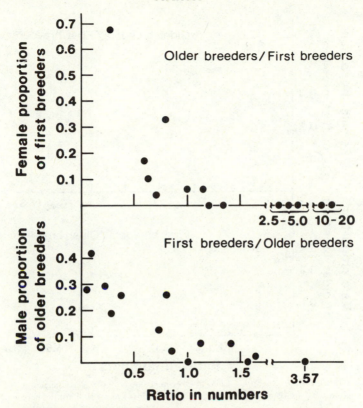

FIGURE 10.8. *Pandalus jordani* in Oregon (fishing area 82–84; see Charnov et al., 1978, for details) for fourteen years. Small ratios of older to first breeders are associated with a positive proportion of females among the first breeders, zero (or small) proportion of males among the older breeders. Age distributions with mostly older breeders give the reverse effect. These age shifts are of the form predicted by sex change theory (Fig. 10.6). Statistical analysis is given in Table 10.2. (From Charnov et al., 1978.)

10.7–10.9). The P (proportion of EMF) values plotted in Figure 10.4 represent (where possible) a within-population average for several years. It is this temporal average which is used in the test of the stable age hypothesis. Elsewhere (Charnov, 1979b) it is shown that this average is very close (in theory) to the value predicted for

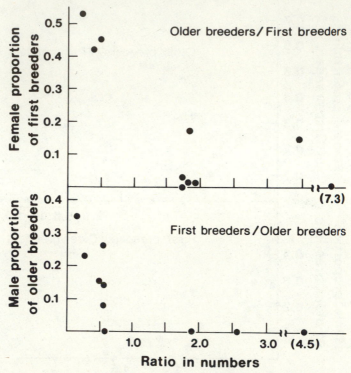

FIGURE 10.9. *Pandalus jordani* in Oregon (fishing area 86; see Charnov et al., 1978, for details) for ten years. Caption below Figure 10.8 applies here also.

a stationary population. A good analogy is that by looking at the average P value, we look at the population's response to an average age distribution. The shrimp data of Figure 10.4 are plotted in a slightly different way in Figure 11.5, which combines shrimp and fish in testing one hypothesis using both.

CHAPTER ELEVEN

Sex Reversal
in Labroid Fishes

In contrast to protandrous shrimp, many coral reef fish are protogynous (sex reversing from female to male). This chapter discusses sex change in wrasses and parrotfish. The most complete and quantitative data come from the genus *Thalassoma*. I discuss these first. I then discuss more general life history correlations of sex change for these two groups of fish.

THALASSOMA SPP.

Both *Thalassoma bifasciatum* of the Caribbean and *T. lucasanum* of the tropical Eastern Pacific are diurnal planktivorous wrasses (Labridae) commonly associated with coral reefs in shallow depths (< 5 m). They have been much studied, particularly by Reinboth (1970, 1973) and Warner, Robertson, and Hoffman (see Warner et al., 1975; Warner and Robertson, 1978; Warner and Hoffman, 1980a,b). Most of my discussion is from Warner and Hoffman (1980a).

Both of these species have two color phases. Brightly colored, *terminal phase* individuals are always males—they are the largest (presumably oldest) fish. The rest of the adult population are called *initial phase;* they are smaller, younger, and may be male or female. A general life history is sketched in Figure 11.1. There are two life history pathways. An individual may first mature as a female, then later reverse sex, change color, and become a terminal phase male. The other alternative is for an individual first to mature as a male, then later change to a terminal phase male. The change to terminal phase is at about the same size down either

161

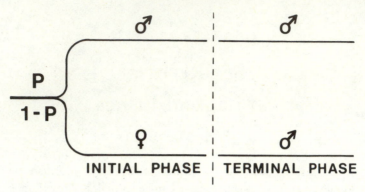

INITIAL PHASE | TERMINAL PHASE

FIGURE 11.1. Alternative life history pathways in the wrasse *Thalassoma* spp. A certain proportion of the cohort (*P*) first mature as males, while the rest (1 −*P*) mature as females. These are *initial phase* fish. Later in life the males change color, becoming *terminal phase* males. They then defend territories and pair spawn with females. Initial phase females later change *both* sex and color to become terminal phase males. Initial phase males (often) group spawn with some females. The ESS *P* equalizes the reproductive gains of the two pathways. This pattern of two pathways is the mirror image of the two pathways for Pandalid shrimp, Figure 10.2.

pathway (Warner and Robertson, 1978, but see below). Both species have pelagic eggs with mating taking place for about 100 minutes each day. Most females mate once each day, and the majority of matings take place at the downcurrent edges of reefs. Here (also see below), the largest terminal phase males set up territories from which they exclude other males. In these territories, the males pair-spawn with individual females. Initial phase males are non-territorial and either group spawn with females, or attempt to interfere with pair spawnings (streaking or sneaking in to release sperm). The territories are on the downcurrent edge of the reef on small reefs, and the group spawns at the reef's edge, upcurrent from the territories. On larger reefs this is reversed, with the territories pushed upstream from the group spawn. An important point for *T. bifasciatum* is that individuals do not leave the reef upon which they have settled (Warner and Hoffman, 1980b). Thus the population is broken into many subpopulations, all interconnected through larval flow. The reefs studied range in adult population size from 17 to about 16,000 fish, with fish density constant at about 1 fish per 3 m^2 of reef. Many reefs are larger than 16,000 fish but these were not studied.

It is clear from Figure 11.1 that these fish are the mirror image of the shrimp. Fish populations consist of pure males and protogynous hermaphrodites, while many shrimp populations consist of females and protandrous hermaphrodites. The ESS proportion pure sex (shrimp = ♀, fish = ♂) must be such that equivalent children are produced on each life history pathway. I provide here that calculation for *Thalassoma,* assuming a large, random-mated, stationary population (from Warner et al., 1975; Warner and Hoffman, 1980a). Suppose that growth, mortality, and age of change to terminal phase are the same down each pathway. After an individual enters terminal phase, its life history should be on average the same regardless of the pathway to get there. Thus, in ESS, the reproductive success of an initial phase male must be the same as that of an initial phase female (during the initial phase). Because initial phase females mate approximately once each day, in ESS *the average initial phase male must mate with one female per day* (Warner and Hoffman, 1980a). (Later in this chapter, we shall alter the assumption of females mating once each day.)

Let:

N = total adult population size;

P = proportion of initial phase which is male;

T^* = proportion of population in terminal phase;

S^* = average number of females mated each day to each terminal phase male.

There are $(1 - T^*)(1 - P)N$ initial phase females, and S^*T^*N of them mate with terminal phase males. Thus $(1 - T^*)(1 - P)$ · $N - S^*T^*N$ females mate with initial phase males. In ESS this must equal the number of initial phase males. Since $(1 - T^*)N$ individuals are initial phase,

$$P = \frac{(1 - T^*)(1 - P)\,N - S^*T^*N}{(1 - T^*)\,N} \quad \text{or}$$

$$P = \frac{1}{2}\left[1 - \frac{T^*S^*}{(1 - T^*)}\right]. \tag{11.1}$$

We can simplify this expression in two ways. T^* is always very small (<0.1) so that $T^*/(1 - T^*) \sim T^*$. Also there are two kinds of terminal phase males: those with territories, and those without (about half these males have territories, R. Warner, per. comm.). Those terminal phase males without territories do not breed. Let T be the fraction of the population in terminal phase with a territory ($\sim T^*/2$), and consider S to be the average number of females per day for a territorial male. Since non-territorial males (in terminal phase) do not breed, $T^* \cdot S^* \equiv T \cdot S$. Equation 11.1 then becomes

$$P \sim \tfrac{1}{2}(1 - T \cdot S). \tag{11.2}$$

That is, P should decrease as more females mate with territorial males (S), or as the fraction of the population with territories (T) goes up.

There are two ways in which we might test equation 11.2. First, we might apply it to an average reef, and second, we might treat each reef as an independent population. The second test will be discussed in detail below. Warner and Hoffman (1980a) provided a calculation for the first test, but Warner (per. comm.) notes that the calculation ignored the fact that half of the terminal phase males were not breeding. He has recalculated the values with the following results. Weighting by reef population size, he constructed an average reef. This reef has $\sim37\%$ initial phase males ($=P$); it also has $T \sim 0.0089$ and $S \sim 27$. Thus, the theoretically predicted P (equation 11.2) is 0.38, almost identical to the observed value.

The second test consists of application of the result (equation 11.2) to each reef independently. Here, we ask if each reef might be itself in ESS. If the reefs differ in some systematic way with respect to T and S, this procedure begins to look plausible. For T, *bifasciatum,* these parameters show some dramatic changes with reef size. Warner and Hoffman (1980a) noted that the number of territories did not increase proportionally with the local population size, but at a slower rate. Thus the proportion of the population with territories (T) decreased with increasing reef size. The average mating success for each territorial male did not change appreciably with reef size (except for tiny reefs); it was a constant at 27 ♀/day (95% confidence interval 22–32). Finally, the most interesting observation: the proportion of initial phase males (P) also changed with reef size. It was zero on very small reefs and showed an asymptotic rise to ~0.5 on the very largest reefs (two reefs with populations of ~3,000 and 16,000 fish both showed $P \sim 0.5$).

This is a remarkable sex ratio shift: note that P increases as T decreases. Warner and Hoffman (1980a) provide data on P and T for 14 reefs. The smallest reef had P equal to zero, the others had P ranging from 0.08 to 0.52. Warner (per. comm.) notes that while there were initial phase males on reefs with <200 fish, these males were excluded from breeding. Since equation 11.2 was derived for breeding initial phase males, I have excluded these small reefs from the analysis. Later, we shall extend the theory to this type of initial phase male. There are 9 reefs left. In Figure 11.2, I have plotted P versus $27 \cdot T$ for these reefs. The relationship is close to linear, with a least squares regression of $y = 0.6 - 0.72x$ $(r = 0.84,\ n = 9)$. With theory predicting $y = 0.5 - 0.5x$, the intercept and slope are both a bit high. However, considering the inherent imprecision of population level data, the relationship is still rather impressive.

Warner has provided me with new data gathered during the winter of 1980, on 8 reefs which had spawning, initial phase males. Again, a series of small reefs (<150 fish) had initial phase males who did not spawn. These data include P and the reef population size (N) but no estimates of T. However, the earlier study (1980a) showed T to vary with local population size. If we assume the same relationship for these data, we can derive and test a theoretical relation between P and the local population size, N.

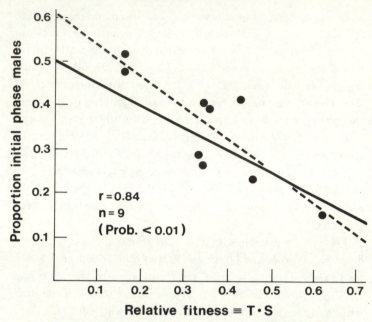

FIGURE 11.2. If each reef (for *T. bifasciatum*) is assumed to be in ESS with respect to the proportion initial phase males (*P*), the theoretical expected relation is $P \sim 0.5(1 - T \cdot S)$. Here, I have graphed data for nine reefs, setting $S = 27$ females/day and $T =$ appropriate value for that reef. Theoretical relation is the solid line; least square regression the dashed line ($y = 0.6 - 0.72x$). (Data from Warner and Hoffman, 1980a.)

Now, Warner and Hoffman (1980a) showed that the number of spawning territories increased at a rate less than proportional to population size. Replotting their data in Figure 11.3, we find that with the exception of the very largest reef ($\sim 16,000$ fish), there is an almost perfect relationship between the number of territories and the square root of local population size. Reefs from size 50 to $\sim 3,000$ fish are represented. The 16,000 fish reef has almost twice the number of territories as this relation would predict, but this will have almost no effect on the predicted P for a reef of this large size, since here $P \sim 0.5$. Since number of territories $= a\sqrt{N}$, T is equal to

$$T = \frac{a\sqrt{N}}{N} = a/\sqrt{N} \quad (a = 0.35),$$

166

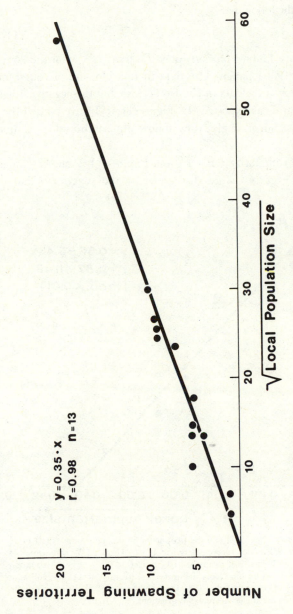

FIGURE 11.3. For *T. bifasciatum*, the number of terminal phase males with territories goes up with the square root of local (reef) population size (=*N*) for reefs ranging from 50 to ~3000 fish. This means that the proportion of the local population with a territory (= *T*) decreases with $1/\sqrt{N}$. (Data from Warner and Hoffman, 1980a.)

Plot axis labels: "Number of Spawning Territories" (y-axis), "√Local Population Size" (x-axis)

y = 0.35 · x n = 13
r = 0.98

Since $S \sim 27$, $a \cdot S \sim 10$. Substituting into equation 11.2, we arrive at the following:

$$P \sim 0.5 - 5/\sqrt{N}. \qquad (11.3)$$

In Figure 11.4a, I have graphed P versus $1/\sqrt{N}$ for the 9 reefs from the 1980a paper. The data in this plot are of course not independent of the data in Figure 11.2, so that the negative, linear relationship is as expected. In Figure 11.4b I have plotted the 8 1980 reefs. Surprisingly, they follow almost the same relationship.

Let me summarize what I think Figures 11.2 and 11.4 might mean. The graphs were stimulated by the suggestion that we

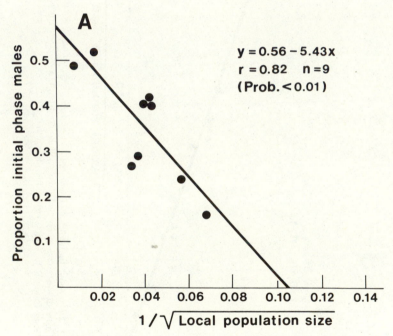

FIGURE 11.4. Reef size and the proportion initial phase males (P) in T. *bifasciatum*. Since T decreases with $1/\sqrt{N}$ (Fig. 11.3), the expected relation, with each reef assumed in ESS, is $P \sim 0.5 - 5/\sqrt{N}$ (equation 11.3). (A) Data for nine reefs of Figure 11.2 (from Warner and Hoffman, 1980a). (B) Data gathered in 1980 from eight reefs (R. R. Warner, unpub. data). Lines are the least squares regressions.

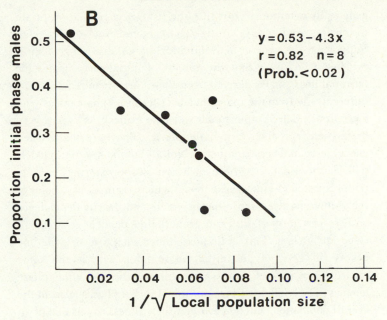

FIGURE 11.4 continued

consider each reef as an independent population, and test each of them for being in ESS with respect to P. This suggestion is not original, since it appears in qualitative form in Warner et al. (1975) and Warner and Hoffman (1980a). What is surprising is the quantitative fit between theory and data, as shown in the figures. However, these reefs are not independent populations. Why, then, should the data show the pattern? There are two ways in which a population such as this might show such spatial differentiation: labile sexuality, or habitat selection with respect to sex. If an individual is not genetically determined to be a male or female (in initial phase), but elects one or the other *after* settlng on the reef, it should adopt the sexuality appropriate to the particular reef. Under the stable age assumption for a reef, each would then show an ESS P as in equation 11.2. There is no evidence which suggests that the fish have labile sexuality of this type.

Warner and Hoffman (1980a) suggest that initial phase sex is genetically determined, but that the fish select reefs appropriate for their sexuality (e.g., initial phase males avoid small reefs). Supporting the genetic determination hypothesis is histological evidence which says that the gonads of initial phase males (or terminal phase males derived from them) are organized in a very different way from the male gonads of terminal phase males who were first female. Young males show no evidence of even a very brief (non-reproductive) female phase. They are male when encountered at a very small size. Not all habitat selection models will lead to a pattern where each reef is approximately in ESS with respect to P. However, a model which assumes easy choice of reefs (any larva can settle on any reef) and density dependence with respect to mortality and growth (independent of sex) will come fairly close. This is because under such a model, lifetime fitness (in ESS) of an initial phase male will be the same regardless of its reef. The same will be true for initial phase females. The equilibrium proportion of initial phase males, in the overall population, will be such that their fitness equals that of an initial phase female. It follows that they will be equal on each reef.

This analysis (Figs. 11.2, 11.4) excluded small reefs (typically <200 fish) which had initial phase males who were themselves excluded from breeding by the territorial males (since the original model was for breeding initial phase males). Warner (per. comm.) suggested that these non-breeding males may well compensate for their status by increased growth and/or survival rates. His unpublished data support the increased growth, but show no increased survival. He notes that it is still possible for these reefs to approximate an ESS P, if the enhanced growth of the little males more than doubles their chances of reaching terminal phase. If all terminal phase males are on average the same, then we can derive the ESS P as a function of the enhanced chances of a young male reaching terminal phase. However, P here refers to the proportion of males among the young initial phase (and not males among all initial phase). It is the proportion at the time an individual elects to be a male. Since these little males grow faster, their proportion

170

should increase as we look at larger initial phase individuals. Let P^* be the proportion of terminal phase males who were initial phase males. The ESS argument $P/(1 - P) = 1 - 2W$, where W now refers to the relative male fitnesses for the hermaphrodite versus pure male, produces the prediction that

$$P^* = 2P.$$

By the time these males reach terminal phase, their frequency is predicted to be double their frequency among the young initial phase. There is an alternative way of writing this result. If $\beta =$ chances of an initial phase, non-breeding male reaching terminal phase, *relative* to the same event for an initial phase female, the ESS argument shows that $P/(1 - P) = 1 - 2/\beta$. Charnov (1983) develops a more general ESS model, which combines differential mortality or growth for the two pathways with some mating for the initial phase males. Warner notes that, assuming habitat choice but no labile sexuality, the growth compensation may fall short of doubling the chances to terminal phase. Here the small males may be making the best of bad reef choice, a choice which puts them on a reef where they are excluded from breeding as young males.

SHRIMP AND FISH TOGETHER

Because the individual reefs (with spawning young males) appear to at least approximate an ESS, in this section I will simply assume they do. Since the shrimp life history is the mirror image of the fish, both may be said to obey the relation

$$P = \frac{1}{2}[1 - W/(1 - W)], \tag{11.4}$$

where P is the proportion of a pure sex among the young animals. In Figure 11.5, I have graphed both data sets plus the theoretical relation. The shrimp data include one new data point (from Charnov et al., 1978). For the fish, $W/(1 - W)$ was estimated as $S \cdot T$ with $S = 27$ and T either estimated from reef size (Fig. 11.3) or as in Figure 11.2. The fish data also include *T. lucasanum*,

171

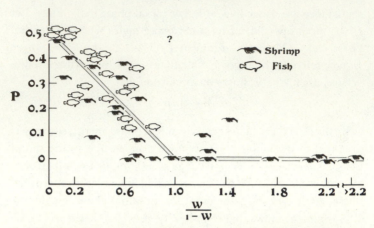

FIGURE 11.5. Letting P = proportion pure sex, and $W/(1 - W)$ the appropriate sex comparison (e.g. $\equiv S \cdot T$ for the fish), the figure shows the shrimp populations of Figure 10.4 (plus one more) and the reefs of Figure 11.4. In addition, there is one data point (see text) for the rainbow wrasse (*T. lucasanum*). The theoretical expected relation is also shown.

which has $P \sim 0.49$ and $S \cdot T < 0.001$ (Warner and Hoffman, 1980a). There is considerable scatter, but this is to be expected, considering the imprecision of these population data. However, the data points are numerous enough for us to ask if the average values, taken over several populations/reefs, converge to the theoretical line. If we lump the points into five ranges for $W/(1 - W)$ (0–0.2, 0.2–0.4, etc.) and calculate for each range a mean ordinate and abscissa value, we can fit a line through the five average values. Figure 11.6 shows that a straight line fits the data almost perfectly ($r = 0.98$, $n = 5$) and that the fitted line is $y = 0.51 - 0.51x$. This is remarkably close to the theoretical expectation of $y = 0.5 - 0.5x$.

WRASSES AND PARROTFISH IN GENERAL

Coral reef fish of the families Labridae (wrasses) and Scaridae (parrotfish) show varying degrees of protogyny. The life history *often* includes two color phases, a duller initial phase followed by a brighter terminal phase, although some species are monochromat-

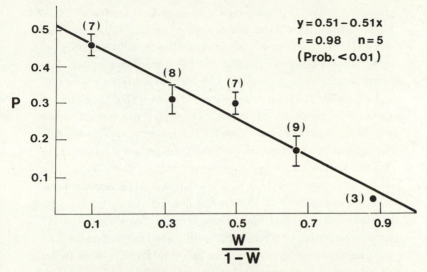

FIGURE 11.6. For each of five $W/(1 - W)$ ranges (0–0.2, 0.2–4, etc.) from Figure 11.5, we calculate a mean abscissa and ordinate value. A regression through the means is linear with the equation very close to the theoretical, $y = 0.5 - 0.5x$. Bars indicate one standard error. Numbers are sample size (reefs or shrimp populations).

ic. Some species have only females among the smaller fish, males among the larger. Some have a life history like *Thalassoma* (Fig. 11.1) with the smaller fish (initial phase) both male and female. Sex change theory says that the presence of initial phase males depends upon opportunities for these small males to breed (or show enhanced growth/survivorship), and that their frequency depends upon the size of breeding opportunity (Robertson and Choat, 1974). For *Thalassoma* we derived equation 11.1 which expresses the ESS proportion of males in the initial phase (P) as a function of the proportion of the population in terminal phase (T^*) and the females/day for each terminal phase male (S^*). The equation was:

$$P = \frac{1}{2}\left(1 - \frac{T^*S^*}{1 - T^*}\right) \tag{11.5}$$

The derivation of this assumed (1) that mortality, growth, and change to terminal phase were the same on average for all initial phase individuals; (2) that females mated once each day, and that there was no tendency for larger or smaller females to mate with terminal phase males; (3) that the life history during terminal phase was on average equivalent for the two sex types.

I would like to retain assumptions (1) and (3) (but see Charnov, 1983, for relaxation of assumption (1)); however, in many Labroid fish, females may spawn less frequently than every day. An argument which equilibrates the fitnesses down either of the two life history pathways (male versus sex reverser—Fig. 11.1), shows that equation 11.5 is a special case of a more general relation. In equation 11.5, the initial phase males each mate with one female every day. Since each terminal phase male gets S^* females each day, S^* is really the fertility of a terminal phase male per unit time compared to the per unit time fertility of an initial phase male. The more general relation for P treats S^* in just this way—thus, if $S^* = 5$, each terminal phase male spawns with five times as many females as each initial phase male. The more general relation is simply equation 11.5 with S^* interpreted in this way. The beauty of *Thalassoma* is that S^* takes an empirically simple form. Since it may be difficult to estimate S^* in the field, I provide here an equivalent relation. Let h = proportion of the females who mate with initial phase males. It is straightforward to show that equation 11.5 is equivalent to

$$P = h/(1 + h). \tag{11.6}$$

Equation 11.6 has a very simple intrepetation; P is adjusted so that each initial phase male ($\tilde{N}P$ of them, where $\tilde{N}$ refers to the number of initial phase individuals) has one female to mate with (there are $(1 - P)\tilde{N}h$ of them). At this point, the average initial phase individual (male or female) achieves the same reproduction while in initial phase. I fully realize that the life histories of Labroid fishes can be exceedingly complex (parrotfish: Randall and Randall, 1963; Buckman and Ogden, 1973; Ogden and Buckman, 1973; Robertson and Warner, 1978; Warner and Downs, 1977; wrasses: Warner and Robertson, 1978; Roede,

174

1975; Thresher, 1979), but I think that equation 11.6 captures the essential reliance of small males (their presence) on the availability of females. For this discussion, I exclude small males who are not reproductive, but gain their increased reproductive success through higher growth or survivorship (although $P^* = 2P$ applies here; see above).

Thalassoma, with its restricted mating sites and high mating population densities (Warner and Hoffman, 1980a,b) provides ample opportunities for small males to breed. At the other end of the spectrum are species like the wrasse *Bodianus rufus* (Warner and Robertson, 1978) or the cleaner fish *Labroides dimidiatus* (Robertson and Choat, 1974; Robertson, 1972, 1974), which have permanent territories, male control of a harem of females, and no initial phase males. *Labroides* are monochromatic as adults. As discussed in Robertson and Choat (1974), the social system consists of a male with 5–6 mature females plus several unrelated juveniles. While reproductive adults remain permanently in one group, juveniles are more mobile, often moving between groups. The male occupies a very large territory and the females usually confine their activities to this area. The male is the oldest, largest individual and dominates the females. Each individual has a feeding area which is the focus of its territory. The females form a simple dominance hierarchy based on size. The largest female dominates and her feeding area roughly corresponds to the male's overall territory. Death of a female results in a lower-ranked female moving into the vacant territory and dominance position. If the male dies, the dominant female takes over his territory and group, rapidly changing sex. *Within one hour* of the male's death, this female is behaving as a male toward the other females. About two weeks later, sperm is being produced. Spawning (with release of eggs into the plankton) takes place within the group territory, with group members spawning only with their male. Almost all spawnings are pair spawnings, and of hundreds observed less than 3% involved a male and female from different groups (Robertson, 1974). Clearly, there is little place for small, cuckolding males in this social system. Probably most wrasses fall somewhere between

175

the open breeding system of *Thalassoma* and the closed system of *Labroides*.

Warner and Robertson (1978) examined life histories for seven wrasses. Three had no initial phase males. One of these (*Bodianus rufus*) had a permanent harem system. One, *Clepticus parae*, had pair spawnings (but no streaking was ever observed), and the third's breeding system was not clear. The four others had various proportions of initial phase males. Two of these had open, non-haremic mating, and evidence suggests that the others lacked any sort of permanent territory. *Halichoeres bivittatus*, a species with a breeding system much like large *Thalassoma* populations, had the highest proportion of initial phase males ($P \sim 0.33$).

Choat and Robertson (1975) examined data for nine Australian parrotfish. In all, terminal phase individuals were typically the largest and were male. Initial phase individuals were smaller and could be either sex, although only three of the species had initial phase male frequencies above 0.20. Five of the others had essentially no initial phase males; one had $\sim$9%. Group spawning was observed in two of the three species with many initial phase males. The other seven species showed only pair spawning. Robertson and Warner (1978) examined nine species of Caribbean parrotfish. Five of the nine do form harem groups. One of these five (*Scarus croicensis*) has about 25% males in the initial phase. It also has a large, non-haremic part of the population. Individuals outside groups may feed within territories by swamping the territory holder (i.e., feeding in mass). Three of the five harem species have 2% or fewer males in the initial phase. There is little or no evidence for the occurrence of non-haremic females and no indication of group spawning (although initial phase males may spawn by streaking). The last species of these five (*Sparisoma radians*) has about 6% males in the initial phase; it has a large, non-haremic segment of the population and regular group spawns. Of the remaining four species, three do not have harems. This suggests ample opportunity for initial phase males to spawn. These species have 10–20% males among the initial phase. The final species has about 5% initial phase males. This one did not

176

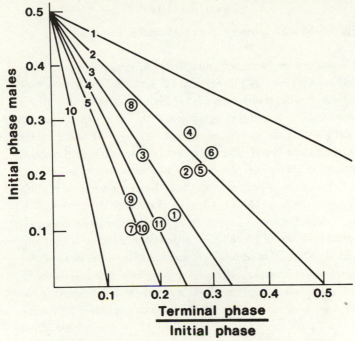

FIGURE 11.7. Predicted relation between proportion initial phase males (P) and the ratio of terminal phase (TP) to initial phase (IP) individuals ($T^*/[1 - T^*]$) for eleven species of Labroid fishes. Theoretical relation is equation 11.5. The predicted relation depends upon the females per TP male compared to the females per IP male (S^*). S^* values from 1 (smallest possible) to 10 are shown. As expected, all species show $S^* > 1$. Species identity (circled numbers) as follows.

Scaridae

1. *Sparisoma viride* (0.15)*
2. *S. rubripinne* (0.27)
3. *Scarus croicensis* (0.32)
4. *S. globiceps* (0.38)
5. *S. fasciatus* (0.27)
6. *S. fosteri* (0.32)
7. *Cryptotomus roseus* (0.11)

Labridae

8. *Halichoeres bivittatus* (0.49)
9. *H. maculipinna* (0.18)
10. *H. pictus* (0.11)
11. *H. poeyi* (0.11)

Data from Robertson and Warner, 1978; Warner and Robertson, 1978; Choat and Robertson, 1975 (only species with ≥10% initial phase males are included). Asterisk indicates proportion of the female population predicted to spawn with initial phase males (= h, equation 11.6).

easily fit into the patterns discussed above, but more data are needed.

To summarize, wrasses and parrotfish strongly support the hypothesis (Warner and Robertson, 1978) that initial phase males are present where factors such as high population density, a non-permanent territorial mating system, or opportunities to interfere with pair spawnings (streaking) give the small males opportunities to breed. They are rare or absent where the social system allows terminal phase males to control access to females. Their frequency when present most likely depends (equation 11.6) upon the fraction of the female population they can spawn with. Although the social system may control the mating opportunities, social systems are themselves determined by the spatial and temporal distribution of basic resources such as food and shelter. Robertson and Warner (1978) have suggested that this explains major differences between Labrids and Scarids. Scarids are herbivores, Labrids carnivores. Permanent territories may have been facilitated by the predictability of benthic, algae food resources. Haremic species are much more common among the parrotfish.

In Figure 11.7, I have graphed the proportion of initial phase maless (P) against the ratio of terminal to initial phase fish, $T^*/(1 - T^*)$, for several Labroid species. I have also graphed the theoretically predicted relations, for various S^* values. If $S^* < 1$, the terminal phase males would do worse than the initial phase males, and protogyny would most likely disappear. Thus, in theory, we predict that all populations will fall inside the $S^* = 1$ line; they will be associated with $S^* > 1$. This clearly is the case. It is interesting that the species range in S^* values from 2 to 6. Of course, the predictions of S^* for these species now become hypotheses to be tested. The species involved are indicated in the figure caption; associated with each is the proportion of the females predicted to spawn with the initial phase males ($=h$).

CHAPTER TWELVE

Sex Reversal in
Some Special Animal Systems

This chapter reviews our knowledge of sex change in fish, two genera of marine molluscs (*Patella, Crepidula*), and one poly-chaete worm, *Ophryotrocha*. The emphasis is on aspects of natural history which seem particularly relevant to evolutionary aspects of sex reversal.

SEX REVERSAL IN FISH

In vertebrates, normal hermaphroditism (including sex rever-sal) is found only in fish. Its occurrence (phylogenetic and ecological) has been reviewed several times (Atz, 1964, 1965; Reinboth, 1970; Smith, 1965, 1975; Chan, 1970; Warner, 1978). Smith (1975) states that hermaphroditism has arisen at least twelve times independently in fish. A summary of our knowledge is shown in Table 12.1, updated from Warner (1978). I think it likely that sex change is more common in fish than these data would suggest (also suggested by Warner, 1978). Anemone fish (Pomacentrids of the genus *Amphiprion*, symbiotic with sea anemones) are a much studied and common aquarium fish. A recent book (Allen, 1972) on their biology does not mention that they are protandrous. A few years later this was known for several species (Fricke and Fricke, 1977; Moyer and Nakazono, 1978b). *Amphiprion* are difficult to breed, and show little or no sexual dimorphism (except females are larger). This may explain why their protandry escaped notice for so long, but this group cannot help but make one wonder about less studied fish. Pandalid shrimp had been fished in northern Europe for hundreds of years,

TABLE 12.1. Normal hermaphroditism in fish (modified from Warner 1978).

Type of hermaphroditism	Order	Family	Degree of occurrence within family	Habit of hermaphrodites
I. Simultaneous	Aulopiformes	All except Harpadontidae and Synodontidae	All species thus far studied.	Bathypelagic
	Atheriniformes	Cyprinodontidae	One species (*Rivulus marmoratus*).	Still freshwater
	Perciformes	Serranidae	Subfamily Serraninae.	Shallow marine
		Pseudogrammidae	One species (*Pseudogramma bermudensis*).	Shallow marine
II. Sequential (A) Protogynous (♀→♂)	Synbranchiformes	Synbranchidae	All species thus far studied.	Still freshwater
	Perciformes	Serranidae	Most species in subfamilies Anthiinae, Epinephelinae.	Shallow marine
		Grammistidae	All species thus far studied.	Shallow marine

	Sparidae	Three species.	Shallow marine
	Maenidae	Three species.	Shallow marine
	Labridae	Almost all species thus far studied.	Shallow marine
	Scaridae	All species thus far studied.	Shallow marine
	Cepolidae	One species (*Cepola rubescens*).	Shallow marine
	Pomacanthidae	Angelfish (*Centropyge interruptus*).[1]	Shallow marine
	Pomacentridae	*Dascyllus*.[2]	Shallow marine
(B) Protandrous ($\delta \rightarrow \varphi$)			
Ostariophysi	Cobitidae	One species (*Cobitus taenia*).	Freshwater streams
Stomiatiformes	Gonostomatidae	One species (*Gonostoma gracile*).	Mesopelagic
Scorpaeniformes	Platycephalidae	At least three species.	Shallow marine
Perciformes	Sparidae	Seven species.	Shallow marine
	Polynemidae	Several species.	Shallow marine
	Pomacentridae	Anemonefish (*Amphiprion*).[3]	Shallow marine
Anguilliformes	Muraenidae	One species of moray eel.[4]	Shallow marine

Data from Reinboth (1970) and Smith (1975), except [1] Moyer and Nakazono (1978b); [2] Schwartz (1980); [3] Fricke and Fricke (1977), Fricke (1974); [4] Shen et al. (1979).

but protandry was recognized only in 1930 (Berkeley, 1930). Since protandry would show an overall male-biased adult sex ratio, plus a sex ratio which becomes more female-biased with size, such patterns might themselves suggest protandry. However, sex differential growth, mortality, or maturation time might also produce similar patterns in dioecious species. Wenner (1972) has summarized sex ratio as a function of size for many marine crustaceans. These data clearly indicate the difficulty of using such plots to infer protandry.

There are no particular habitat correlations with sex change in fish. It is found in species associated with freshwater swamps, the continental shelf, coral reefs, and the deep sea (Smith, 1975). Since egg production typically increases with adult size in fish, we would expect protandry where size adds little or nothing to male reproductive success. Protogyny would be expected where an individual must be larger in order to compete effectively for females (Choat and Robertson, 1975; Robertson and Choat, 1974; Warner, 1975, 1978).

Only two families (Pomacentridae, Sparidae) have both directions of sex change. Reinboth (quoted in Atz, 1965) stated that protandrous Sparids lack sexual dimorphism, lay pelagic eggs, and take several months to complete sex reversal after its onset. The protogynous species have more pronounced sexual dimorphism, lay adhesive eggs, and sex reverse in as little as 1.5 months. This suggests (with data for one species—discussed in Warner, 1975) that here males may be territorial, competing for limited breeding sites. This would favor larger male size. Apparently nothing is known about the mating habits of the protandrous species (Warner, 1975). Since some species of Sparids are common and heavily fished in the Mediterranean, they may provide very useful comparative material. I will discuss the Pomacentrids below.

Equally little is known about the other four protandrous families. Warner (1975) notes that the families Gonostomatidae, Polynemidae, and Platycephalidae all contain common, heavily fished species (off Africa, India, and Japan). Longhurst (1965) reviewed fishery data for two common Polynemid species off Nigeria. One was dioecious, with a maximum life span of two years. The other was protandrous, with some individuals maturing as females when they first breed. About 25% of the reproductive females were early-maturing. With a life span of at least three years, this would mean that about 8-20% of a cohort matures as females. The dioecious species breeds the year round, while the sex changer almost ceases breeding during the rainy season. This strongly suggests a discrete fitness set (Fig. 10.1) for the sex changer, reminiscent of Pandalid shrimp.

Of the protogynous species, only the eel-like fish of the family Synbranchidae are found in fresh water. The physiology of sex change has been much studied in this group (Chan, 1970; Chan et al., 1975). These eels have no external sexual dimorphism (Liem, 1963, 1968). Male parental care is the rule, with the eggs guarded in breeding burrows (Wu and Liu, 1942). Liem (1963) studied the Asian *Monopterous albus*. In the lab, one-year-old fish were mature females and sex change took place at the age of 2½ years. The life span was not known. Using histology of the gonads, Liem (1968) identified two kinds of males in the tropical new world *Synbranchus marmoratus*. One male class showed evidence of prior reproduction as females, the other showed no such evidence. Members of the second class of males were found in the smallest size class of reproductive individuals. Based on what is known about gonad organization in other fish which change sex (e.g., Smith, 1965), the second class of males were most likely pure males. If so, then this species shows a life history similar to *Thalassoma*, with pure males and sex reversers present. However, there is much geographic variation. Eleven locations from South America showed these small, pure males. In Brazil they made up 20% of the smallest reproductive class. However, only pure males were found in Trinidad, while no pure males (all small fish were female) were found in samples from Pearl Island. It would be interesting to know if this life history variation correlates with changes in the social system, changes which influence the chances of small males to reproduce.

Zei (1949) reviewed protogyny in the Maenidae. At least three species reverse sex. They show sexual dimorphism (with bright males), adhesive, demersal eggs, and rapid sex change (as in protogynous Sparids).

In Table 12.2, I have summarized life history data for four species of Serranids. Groupers showed little sexual dimorphism, and determination of sex requires a ripe gonad. Little is known about their spawning habits (Thompson and Munro, 1978; Moe, 1969), except Smith (1972) reports a spawning aggregation (??) of 10^4-10^5 fish for the Nassau Grouper, *Epinephelus striatus*. As shown in the table, increase in life span goes along with more years in the female phase. Since many species of Serranids are of commercial importance, it would be useful to contrast sex reversal in exploited versus unexploited populations. Thompson and Munro (1978) have suggested that the population sex ratio (proportion of males) increased in exploited populations of *Epinephelus guttatus* in the Caribbean. The meaning of this is unclear.

In the Serranid subfamily Anthiinae, the planktivorous reef fish *Anthias squamipinnis* shows protogyny (Fishelson, 1970; Shapiro, 1979). It is a very common fish which has been much studied in the Red Sea, off the Sinai Peninsula, and in the Philippines. My discussion is a composite, drawn from these three locations. The fish typically occurs during the day in large (10^1-10^3 fish) stationary groups around coral heads (Popper and Fishelson, 1973). At night the fish hide in coral crevices. The groups consist of mostly immatures and females, the adult sex ratio being less than 10% males (Fishelson, 1975). Shapiro (1977a,b, 1979–1981) studied 45 groups for several months. The groups ranged in size up to 370 fish with a median size of 31. The total composition was 220 male, 1856 female, and 510 juveniles, for an adult sex ratio of 11% males. Even though Shapiro's work provides incredible detail in observations of social behavior (his 1979 monograph is a small book itself), he gives no information on reproduction. Popper and Fishelson (1973) provide the only study of breeding behavior.

TABLE 12.2. Summary of data on sex reversal for groupers and sea bass (Serranidae).

Species	Location	Life span (maximum)	When sex change?	Reference
(1) *Centropristes striatus* (common Atlantic bass)	New York	12 yrs	1. ♂ 50% at 6 yrs 2. ♂ 80% at 7 yrs	Lavenda, 1949
(2) *Mycteroperca microlepis* (the Gag)	Florida	15 yrs	1. ♀ mature at 5–6 yrs 2. ♀ till age 10–11 3. ♂ at age 13–15	McErlean & Smith, 1964
(3) *Epinephelus morio* (Red Grouper)	Florida	>20 yrs (maybe 30 yrs maximum)	1. ♂ 10% at 9 yrs 2. ♂ 50% at 15 yrs	Moe, 1969
(4) *Epinephelus diacanthus*	Taiwan	7 yrs*	1. ♀ mature at 1 yr 2. ♂ 50% at 4 yrs 3. ♂ 72% at 6 yrs*	Chen et al., 1980

*This may reflect recent fishing exploitation. The natural life span may be longer, with a greater fraction of the females changing sex.

Breeding is seasonal with a peak from November to March. They found no small males, indicating that everyone begins life as a female, later reversing sex. The males form two categories. A minority hold defended territories over the reef surface—here they pair-spawn with females. A majority of males do not hold territories and swarm lower on the reef. These non-territorial males are sometimes attacked by the breeding males, and the authors did not know if they succeeded in breeding. Space on the reefs limits the number of territories, and in small groups all the males may hold territories (Fishelson, 1975). Females and immatures often swarmed apart from the males. Shapiro (1979) also notes that some groups existed with no male. However, in the absence of breeding data it is difficult to argue (as Shapiro, 1980, does) that these groups were never associated with males.

Shapiro (1977 a,b, 1979) also observed that large groups often were broken down into several subgroups. The groups may change in size by three means: death, recruitment of immatures, or fission. From the structure of groups of different sizes, Shapiro inferred that as the group grows larger, it may split into two or more smaller groups. If this is true, the most common situation would be a male splitting away with a group of females (see also Fishelson, 1975). It would be very interesting to know which males and females typically split off.

Sex reversal is socially controlled. Fishelson (1970) noted that removal of a male from a group induced a female to sex reverse. Shapiro and Lubbock (1980) watched several groups in the field. As the groups grew through addition of young fish, the sex ratio drifted toward females. It appeared that when a threshold sex ratio was reached (about 10% female) one female changed sex. The females formed a dominance hierarchy in which the largest and first-ranked fish was most likely to sex reverse. In another study Shapiro (1980) removed from 1 to 9 males from each of 26 groups. There was an almost one to one replacement of the lost males. Where one male was removed a mean of 1.17 females sex reversed. In the groups where 3–9 males were removed, 58 removed males were replaced by 57 sex reversals. Duplication of these experiments in another location produced virtually the same results (Shapiro, 1981). Given the social control of sex change, it should not be surprising if the male size range varies dramatically from place to place. The largest 10% of the population should be male, but the size range must vary with growth and death rates. Shapiro (1979) shows two locations about 800 meters apart. They are not separate genetic populations, yet the size of sex reversal is very different in the two areas (Fig. 12.1).

The Angelfish (*Centropyge interruptus,* Family Pomacanthidae; Moyer and Nakazono, 1978b) is a benthic/algae feeder which is sexually dichromatic (bright males) and protogynous. One male holds a harem of one to four females. The females form a dominance hierarchy based on size, and death of the male results

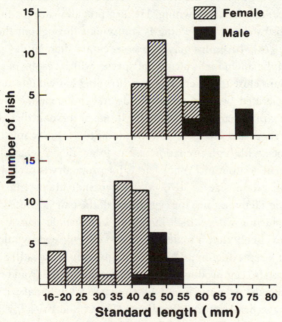

FIGURE 12.1. Size distribution for male and female *Anthias squamipinnis* from two locations (800 m apart) on the same Aldabra Island reef. The largest 10% are males, but the sizes differ dramatically between the two locations. Populations are probably not genetically distinct. (Data from Shapiro, 1979.)

in the sex reversal of the first-ranked female. Mating takes place just before sunset, mostly between a male and a female in his harem. Nearby males may attempt to streak the spawning pair.

Sex reversal in the Pomacentridae was only discovered in the late 1970's (Fricke, 1974; Fricke and Fricke, 1977; Moyer and Nakazono, 1978a). Damselfish of the genus *Dascyllus* (Schwartz, 1980) are protogynous while the Anemonefish (*Amphiprion*) are protandrous. *Dascyllus* form harem groups with a single male dominating several females. In Anemonefish, the typical social unit consists of one adult pair plus unrelated juveniles inhabiting a single sea anemone individual (Fricke and Fricke, 1977). The pairs are very stable, as some fish were observed for three years in the same place. The female behaviorally dominates the others while the largest male dominates the smaller (potential males) and prevents them from spawning. He also provides care for the eggs in a substrate nest. Spawning is continuous throughout the year (Ross, 1978). Juveniles may be less sedentary than adults, particularly if the anemone is a colonial species which results in several fish groups close together. The non-breeding individuals are most likely tolerated because they help defend the anemone and will provide a replacement reproductive if one of the pair dies. Fricke (1979) suggested that the low availability of unoccupied hosts (combined with high predation risk to locate them) selects for the permanent occupation. What selects for protandry is probably the breeding group size of two. With two individuals, the larger should be a female since the egg output of the pair is limited by the egg production rate, which increases with female size. It seems much less likely that a male's ability to care for eggs would limit the pair's reproduction. The male might gain if the still smaller fish were also egg producers, but they are prevented from being so by the female. An experiment which paired adult females resulted in injury or death to the subordinate (Fricke and Fricke, 1977). If the breeding group were of size three or more, the protandry would probably not be stable. Here the largest individual would likely become a male; he could then fertilize the two smaller females, whose combined egg output would be greater than his potential egg production as a female. This may be why the *Dascyllus* are protogynous.

SEX REVERSAL IN MOLLUSCS: *PATELLA* AND *CREPIDULA*

In this section and the next, I discuss sex change in two groups of molluscs, and one genus of polycheate worms. The purpose of the discussion is to point toward these organisms as systems for testing aspects of sex allocation theory, even though they have typically not been viewed in this way. Since they are easily reared and/or sampled, they provide ideal material for experimental work. Two of the groups also contain congeners which are dioecious and/or simultaneous hermaphrodites. The emphasis is on aspects of natural history particularly relevant to the book's theme.

Sex reversal is rare in molluscs, being confined to a few limpet-like Prosobranch Gastropods (particularly the genus *Patella* and the family Calyptraeidae, genera *Calyptraea, Cricibulum,* and *Crepidula*—Webber, 1977; Hoagland, 1975, 1978; LeGall and Streiff, 1975; Fretter and Graham, 1962; Coe, 1944), oysters of the genus *Crassostrea* (Andrews, 1977; Galtsoff, 1964), and a few other pelecypods (Sastry, 1977; Coe, 1943) (for example, shipworms of the genus *Teredo*—Coe, 1941, 1943; Turner, 1966; Herlin-Houtteville and Lubet, 1975). In all cases, the sex reversal is from male to female.

Since the early work of Orton (1920, 1928, 1946) and colleagues (Orton, Southward, and Dodd, 1956; Dodd, 1956; Orton and Southward, 1961) and cytological work by Bacci (1952, 1965), it has been known that some species of intertidal, herbivorous limpets of the genus *Patella* are protandrous hermaphrodites. The ecology/natural history of the genus has been widely studied in Europe and the U.K. (Ballantine, 1961; Fischer-Piette, 1948; Blackmore, 1969; Das and Seshappa, 1948) and in South Africa (Branch, 1971, 1974a,b, 1975a-d, 1976). The genus is of particular interest since it contains both dioecious and sex-changing

189

species. Sex change is the rarer of the two conditions (e.g., of eleven South African species, at least one but perhaps up to three change sex—Branch, 1974a; only one of the three British species changes sex—Dodd, 1956). The most widely studied species of sex changer is undoubtedly *Patella vulgata* in Europe/U.K. Fewer data exist for two other sex changers; *P. caerula* in the Mediterranean (Bacci, 1965; Montalenti, 1958) and *P. oculus* in South Africa (Branch, 1974a). As noted by Branch (1974a), nothing in the ecology of the sex changers particularly suggests why they do and the other species do not. Females are the larger sex even in the dioecious species, and Branch could show no sex differential in growth rates. All species are external spawners (in contrast to protandrous *Crepidula* where all species copulate and brood eggs for at least a while) with males typically devoting a greater proportion of their biomass to gonads (*P. vulgata* follows this rule—Ballantine, 1961; while the rule is reversed in *P. oculus*—Branch, 1974). Breeding is synchronous in a given location. *P. vulgata* spawns in the fall and Ballantine (1961) observed that it spawned over a one-day period in one year, a nine-day period in another. Female egg count increases exponentially with female shell length (Ballantine, 1961, for *P. vulgata*).

Here, I shall briefly review the data for *P. vulgata*, particularly the less familiar work of Ballantine (1961). Orton's data suggested that small limpets (< 10 mm shell length) were immature and that males made up 90% of those in the 16–25 mm category, with female frequency increasing with size (50% of 40 mm; 75% of 60 mm). Das and Seshappa (1948) showed a similar pattern with females making up ~80% of the largest size category (56–60 mm). Their data lumped together all the limpets on a particular shore, regardless of tidal height. Fischer-Piette (1948) compiled growth curves for many limpet populations, from locations all over Europe, and showed tremendous variation from place to place. From these data came the general pattern that absolute growth rate was inversely related to longevity. Limpets with short life spans were on average much larger than those in populations with long life spans. He also noted that different habitats on the same shore could be ranked by limpet growth rate.

Building on this, Ballantine (1961) studied *P. vulgata* in Batten Bay (Plymouth, U.K.) and separated the bay into four populations. While there was undoubtedly much larval flow between them, it seems likely that the areas were distinct with respect to the adults. In Figure 12.2, I show the growth curves for his areas 1 and 4. These curves are the upper and lower bounds for the growth curves observed by Fischer-Piette (1948) when considering the species all over Europe. *That is, in one English bay we find almost all of the life history variation for the species!* In area 1

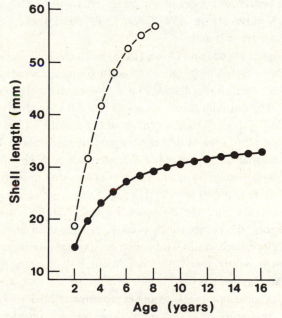

FIGURE 12.2. Growth of the limpet *Patella vulgata* in two parts of Batten Bay, Plymouth, U.K. Note that lifespan and growth rates are inversely related. These two areas are at the extremes of lifespan and growth for the species in Europe. For reference, open circles are area 1, solid circles area 4. See text for more details about the two areas. (Data from Ballantine, 1961.)

maximum life span was 8 years with an asymptotic size of 60 mm. In area 4, the corresponding values were 16 years and 35 mm. Area 4 was the highest population on a shore which was greater than 90% barnacle-covered. Limpet density was $\sim 100/m^2$. Area 1 was around *Fucus*. Here the limpets grazed and maintained clearings in the algae; they also occurred in semi-isolated groups made up of a few large limpets (in the center of the clearing) surrounded by many smaller limpets (at the edge). Limpet density was $\sim 150/m^2$. Figure 12.3 shows the typical sexual development of a limpet in each of these areas, related to both size and age. The absolute size relations are vastly different between the two areas, although every individual apparently matures as a male. Sex reversal occurs over a broad size range even within each area— and 20% (area 4) to 40% (area 1) of the largest (oldest?) individuals are still male.

Both Bacci (1965) and Orton (1928) had suggested earlier that protandrous *Patella* populations typically contained some individuals who never changed sex. The *P. vulgata* data support this (Fig. 12.3A) but data for *P. oculus* do not. All individuals in the upper 30% of body weight were females in Branch's 1974 study. Ballantine (1961) noted that the remarkable thing about Figure 12.3A was that the course of sex change appeared to be related to time in both populations, independent of absolute growth rates. That is, all individuals were male at age 3 years, 40% were female at age 5 years, etc. He produced Figure 12.3B to show this. Remarkably, the curves much overlap, at least until about 60% female. Here, they would have to diverge, as area 4 increases up to 80% female, while area 1 does not. While Ballantine considered limpet development related to age or absolute size, we may also ask if the developmental sequence appears related to *relative growth*. In Figure 12.4, I have graphed percent female versus relative limpet size (proportion of the asymptotic length) for the two areas. The curves are very similar (they must diverge at the upper end). Ballantine (1961) may be correct that sex development is strictly related to age (Fig. 12.3b), or it may be related to some relative size distribution (perhaps keyed to aspects of the

192

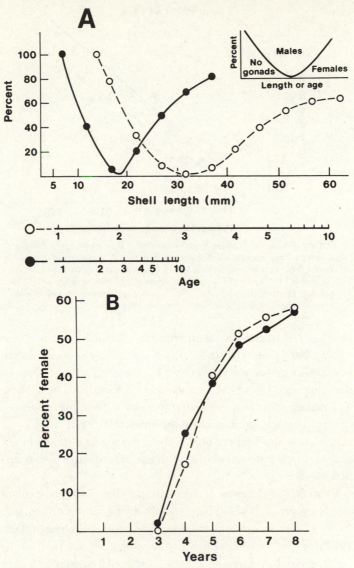

FIGURE 12.3. Sexual development versus size (A) and age (B) for *P. vulgata* for two areas in Batten Bay, Plymouth, U.K. Open circles are area 1, solid circles are area 4. The curves in (B) show that sexual development *appears to be* related to age, independent of the absolute size distribution. (Data from Ballantine, 1961.)

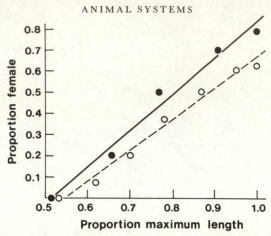

FIGURE 12.4. An alternative hypothesis for sexual development of *Patella* in Batten Bay. Figure 12.3B suggests that sexual development is age-related. This graph suggests that sexual development is related to *relative size*. Areas 1 (O) and 4 (●) show almost equivalent sexual development at a specified relative size. Relative means scaled to the largest individual present in each area. (Data from Ballantine, 1961.)

social system). He had no direct age estimates, and age was reconstructed from growth relations. Since there is such a broad size/age range for sex change (with a significant proportion not changing sex), I have not attempted any ESS calculations. These data make it clear that the spatial scale for considering limpet sex change is much smaller than the intertidal region itself, and suggest that the limpets may well be responding (in their sex change) to microvariation in growth and reproductive opportunities.

Crepidula is a genus of small limpet-like gastropods, all of which are protandrous. There are ~30 living species (Hoagland, 1975, 1977). Protandry was first discovered by Orton (1909, 1919) for *C. fornicata,* which had become a serious pest on the oyster ground in England (Yonge, 1960). All species are filter feeders. All copulate and brood their young through early development. Typically, small species brood their young completely through development and they emerge as miniature adults. The larger species typically produce pelagic young which spend various amounts of time (two weeks for *C. fornicata*) in the water column before settling (Hoagland, 1975, 1977, 1978). The genus has been much studied, particularly relative to social control of sex reversal. The early work is by Orton (1912), Coe (1935, 1938a,b, 1944, 1948, 1953), Gould (1917a,b, 1919, 1952), and Ishiki (1936).

Hoagland (1975, 1977, 1978) provides a fine set of studies on sex reversal on four species. She proposed that the genus could be divided into two types of species:

(1) *Large species with planktonic larvae.* They are long-lived (~ 10 years for *C. fornicata*), typically forming stacks of 5–20 individuals and often inhabiting muddy bays. They are gregarious, with immatures (or less mature individuals) actively joining stacks, and with social control of sex reversal. A stack of *C. fornicata* is shown in Figure 12.5. Typically the larger (usually older) individuals are on the bottom and are females; smaller individuals are on top and are males. Very little is known about

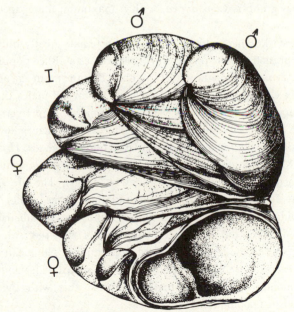

FIGURE 12.5. A stack of *Crepidula fornicata* in life position. Sexes of the individuals are indicated. I = intermediate. (From Hoagland, 1978.)

stack dynamics. Large individuals are relatively immobile, but small ones are mobile. Depending upon stack density, it would seem that small males would be able to wander from stack to stack. These males may even be better than somewhat larger males (who would be less mobile) at inseminating females, but we know little of male-male reproductive competition. Early work by Gould and Coe in *C. plana* demonstrated that males simply do not grow in the presence of females, suggesting that males may gain by being small.

(2) *Small species without planktonic larvae.* These individuals are short-lived (life spans about half that of the large species), do not form permanent stacks, and do not have social control of sex reversal. The juveniles are not attracted to the adults. The males and females are together for only a short period, and the females store sperm. For both groups of species, egg count increases with the 2nd or 3rd power of female length. Clutch size is approximately 1% that of planktonic species. A good example of this second group is *C. convexa,* with a maximum life span of ~ 5 years.

In stack-joiners, close proximity of a female greatly influences the duration of male phase. For three well established populations of *C. fornicata,* Hoagland (1978) found that the mean age and size of sex change was 2–3 times greater for mated males than for solitary males (16 months versus 5.5 months; 3 gms versus 0.9 gms). It has been repeatedly shown (Coe, Gould) that removal of a female cues the small male to grow fast and change sex. Hoagland (1978) also studied two populations of *C. fornicata* which she characterized as colonizing, or newly formed. The life span is about 10–12 years, but these populations lacked older/larger individuals. The downward shift of the age/size distribution should select for a lowered age/size of sex reversal, when compared to the long-established populations. The mean age of sex reversal here was about 7 months for mated males and about 3.5 months for solitary males (contrast this with the well-established populations).

In addition to these field data, Hoagland (1978) carried out some lab experiments on sex reversal in *C. fornicata.* She placed limpets in large tanks, at various starting sex ratios, and observed the sex ratio one year later. While the starting ratios were 0.5, 0.67, and 1.0 proportion males, the final ratios were all very close to 0.5 (0.48, 0.53, 0.53 respectively). Similar work for *C. convexa* showed no social effect on sex reversal (but see below). Lab experiments (identical to the above) showed that in one year, almost all the limpets had changed sex (starting male proportions were 0.5, 0.67, 1.0, while the final percentage of males ranged from zero to only 20%). In addition, her three study populations for *C. convexa* showed little variance in the age (or size) of sex reversal, being about 6.7 months (and 24 milligrams) in each. Earlier, Coe (1938a, b) had claimed that association had little or no effect on the age of sex reversal for three brooding (non-stacking) species (*adunca, convexa, nummaria*), but dramatic effects in three planktonic species (*plana, fornicata, onyx*). For both *C. convexa* and *C. fornicata,* Hoagland (1978) found that the proportion of the adult populations in male phase increased with population density. This may indicate alteration with density in the opportunities for larger males to reproduce, as discussed at the end of Chapter Nine.

There is one social aspect to sex change in *C. convexa*. Certain populations occur on substrates where growth is limited (e.g., eel grass—Hoagland, 1978; hermit crab shells—Hendler and Franz, 1971). Such populations are said to be dwarf. Because larval flow between populations is restricted (young emerge as miniature adults, and are never in the plankton), selection may act to lower the size of sex change in such groups. Indeed, such shifts have been noted by Coe (1938a, b), Hoagland (1978), and Hendler and Franz (1971). Hoagland (1978) claimed that populations on eel grass lowered the size but not the age of sex change.

Hoagland (1978) proposed that stacking species should show much variation in mating opportunities from stack to stack, and that this variation selects for labile sex change. In contrast, the species without stacks or planktonic larvae may show much less variability. One population of *C. convexa* was stationary over a three-year period. This correlates well with the lack of a labile sex change.

197

What selects for sex reversal in molluscs? D. R. Lindberg (unpub. ms) first noted that virtually all sex-reversing gastropods are limpet-like, with high shell whorl expansion rates or increasing whorl expansion rates with age. Most coiled gastropods have apical angles less than 17°, while those of most limpet-like gastropods are greater than 90°. He also noted that territoriality is very common among limpets. Here, larger individuals tend to exclude other larger individuals. He proposed that this would select for protandry if the exclusion meant that large individuals as males would not be able to mate with large females. Only small males (or females) would get near a large female (or male). In effect this greatly limits the reproductive opportunities for a large male. Following this theme, it would be very useful to compare the social systems of sex-changing and dioecious members of the genus *Patella*. In *Crepidula,* my own observations suggest that size greatly limits mobility. If mobility is important in male reproduction, but not in female, then again larger individuals gain relatively more by being female (Ghiselin, 1974). Both of these hypothesis relate to *factors which limit male reproduction by larger individuals.* Since female egg production increases with size in molluscs (and in many other invertebrates), the size-advantage hypothesis (Ghiselin, 1969, 1974) points toward size-related male reproduction as a key to understanding protandry and its selection over dioecy.

SEX REVERSAL IN THE POLYCHAETE, *OPHRYOTROCHA PUERILIS*

While most of the ~20 species in the polychaete genus *Ophryotrocha* are either dioecious or simultaneously hermaphroditic (Akesson, 1977, 1976, 1973) at least one, *O. puerilis,* is a protandrous sex reverser. Hermaproditism is widely scattered but rare in Polychaetes (reviewed in Schroeder and Hermans, 1975; Reish, 1957). *O. puerilis* has been widely studied, particularly with respect to the control of sex reversal (Bacci, 1965, 1978; Akesson, 1973). The species differs from the previously discussed fish, shrimp, and molluscs in that an individual can sex reverse many times.

Bacci (1965, 1978; Bacci and La Greca, 1953) found that in lab cultures, sex reversal was related to size. He contrasted the size at sex change in two subspecies (Naples, Plymouth) and showed a large difference (see Fig. 12.6). We should perhaps not call these groups "subspecies" as they show clear morphological differences, and crosses between them show almost perfect reproductive isolation (Akesson, 1977). Interestingly, the few surviving off-spring from these crosses show hybrid vigor, with growth rates increased over intrapopulation crosses. Sex change theory would suggest that the reversal time differences of the Naples versus Plymouth populations reflect underlying differences in the size fertility relations, or more likely the size distributions themselves. At present there are no data on this. The differences in the size at sex change for these two populations are most likely maintained by selection, since Bacci has demonstrated that genes affect the size of reversal. Using *O. puerilis* from both areas, Bacci (1955) and Bacci and Bortesi (1961) (both reviewed in Bacci, 1978, 1965) carried out artificial selection for size at sex reversal. At the

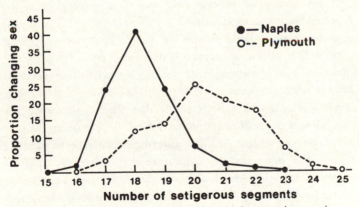

FIGURE 12.6. Sex reversal as a function of size in the protandrous marine polychaete *Ophryotrocha puerilis,* for two locations in Europe. The differences are probably genetic, as discussed in the text. (Redrawn from Bacci and LaGreca, 1953.)

beginning of one experiment, the average size of sex change was 18 segments. After only four generations, the early sex change line had individuals reversing at an average of 13 segments. In the late line, the average size was 25 segments. These lines were almost pure males and females. Other artificial selection experiments have shown similar responses with this species (Bacci, 1965, 1978; Muller, 1962). Crosses between the selected lines showed an intermediate size of reversal.

In addition to the patterns discussed above, sex reversal in this species has a large social and developmental component. Hartmann (1956) demonstrated considerable environmental influence. When he amputated 15 chaetigerous segments from female animals, leaving 10 segments, the anterior part regenerated into a male. Reversal from female to male also results from starvation (Hartmann, 1956; Bacci, 1965). The male phase may be extended by contact with larger females (or maybe even the water which contained larger females!). Perhaps the most interesting (if puzzling) aspect of sex reversal in this species is what I shall term "pair formation." At least in the lab, two females brought together will pair up, one (the smaller) will sex reverse to a male, and the couple will bring forth fertilized eggs. At some future time, they will simultaneously reverse sex, and this sequence may be repeated several times (discussed in Pfannenstiel, 1975). Since the eggs are costly, relative to the few sperm necessary to fertilize them, it may be that the female is drained of resources while the male stores up resources. Since the pair's reproductive success is limited by egg production, the sequential switching of roles seems reasonable. Akesson (1973) states that this simultaneous sex reversal may occur after spawning only if the animals in the pair are of about equal size. Animals differing considerably in size may remain the same sex throughout several spawnings. This is consistent with the hypothesis about the energy cost of egg versus sperm production. Apparently nothing is known about the timing of this switch, but it should be related to the energy input rate, the rate at which resources are drained from the female. However, it is not obvious why the pairs stay together: why do males not

200

simply abandon their mates after a period? At least some cheating would be expected. Obviously, the availability of partners is important, and all these experiments were done with isolated pairs. Nothing is known of what goes on in a more natural setting.

Two other aspects of pair formation are particularly interesting. First, both parents help care for the eggs, which are laid in a gelatinous matrix. Removal of the parents results in death to the brood (Akesson, 1973). Second, when two females of about the same size pair up, the first one to become a male also grows a new and larger upper jaw (Pfannenstiel, 1975). Now the pair has one individual with a large jaw and one with a small jaw. This suggests differential resource utilization within the pair, but there are no data on this.

This genus may be very important for sex allocation studies, since it contains all three of the basic forms of sexuality found in animals. At present we simply do not know why the "cake is cut this way" within *Ophryotrocha*.

201

CHAPTER THIRTEEN

Labile Sexuality
(Sex Choice) in Plants

Much of this book is devoted to asking when it is that individuals are selected to alter their allocation to male versus female function, in response to short-term alterations in environmental or social conditions, or in response to increasing age or size. Examples are the LMC sex ratio response to superparasitism of *Nasonia* (Werren, 1980a,b, 1982, Chapter 5) and the response to fluctuations in age distribution shown by protandrous shrimp (Charnov et al., 1978, Chapter 10). Most higher plants are fairly immobile as adults, and an individual must literally breed where it is rooted. As a consequence, plants are usually very plastic in their growth (Harper, 1977). Since opportunities to reproduce through male versus female function might be expected to vary greatly with microhabitat or plant size, we should expect many plants to show the ability to adopt the sexuality appropriate for the individual's particular condition. This chapter reviews the evidence for such responses, discusses some of the theory proposed to account for them (i.e., in what way, if at all, is the response adaptive? what kinds of predictions can sex allocation theory make?) and finally, briefly reviews data on two of the best-known systems.

Botanists have long been aware that, at least for some species, sexuality is responsive to external, environmental, or growth conditions. Maekawa (1924) reviewed early data for many species. The physiologist Heslop-Harrison (1957, 1972) provides more recent reviews. In the middle of this century, much work was done in Russia on the physiology of labile sexuality. Reviews are in Minina (1952), Dzhaparidze (1963), and Chailakhyan (1979). However, that such responses might be adaptive (in the sense of

202

altering sex allocation) has only recently been discussed (Freeman et al., 1976; Charnov and Bull, 1977; Smith, 1981). Much of my discussion is drawn from the review article by Freeman, Harper, and Charnov (1980).

Many publications support the fact that various environmental factors can alter sex expression in dioecious species. Likewise, the ratio of male to female flowers on individuals of monoecious species has often proved manipulable through alteration of the plant's environment and (less often) the ratio of male to female organs of perfect flowered taxa. As summarized in Table 13.1, age, injury, and disease have all been shown to alter the sexual expression of individuals of some species. Similarly, physical and nutritional characteristics of the environment (e.g., light intensity, soil fertility, soil moisture) are reported to affect the sexual expression of a variety of species. In addition to the factors listed in Table 13.1, various chemical, hormonal, or light treatments, or

TABLE 13.1. Some factors known to modify the sexual expression of vascular plants under controlled conditions. Table modified from Freeman, Harper, and Charnov 1980. Consult this reference for original citations and certain qualifications on data.

Factor	Direction of shift	Number of species listed in Freeman et al., 1980
1. Increasing age or size	Male to Female	8
2. Cold weather	Female to Male	2
3. Dry soil (wet soil often the reverse)	Female to Male	7
4. High light intensity (low gives the reverse)	Female to Male	1
	Male to Female	12
5. Manure	Male to Female	2
6. "Rich" soil	Male to Female	5
7. High temperature	Female to Male	6
8. Trauma—removal of leaves, flowers; or crown pruning	Male to Female	8
9. Removal of storage tissue	Female to Male	2

additions to the soil (e.g., abscisic acid, boron, auxin, ethylene, gibberellins, potassium, photoperiod) may affect sex expression. Some of these factors (e.g., hormonal) are probably the proximate causes of sex shifts and not themselves the ultimate factors. At present however, this proximate-ultimate distinction is difficult to make for much of the literature. For example, photoperiod may often be a proximate cue for the seasonal scheduling of male versus female function. Light intensity, variable from place to place on the forest floor, may be an ultimate factor in sex expression for several species (Table 13.1). However, much experimental work confounds these two aspects of "light" (reviewed by Heslop-Harrison, 1957).

Some variables predispose individual plants of labile sex expression toward femaleness, while others favor maleness (Table 13.1). The data reveal a strong tendency for stress (broadly defined) to induce maleness. By "stress" I mean conditions which reduce growth, reduce a plant's ability to allocate resources to reproduction, or lessen an individual's chances for survival. For example, small size, cold weather, dry or low nutritional soil, low light intensity, or removal of storage organs all tend to incline the individual toward maleness. The exception is trauma in the form of leaf removal or crown pruning which in at least eight species causes shifts toward femaleness.

Recent work by Freeman and Kalled (unpub. data) demonstrates the role of water stress on sex ratio of spinach populations. They transplanted spinach seedlings (from a common seed source and grown in a common environment) into wet and dry soil environments. The wet environment received 5 times the water applied to the dry environment. They obtained ratios of 82 females to 42 males in the wet environment and 46 females to 79 males in the dry environment. Since only three plants died in each treatment and all plants flowered, the results are best explained by the hypothesis of labile sexual expression.

Most of the work described above (and summarized in Table 13.1) was done under controlled laboratory conditions. However, recent work shows that sex choice is a usual feature of the life

204

history of several species. Barker et al. (1982) studied the maple, *Acer grandidentatum,* which is a small tree showing either monoecy or purely male individuals. They surveyed the floral sex ratios and showed that trees on xeric sites were relatively more male, while trees on mesic sites were more female. In the two-year period 1977–1979, sex expression altered in 12 of 46 trees in Logan Canyon, Utah. Nine individuals changed from male to monoecious, 3 the reverse. Freeman et al. (1976) showed a similar xeric versus mesic site trend for five dioecious species in the intermountain west of the U.S. They argued for sex choice, but the data did not eliminate a differential mortality hypothesis (see also data in Waser, 1981). Freeman et al. (1981) studied three woody monoecious species, and again compared a xeric site (steep midslope) with a mesic site (stream side or bottom land). They found that the number of male flowers per standard branch did not change across sites. However, the number of female flowers doubled in two species and went up by ~30% in the other, in the shift from xeric to mesic.

Natural sex change has also been documented for two species of *Juniper* by Vasek (1966). He showed that over a two- to five-year period 7% of the individuals of one species, and almost 25% of individuals of the other changed sex. Freeman and McArthur (1981) marked over 1400 individuals representing six species growing in natural populations in Utah. They found that 13.5% of the *Atriplex canescens,* 15.5% of the *A. confertifolia,* 34% of the *A. corrugata,* 18.5% of the *A. cuneata,* 35% of the *A. lentinformis,* and 31.5% of the *A. tridentata* individuals changed sex between 1978 and 1981. Hermaphrodites were observed in all species, and hermaphrodites displayed a larger percentage change in sexual expression between the two years than was recorded for either males or females.

In other recent work, McArthur (1977), and McArthur and Freeman (1981) have demonstrated that environmental factors are strongly correlated with the sexual expression of individuals of the subdioecious species *Atriplex canescens.* They document sex switching following three environmental stresses: (1) an unusually cold winter, (2) drought, and (3) heavy seed set by females. During the flowering period following each of the stressing events, there was a pronounced shift toward maleness in the population of over 600 individuals. For example, following an unusually severe winter, 86 females become male or monoecious, 10 monoecious individuals became male, and only 11 non-females became female. When each stressing condition was lifted (i.e., the year following the severe winter), the proportion of females in the population increased. Over 40% of the plants involved in the study changed their sexual state during the seven years of observation. Their data also support the idea that the switching toward maleness during stressful years enhances the individual's chances of survival during that period.

These data argue that sex choice is a typical part of the life history of at least some species, and that "stress" shifts toward maleness. We do not know how widespread sex choice in plants is. Freeman et al.'s (1980a) literature search (their Table 1) showed over 50 dioecious species in 25 families with evidence of individuals having altered their sex expression. Also of importance is that the species discussed represent a variety of life forms (trees, shrubs) and taxonomic groups. I doubt that any botanist would have guessed that a maple would show sex choice. What I conclude from this brief survey is that sex choice in plants is probably much more common than we realize.

If at present we cannot ask how common the phenomenon is in nature, the environmental correlates (e.g., "stress" $\rightarrow$ maleness) are at least suggestive of hypotheses relative to *its* adaptive significance. The word "its" may be a misnomer, since it seems likely that the shifts in sexuality which we have collectively termed sex choice actually represent several somewhat distinct adaptations. "Somewhat distinct" should be taken to mean that the factors which cause variation in the relative opportunities for female as opposed to male reproduction may well differ between species. The generalization is, of course, that the shifts in sexuality represent adaptive responses to those opportunities. Some of the shifts may not be adaptations at all, but since physiological and non-adaptive explanations have held the field for the last sixty or so years, it seems time to see what selection theory can do.

In general the plants (= individuals) just discussed alter their sexuality in response to factors which themselves vary through space (e.g., wet and dry patches), time (e.g., a dry year), or with size (condition or age) of the individuals. For example, a hermaphroditic species with discrete generations (no age structure) inhabiting a perfectly uniform environment might well show alteration in sexuality from year to year if the male versus female gain curves (discussed in Chapter Fourteen) changed from year to year. Likewise, a sequentially hermaphroditic species (with no spatial or temporal variation) would show sex change each year in the individuals who passed the threshold age or size. Also, the threshold itself might alter from year to year, as in shrimp, or spatially as in *Crepidula*'s response to microvariation in stack structure. All of these (and more) we would lump under the term "sex choice," since field or lab observations would show individuals altering sexuality.

Ignoring for a moment year-to-year variation, it seems clear that in general sex choice may be due to:

(1) A form of sequential hermaphroditism, where an individual changes sex as it grows larger. As previously noted (Chapter Nine), two major factors might play a role here. First, larger (older) individuals are relatively better at being one sex—for example, at attracting pollinators and dispensing pollen (*male function*), or producing and dispersing seeds (*female function*). Second, reproducing through one sex is relatively more costly than through the other, so that growth and/or mortality is sex specific (Policansky, 1982; Bierzychudek, 1981b; Freeman. et al., 1980a). Selection then delays to a larger size or later age reproduction in the sex which pays the higher mortality/growth cost. The early years are spent in the sex with lower mortality and/or higher growth rates. For example, small individuals may not bear well the cost of being female. Note that this does *not* answer the question as to why the costs differ between the sexes; why (for instance) small individuals do not just allocate much less to being a

female. One possibility is that the fixed cost for being (say) female is so high that small individuals cannot afford it (Bierzychudek, 1981b).

(2) Sex choice may also be a response to a spatially patchy environment. A seemingly uniform habitat might well have microsite variation, so that even assuming discrete generations, some individuals are robust at the time of breeding, while some are small. If size (or condition) translates differentially into male versus female fitness, individuals might be expected to choose the sex appropriate for their size or condition. The model situation is like the host-size wasp model of Chapter Four. The sex ratio response then depends upon the male/female fitness curves, as well as the distribution of sizes in the breeding population. Some of the species previously discussed have sex ratio varying with a major environmental gradient, such as soil moisture. If the individuals from the various patches interbreed, the situation is again like the host-size model.

These two situations—sequential hermaphroditism and a spatially patchy environment—may, of course, interact. For example, one sex may die faster in the dry patches. Freeman et al. (1980, 1981) suggested that in the U.S. intermountain west soil moisture is often correlated with sexuality (females in wet) because pollen production takes place in the spring when moisture is everywhere abundant, while seed and fruit maturation take place later in the year when patches far from permanent water are very dry. Females would then suffer relatively higher mortality in dry patches, contrasted to males in those patches. Freeman and McArthur (1982) measured internal water stress in individuals of five dioecious species of desert shrubs (in the genus *Atriplex*). The tests were conducted during the summer months, while fruits were developing. Paired comparisons between males and females showed that females were under significantly higher internal water stress (in all species) when fruits were in the late stages of development. The data suggest that males may be relatively better able to reproduce on sites which are dry late in the summer. As noted earlier in this chapter, these species all show sex choice.

On top of these *spatial* and *age* (= *size*) patterns, we must add year-to-year variation in any of the various costs. An example would be the *Atriplex* study where a particularly dry winter caused mass reversion to maleness. One thing which should be kept in mind is that if the patches do not form an interbreeding group of individuals, the conception is quite different—each patch must be treated as a separate population, which may still show year-to-year or size-related changes in sexuality for the individuals.

One other factor should be mentioned with respect to sex choice. In many of the animal examples of labile sexuality, the thing that varied was the social environment into which the individuals or their offspring were put. I know of no such effects for higher plants, but several studies have documented socially induced shifts in sexuality for lower plants such as fungi, algae, or ferns (physiological review in van den Ende, 1976; related to sex allocation theory, at least for the fern prothallus, in Willson, 1982).

I have sketched without formal development the four factors probably involved in "sex choice" in plants (*sequential hermaphroditism, spatially patchy habitat, social environment, year-to-year variation*). Many of the analytical techniques used elsewhere in this book are easily applied to calculate consequences which may help to distinguish alternative hypotheses (e.g., does age or size correlate with sexuality? is mortality sex specific?). We now turn to two particular case histories: orchids of the subtribe Catasetinae, and perennial, herbaceous plants of the genus *Arisaema*.

Of all orchids, only the three genera of the subtribe Catasetinae have separate male and female flowers. Dodson (1962) noted that field populations usually had less than 5% females, and suggested sex choice for the group. He picked 15 females (from a species of *Catasetum*) from full sunlight and moved them to dense shade— all then bloomed as males. A control experiment moved 15 females from full sun to full sun—13 of these remained females. By moving plants from shade to sunlight, he also produced the reverse shift. In her thesis (1973) and two papers (1975, 1978), Gregg greatly extended these observations. She studied several species in the genera *Catasetum* and *Cycnoches*. Defining full sunlight (FSL) to be ~10^4 lux (at sea level), she exposed individuals to medium shade (0.33 FSL), bright shade (0.50 FSL), and sun (0.75 to 1.0 FSL). Her data showed that most of the species studied produced significantly more female inflorescences when grown under sun, compared to shade conditions. However, the species were not at all uniform in response. Plants of two species (*Cycnoches densiflorum* and *Cy. stenodactylon*) required lower light intensities (0.50 FSL versus 0.75 to 1.0 FSL) to produce substantial proportions of female inflorescences, compared to individuals of four other species (*Catasetum expansum, C. tabulare, Cy. dianae,* and *Cy. warscewiczii*). Catasetinae lose their leaves just prior to (or just after) flowering, so that all of the resource for reproduction is contained in the storage organ, called a pseudobulb. It appears that plants under good growth conditions typically became females. In *C. macrocarpum*, females had much larger pseudobulbs than males (256 versus 58 gms mean weight). High nutrition, in this case sheep manure, also increased pseudobulb weight in two of three species tested.

The picture which emerges from this work is that photosynthate is stored, expended for reproduction, and then replenished. Light and other growth factors influence the resource available for reproduction. These orchids are probably pollinated by large bees, which means that breeding takes place between individuals from many patches (e.g., light and shade areas). While complicated by the possible accumulation of resource in the pseudobulb, the situation seems analogous to the wasp host-size model. In addition to asking just why females gain more by being large, the most interesting comparison is probably the one analogous to shifting the host-size distribution. If a species can be compared over several locations, some of which have on average high light levels, some of which have on average low, we expect different responses to a given light level from individuals in the separate locations. Whether 0.5 FSL is high sunlight or low depends upon what kind

210

of sunlight patches are present. If most patches have less sunlight, then the individuals in 0.5 FSL should be more female, compared to habitats where most patches have greater than 0.5 FSL. Here, individuals in 0.5 FSL should be more male. Gregg's (1973) cross-species comparison noted earlier, which showed that two of six species differed in the response to 0.5 FSL, hints at this predicted shift. Do these two species differ from the others in being found under generally shadier conditions?

Arisaema is a large genus (over 100 species) of herbaceous perennials, mostly restricted to forests of Africa and eastern Asia (Wilson, 1960). One of the two North American species, *A. triphyllum* (Jack-in-the-Pulpit), and one Japanese species, *A. japonica*, have been much studied (Schaffner, 1922; Maekawa, 1924; Policansky, 1981; Bierzychudek, 1981a,b; Lovett-Doust and Cavers, 1982) from the viewpoint of sex reversal. This general discussion is from Bierzychudek, 1981b. *Arisaema triphyllum* overwinters as a corm. The leaf and inflorescence primordia, formed the previous fall, expand in the spring. The inflorescence consists of a cylindrical column of tissue, the spadix, which bears flowers at its base. A modified leaf, the spathe, wraps around the spadix. The sexes are usually separate. Pollination is by small flies who enter into the top of the spathe tube. They receive no reward and are presumably tricked by some quality of the inflorescence. Once in the tube, they become trapped and are unable to move upward, only downward. In males they are able to escape through an opening at the base. In females, they simply die. Seed maturation takes most of the summer and the bright red berries are dispersed in the early fall. In addition, individuals may reproduce vegetatively by producing small cormlets at the edge of the parent corm.

Schaffner (1922) studied this species in five eastern U.S. habitats. He found a male-biased adult sex ratio (23% female, 62% male, 14% monoecious; $N = 1874$). In summer experiments in 1919 he dug up 25 female plants, cut off a good portion of the roots and foliage, and replanted them under poor growth conditions. Twenty-one of these reverted to males the next spring. In

211

another experiment he cultured males under excellent growth conditions. Thirty-one of 32 turned into females the next year. Maekawa (1924) studied even more intensively the Japanese species *A. japonica*. Like *A. triphyllum,* this species has a corm and shows sexual differentiation in buds late in the summer. Differentiation occurs after most of the year's growth has taken place. He showed that corm weight was strongly related to sex. In the range 14–24 gms, 91% of the individuals were males, while 25–35 gms gave 65% females, and above 35 gms all were females. He caused sex change (here, female to male) by any of several treatments which interfered with the storage or growth ability of the plants, or by mutilation of the corm itself.

Bierzychudek (1981a,b) studied the demography and reproduction of *A. triphyllum* on two sites near Ithaca, New York. In her populations, 60–80% of the females failed to set seed. She suggested that this was due to low pollination activity. Artificial pollination dramatically increased seed set (about 10 times), and showed a high, positive correlation between plant size and seed number. Mortality was size dependent, but not sex dependent. She also provides a detailed discussion of the demography (and its year-to-year variation) for the two sites. Her data on reproduction suggest that individuals might change sex because females allocate a good deal more of their resource to reproduction than do males. Lovett-Doust and Cavers (1981) showed that fruiting females of *A. triphyllum* allocated (on a percentage basis) about three times as much resource to reproduction as males. Bierzychudek's studies further supported this comparison. Average reproductive effort at the time of flowering was ~11% for males and ~7% for females. This represents a male's total reproductive effort, but females must pay the additional costs of seeds. Further calculations strongly suggest that small plants would have great difficulty reproducing as females. In a sense, the flowering cost for a female is a fixed cost; it must be paid prior to production of any seeds. However, it represents all the male's reproductive cost. By reproducing as a male when small, an individual avoids this excessive cost and frees resource for growth.

212

Policansky (1981) also studied *A. triphyllum,* in a wood at Concord, Massachusetts. He estimated seed production versus female size, and, as a measure of male reproductive success, estimated flowers per inflorescence versus male size. Male reproductive success (RS) did not increase with plant size, while female RS went up significantly. His female RS curve excluded females who set no seed. The probability of this event was independent of female size (Policansky, per. comm.), so the calculation to be presented here is still valid. Using the estimated female RS curve, and assuming that male RS does not go up with size, he then combined these with the observed size distribution (Fig. 13.1) to estimate, using the product theorem for sex change (Chapter Nine), an ESS size of transform. Figure 13.1 shows much overlap in male/female sizes, but the size at which 50% are each sex is 380 mm in height. The product theorem predicted a value between 380 and 400 mm. Policansky's (1981) calculations are the first of their kind for a plant. They assume that females gain by being large, while males do not. Bierzychudek's (1981b) calculations suggest that small individuals cannot pay (or have difficulty paying) the cost of being female. Both factors may be involved in selecting for sex reversal here; at least both favor protandry. The ESS prediction is a bit higher than the value where 50% are each sex—this deviation may reflect the element of female mortality or growth versus reproduction. It would be very interesting to apply the product calculations to several populations of *A. triphyllum,* populations which differ in their adult size distribution. Lovett-Doust and Cavers (1982) studied this species near London, Ontario. Data on size versus sex from four locations strongly suggest that if the general size of the individuals is adjusted upward, so is the size of transform. In one location the average height of reproductive individuals was ~49 cm, in another location ~37 cm. The average height of females in the first location was 55 cm, in the second 43 cm. The same comparison for males is 41 cm versus 33 cm. Thus females in one population were almost as small as males in the other. Interestingly, these two populations also represent extremes in available sunlight. Of the four popula-

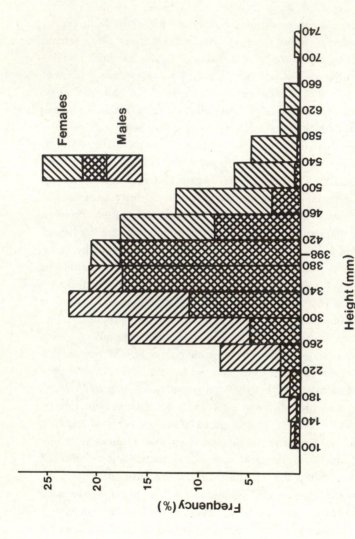

FIGURE 13.1 Size-frequency distributions for males and females of *Aris-aema triphyllum* (jack-in-the-pulpit). Data for three years combined. At ~380 mm in height, 50% of the individuals are each sex. This is very close to the ESS size of sex change, as discussed further in the text. (Figure from Policansky, 1981.)

tions studied, the location with small plants had the lowest light intensity, the location with large plants the highest.

I summarize this chapter by noting that we have just begun to explore sex choice in plants, at least from the viewpoint of sex allocation theory.

Simultaneous Hermaphroditism

Many animals and most higher plants are simultaneous hermaphrodites, here defined to mean that sperm and eggs are produced by a single individual in a single breeding season. In this section of the book I will review sex allocation theory and data relative to the selective advantages of simultaneous hermaphroditism (in this section referred to simply as hermaphroditism). There are three sex allocation questions which are of general interest about hermaphroditism.

(1) When (under what conditions) is it selected for, contrasted to dioecy or sex reversal?
(2) Within hermaphroditism, what fraction of resources should be allocated to male as opposed to female function?
(3) If the allocation to male as opposed to female function is labile or facultative, how is the response used? What conditions favor the input of more resources to (say) male function?

The first chapter of this section (Chapter Fourteen) reviews the basic discrete generation theory, first looking at outcrossed hermaphrodites and then looking at the role of selfing. The simple theory developed here is, with the exception of one barnacle example, without a role for age or size structure in the population; that is, we assume discrete generations. As the barnacle example will show, size or age structured models for hermaphroditism admit many possibilities for degrees of sex reversal within simultaneous hermaphroditism. These added complications are not pursued further here, although Chapter Thirteen discussed some biological examples.

Chapters Fifteen and Sixteen look at sex types in animals and higher plants, respectively. The animal chapter concentrates on barnacles, suggesting them as a model system for critically testing hypotheses about hermaphroditism. In the final chapter (Chapter Seventeen), I use the tools of sex allocation theory to look in more detail at two particular sex types in plants: heterostyly and dioecy. For both of these I pose questions (1) and (2) above.

CHAPTER FOURTEEN

Basic Discrete Generation
Theory for Hermaphroditism

This chapter first looks at outcrossed hermaphrodites, then examines the role of self-fertilization. I am concerned with the stability of hermaphroditism (contrasted to dioecy) and the resource allocation to male versus female function within hermaphroditism.

OUTCROSSED HERMAPHRODITES

Since a hermaphrodite individual allocates its reproductive resources to both male and female function, we will ask when such an individual will have higher fitness than a pure male or female. This is termed the "resource allocation model" for hermaphroditism. My discussion is drawn primarily from Charnov et al., 1976, Maynard Smith, 1978, and Charnov, 1979c. As in other chapters of this book, the goal is first to develop the theory at the general level of a tradeoff between male and female function (i.e., the fitness set), then to ask just what biological conditions give rise to which tradeoff relations. At first I will consider random mating and self incompatibility (outcrossing); then I will discuss selection for selfing and the Charlesworths' (1981) extension of the resource allocation model to this situation.

Consider, for concreteness, a plant species with discrete generations, and let n_1, n_2, and n_3 be the numbers of male, female, and hermaphrodite individuals respectively in a population (counted at conception). For simplicity all individuals are assumed to have the same survival rate to adulthood. Let there be random mating among the gametes and suppose that a female can produce k_1 seeds, a male k_2 pollen grains, and a hermaphrodite individual

$m \cdot k_2$ pollen grains and $f \cdot k_1$ seeds. Even though in this simple model reproductive success is proportional to number of gametes shed, the m and f actually have more general interpretations. Thus the hermaphrodite has a proportion f of a female's fitness (through seeds) and a proportion m of a male's fitness through pollen. Factors, such as the ability to attract vectors to carry pollen or seeds away (in addition to the actual number of gametes), affect the chances of an individual to gain reproductive success via sperm or eggs.

In Figure 14.1, I have graphed two possible fitness sets, i.e., the relation between m and f. Suppose that the population produces K offspring. These offspring will have $2K$ haploid chromosome sets,

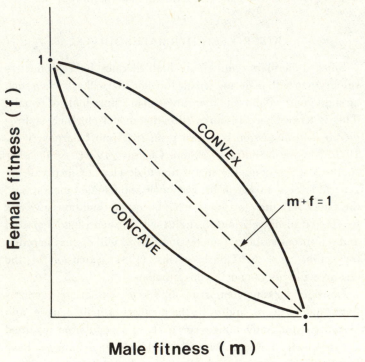

Male fitness (m)

FIGURE 14.1. Possible fitness sets (*convex, concave*) for the tradeoff between male and female reproduction in a simultaneous hermaphrodite. Here, pure males and females (end points of the fitness set) have a relative fitness of one.

220

K of which were contributed via pollen, K via seeds. Let W_f, W_m, W_h be the fitness (here taken to be the number of haploid chromosome sets contributed to the offspring) of a female, male, and hermaphrodite respectively. It follows that (with self incompatibility):

$$W_f = \frac{K}{n_2 + f n_3}, \; W_m = \frac{K}{n_1 + m n_3},$$

$$W_h = \frac{Km}{n_1 + m n_3} + \frac{Kf}{n_2 + f n_3}. \tag{14.1}$$

If there are no hermaphrodites present $n_3 = 0$. The ESS sex ratio is $\frac{1}{2}$, and $n_1 = n_2$. A rare ($n_3 \sim 0$) hermaphrodite phenotype can invade this population if it has higher fitness than a male or female ($W_h > W_f$ or W_m), or if (14.2) $(m/n_1) + (f/n_2) > 1/n_1$; since $n_1 = n_2$ in the dioecious population, this reduces to $m + f > 1$. Likewise the dioecious population is stable if the hermaphrodite phenotype has less fitness, or if $m + f < 1$. Of course $m + f = 1$ is the equation of a line linking $m = 1$ to $f = 1$ (Fig. 14.1). It follows that the dioecious population will be stable if the fitness set is concave (Fig. 14.1). If the fitness set is convex, the hermaphrodite population will be stable (see below). This is the same condition as was derived earlier for dioecy versus sex change (Chapter Nine).

Consider a population with a convex fitness set where all members are hermaphroditic. If most members of the population are at (m, f), then the fitness ($\hat{W}_h$) of a mutant individual that alters its male/female fitness values to $\hat{f}$, $\hat{m}$ is given by

$$\hat{W}_h = \frac{\hat{m}}{n_3 m} + \frac{\hat{f}}{n_3 f} \propto \frac{\hat{m}}{m} + \frac{\hat{f}}{f}. \tag{14.3}$$

This is the familiar Shaw-Mohler equation. It follows immediately that the ESS (m^*, f^*) are the values which *maximize the product* $m^* \cdot f^*$. By the methods of Chapter Two, we also know that $m^* \cdot f^*$ may be found by looking for a pair (m^*, f^*) such that the line through that pair, with slope minus f^*/m^*, is a tangent to the curve at the * values. Such a line has the equation $2 =$

$(\hat{m}/m^*) + (\hat{f}/f^*)$ (14.4) and is the locus of points such that $\hat{W}_h$ does not change. Note (Fig. 14.2) that the intersections of the line with the axes are the points $\hat{f} = 2 \cdot f^*$, $\hat{m} = 2 \cdot m^*$: that is, the pure male and female values which are exactly twice the hermaphrodite's male and female fitness values. If a mutant phenotype completely gives up male function ($\hat{m} = 0$), then its fitness is $\hat{W}_f = \hat{f}/f^*$; but for the morph to be favored, $\hat{W}_h$ for a typical hermaphrodite ($\hat{m} = m, \hat{f} = f$) must be $< \hat{W}_f$ or $\hat{f}/f^* > 2$. For a male morph to be selected in this hermaphrodite population the same argument applies, i.e., $\hat{m} > 2 \cdot m^*$. But these conditions reduce simply to looking at the intersections with the axes of the $(\hat{m}/m^*) + (\hat{f}/f^*) = 2$ line (Fig. 14.2). If the fitness set is convex, no points on the set will fall to the outside of this line; thus, hermaphroditism will be stable to pure males or females.

If the fitness set is a mixture of convex and concave, then a mixture of hermaphrodites and a pure sex may be the only stable state (see Charnov et al., 1976). (If some part of the fitness set satisfies $m + f > 1$, hermaphrodites must be present at equilibrium.)

The biological questions now reduce to asking what factors give rise to what shapes for the m, f tradeoff. It will be useful here to introduce one new variable. For simplicity, suppose that some resource exists which an individual can allocate to male versus female reproductive function. Let r proportion of it be given to male function. In general m will be a function of r, f a function of $1 - r$. Males will have $r = 1$, females $r = 0$. The shape of the fitness set will be determined by how m and f change with changing r. The thought experiment which lies at the heart of the resource allocation model for hermaphroditism is to consider how sperm versus egg fitness (m, f) alters as resources are shifted from one to the other. It will often be useful to plot them (m, f) separately, versus a variable like r. In such a plot $m(r)$ may be termed the *male gain curve*, $f(r)$ the *female gain curve*. In many places in this chapter I will discuss possible biological bases for particular shapes for $m(r), f(r)$. By way of illustration, I discuss here one general case.

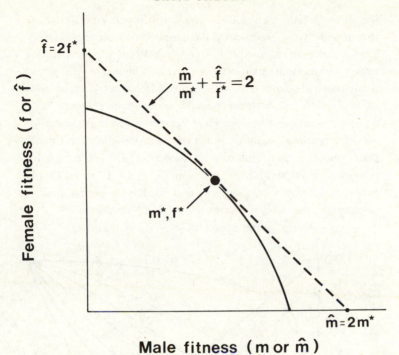

Male fitness (m or m̂)

FIGURE 14.2. The ESS allocation to male versus female function maximizes $m^* \cdot f^*$. Here (m^*, f^*), a line with slope *minus* f^*/m^* is just tangent to the fitness set, and no points on the fitness set fall to the outside of the line. In a hermaphroditic population, mutant pure males are only at a selective advantage if the male's fitness is more than double the male fitness of the hermaphrodite (the reverse for a pure female). But the intersection of the tangent line with the axes gives fitness values which are double the hermaphrodite's $(2f^*, 2m^*)$. Thus, for this curve (*convex fitness set*) pure males and females fail to have more than double the hermaphrodite's male or female fitness. Here, hermaphroditism is stable to dioecy. Likewise, a *concave fitness set* favors dioecy.

Suppose that the production of fertilized eggs is not limited by the availability of sperm (pollen), but strictly by the resource $(1 - r)$ put into eggs (Bateman's principle—Bateman, 1948; Charnov, 1979c), and that the eggs are randomly distributed in the habitat (i.e., no added sibling competition). Suppose further that the resource available for input into eggs is also freely available for input into male function (e.g., this might not be so if the sperm versus egg resources were of different kinds, or if the investments were temporally displaced; more on these later). Under Bateman's principle $f = (1 - r)$. What shape might we expect for the male gain relation, $m(r)$? A model which allows many possible shapes is $m = r^n$. Figure 14.3 shows m versus r for various n. If $n < 1$, male reproductive success shows *saturation, or a law of diminishing returns.* Here the increase in m is greater for the first resources shunted into male function than for further resources. If $n > 1$, there is an increasing rate of return for resources invested in male function. At $n = 1$, m is simply proportional to r. Now, suppose that we have a hermaphrodite population; the ESS r maximizes $m^* \cdot f^*$ or *maximizes* $r^n \cdot (1 - r) = H$. By setting $\partial \log (H)/\partial r = 0$, we find that $r^* = n/$

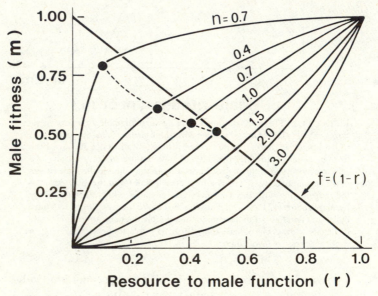

FIGURE 14.3. If r is the proportion of resources given to male function, male fitness is given by $m = r^n$. This graph shows the male fitness (the *male gain curve*) for various n. Female fitness is assumed proportional to resource input into seeds, or $f = 1 - r$. Hermaphroditism is stable to dioecy only if $n < 1$; that is, only if male reproductive success *saturates* or *shows a law of diminishing returns* with resource input. The solid dots show the ESS allocation to male function (r^*) for four n values. The faster the saturation of male fitness (i.e., the smaller n), the smaller the r^*.

$(n + 1)$. Likewise, hermaphroditism itself will be stable if m^* and $f^* > \frac{1}{2}$ or if

$$\left(\frac{n}{1 + n}\right)^n > \frac{1}{2} \text{ and } \frac{1}{1 + n} > \frac{1}{2}.$$

It is clear that both these condtions are satisfied only if $n < 1$; hermaphroditism is favored if and only if male reproductive success shows a law of diminishing returns with the shunting of resources from female to male function. Alternatively, dioecy is here favored by increasing male returns for investment in male function.

It is possible to imagine situations in which the female gain curve, $f(r)$, is likewise nonlinear (e.g., enhanced sibling competition among one's own seeds as their number increases). It seems clear that hermaphroditism will be favored if both curves show diminishing returns, and dioecy if both are bowed upwards. If one is bowed up, and the other down, then the outcome depends upon the relative degree of nonlinearity. For example, suppose that the female gain curve may be written as $f = (1 - r)^{\bar{x}}$. The $m^* \cdot f^*$ product is maximized at $r^* = n/(n + \bar{x})$. If n and $\bar{x}$ are both < 1, hermaphroditism is stable and r^* reflects the relative rates at which reproductive success saturates within each sex function; more resource is expended on the sex function with the slower rate of diminishing returns. If the gain curves are symmetric, $n = \bar{x}$ and $r^* = \frac{1}{2}$. If one curve (say, m) saturates, while the other is bowed upwards, hermaphroditism is stable only if n and $\bar{x}$ are both small. For example, if $n = 0.5$, $\bar{x}$ must be <1.5 for stability of hermaphroditism.

Let me provide here a biological example of the use of $m(r)$ and $f(r)$ curves. Heath (1979) suggested that the well-known correlation in animals of hermaproditism with brooding of offspring might obtain because space in the brood-pouch limits egg production, and the excess energy could be used for sperm production. Let us see how this can be represented in terms of male and female gain curves. Suppose m increases proportionally to resource input; f does so likewise, but at some point space limits the number of

225

offspring produced. More input of resource to eggs now does not increase female reproductive success. This is illustrated in Figure 14.4. We can write the m, f functions as

$$m = r;$$

$$f = \begin{cases} c_1(1 - r) \text{ for } 1 - r < 1/c_1, & \text{where } c_1 > 1; \\ 1 & \text{for } 1 - r > 1/c_1. \end{cases} \quad (14.5)$$

It is clear from the figure and (14.5) that: (1) hermaphroditism is favored; (2) the ESS r^* is ½ if $c_1 < 2$ (i.e., $f = 1$ at $r < ½$, as in the figure). If $c_1 > 2$ (brood-pouch filled, with less than half of the resource allocated to eggs) the ESS r^* is that which fills the brood-pouch. If Heath's (1979) suggestion and my simple model of it are biologically reasonable, the calculations provided here

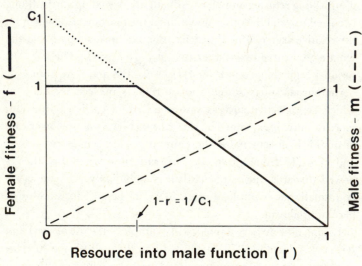

FIGURE 14.4. Male (dashed line) and female (solid line) gain curves when brood space limits female reproduction. Male fitness is proportional to resources put into male function (or, $m = r$). Female fitness is likewise proportional, *but* only until the brood space is filled (here shown at $1 - r = 1/c_1$). At this point, hermaphrodites and females have the same female fitness. These curves favor hermaphroditism over dioecy. I invite the reader to construct the fitness set associated with these curves. The ESS r^* is either 0.5 or the value $1 - r^* = 1/c_1$. See text for further discussion.

immediately suggest some testable hypotheses. According to theory, brood space limitation may well favor hermaphroditism, even though the hermaphrodite individual at the ESS does not use all the brood space. However, here we predict half the resources to go to each sex function. If brood space is filled, less than half the resources are going to eggs.

Let me end this introduction to sex allocation in outcrossed hermaphrodites by consideration of one other factor. Heath (1977) suggested that it might be useful to consider two types of costs associated with reproduction. The first might be termed a fixed cost or fertility independent cost. It involves structures that must be built simply in order to reproduce, but which do not quantitatively affect the amount of reproductive success (other than allowing it to be greater than zero). The second cost involves the resources left after the fixed cost is paid. Allocation of these resources to reproduction increases the individual's reproductive success. A simple example would be the construction of a duct to transport gametes (a fixed cost) compared to resources put into the gametes themselves. Reproductive success should increase with resources put into gametes, but only after the duct is built. Suppose that R units of resource are available for reproduction. The female will have R minus the fixed cost (for being female) left after set-up, the male R minus the male fixed cost. However, the hermaphrodite must set up both systems. As noted by Heath (1977) the hermaphrodite must pay both male and female fixed costs, while each pure sex pays only one. This is the reason behind considering costs to be of these two types. The dichotomy is a simple one and I use it here mostly for illustration (as we know almost nothing about the relative magnitudes of the costs, or just what structures can be considered a fixed cost). Note that any fixed cost that is paid by all three types is simply included in the determination of R.

To incorporate this idea into a model for f and m, I will assume as follows. Let r be the proportion of resources (left after the fixed costs are paid) that is allocated to male function. Under Bateman's principle, f is proportional to $1 - r$; fertilized eggs depend only

227

upon resources diverted into eggs. Thus, we may set $f = (1 - r)b$; $b < 1$ refers to the fixed cost the individual pays for *also* reproducing through male function., For m, we need to specify how reproductive success through male function increases with r. Again, the hermaphrodite may pay some additional cost for also reproducing as a female. Let $m = cr^n$ where $c < 1$ refers to this female fixed cost. Note here that these fixed costs do not affect the ESS r since they become constants when we form the $m \cdot f$

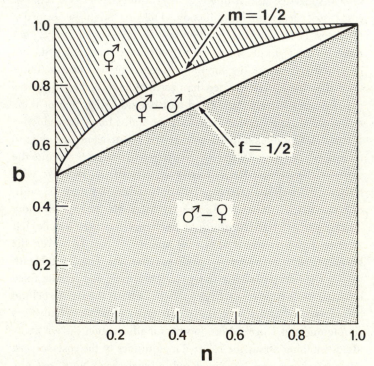

FIGURE 14.5. Fixed costs which are sex specific tend to favor dioecy. The female gain curve is $f = (1 - r)b$, the male gain curve $m = br^n$ (while pure males and females each have a fitness of 1). When $b < 1$, then to be a hermaphrodite an individual must pay some additional cost which need not be paid by a pure sex. This figure shows fixed cost values (b) and the rate of saturation for the male gain curve (here indexed by n) which favors hermaphroditism (⚥), androdioecy (⚥-♂), and dioecy (♀-♂). If $b = 1$, $n < 1$ is sufficient to favor hermaphroditism. If $b < 1$, n must be even smaller to favor hermaphroditism.

product. However, they greatly affect the stability of hermaphroditism (versus dioecy), since a pure sex need only pay one fixed cost. For symmetric fixed costs ($b = c$), Figure 14.5 shows values of n, b which favor hermaphroditism (versus dioecy or androdioecy). Figure 14.6 is an even more graphic illustration of the effect of fixed costs (contrast this to Figure 9.3 for sex reversal). Applying our usual tangent argument to f^*, m^* shows that, for this fitness set, both male and female morphs can invade the hermaphrodite population.

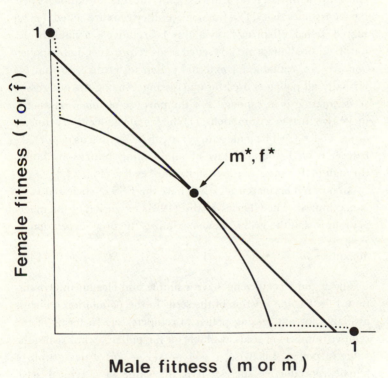

FIGURE 14.6. At the ESS allocation to male versus female function (m^*, f^*), construction of the tangent line (as in Fig. 14.2) shows that this hermaphrodite population is not stable to invasion by pure males or females. Sex-specific fixed costs push the hermaphrodite curve inward, relative to the pure male and female fitnesses (which are equal to 1), and tend to favor dioecy.

SELF-FERTILE HERMAPHRODITES

Charlesworth and Charlesworth (1981) have extended the basic resource allocation model to conditions of selfing, with inbreeding depression in the fitness of selfed offspring. Their model was discussed in terms of a plant, so here I shall talk of pollen and seeds. They considered two types of situation. In the first, the level of selfing does not depend upon the sex allocation (i.e., does not depend on the level of pollen production). In the second, the selfing rate does depend upon the pollen production, going up with it. Here, I discuss only the first situation. Their model assumes that: (1) a fraction S of the seeds are selfed. (2) an inbred (selfed) offspring has viability 1-δ relative to a viability of 1 for an outbred offspring, (3) selfed seeds require negligible pollen and are not available for external pollen to fertilize, so that (4) virtually all pollen is used for outcrossing. Among the outcrossed seeds, mating is at random. For the purpose of this discussion I make two further assumptions: (1) the female gain curve is linear, or $f = 1 - r$. (2) The male gain curve can be written as $m = r^n$. As before, $n < 1$ shows a law of diminishing returns in fitness through male function; $n > 1$ shows the reverse (Fig. 14.3).

An outbred hermaphrodite will have the ESS r^* such that $m \cdot f$ is maximized. The Charlesworths' (1981) extension of the model is to show that the ESS r^* now maximizes the product relation:

$$\text{maximize } m^x \cdot f^y \text{ where } x = 1 - S; y = 1 + S(1 - 2\delta). \quad (14.6)$$

The x and y coefficients have a simple and elegant interpretation. $1 - S$ is the fraction of the seeds in the population which is available for outcrossing pollen to compete for. In terms of the relative numbers of seeds available for the pollen, x thus scales the value of pollen. Likewise, $y = 1 + S(1 - 2\delta)$ scales a unit of female reproductive success; it is the value of a typical seed. Suppose that c seeds can be produced. S proportion of them are selfed and here each contains a double dose of the mother's genes. However, each of these offspring has fitness $1 - \delta$. This hermaphrodite will produce $(1 - S)c$ outcrossed offspring via its own seeds.

Thus, its total fitness via seeds is (omitting the c multiplier) $1 - S + 2S(1 - \delta)$, which equals y.

The exponents in equation 14.6 play the same role here as did the exponents in the Trivers-Hare model for worker control of sex ratio in eusocial hymenoptera (Chapter Eight) or the LMC sex ratio model (Chapter Five)—they scale the relative fitness value of a unit of male (m) versus female (f) function.

Under my assumptions for the male and female gain curves, the product (equation 14.6) takes the form:

$$H = (1 - r)^y \cdot r^{nx}. \tag{14.7}$$

Equation 14.7 is maximized (by choice of r^*) when $\partial \log H / \partial r = 0$, or when:

$$\frac{r^*}{1 - r^*} = \frac{nx}{y} = \frac{n(1 - S)}{1 + S(1 - 2\delta)}. \tag{14.8}$$

For any fixed male gain relation and level of inbreeding depression (n and δ fixed values), equation 14.8 shows the relative allocation to male function ($r^*/(1 - r^*)$) to be inversely related to the selfing rate. In Figure 14.7 I have graphed $r^*/(1 - r^*)$ versus S (for $n = 0.5$ and three levels of inbreeding depression). For levels of inbreeding depression (δ) between 0.35 and 0.65 the predicted relation is rather insensitive to the depression level. In fact, the predicted relation is approximately linear with slope of minus n. The intercept on the abscissa is predicted to be near one (i.e., almost no pollen needed to fertilize selfed seeds); the intercept on the ordinate is predicted to be n.

The relation shown in Figure 14.7 is analogous to LMC. As competition among unrelated pollen grains goes up (S goes down), more resource is given to male function. Qualitative versions of "this LMC" hypothesis have been proposed by Williams, 1975, Charlesworth and Charlesworth, 1979c, and Charnov, 1979c; and for total self-fertilization, Darwin, 1877. Maynard Smith (1978) proposed a model for a situation with zero inbreeding depression ($\delta = 0$).

In addition to the sex allocation within self-fertile hermaphro-

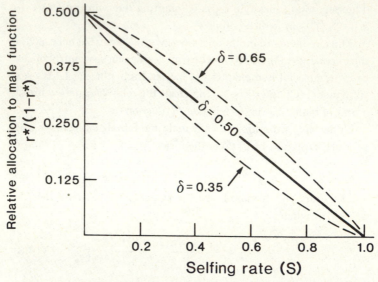

FIGURE 14.7. The resource allocation to male versus female function $(r^*/[1 - r^*])$ is predicted to be inversely related to the selfing rate (S). The graph shows the relations for one male gain curve ($m = r^n$ where $n = 0.5$) and three levels of inbreeding depression for selfed offspring ($\delta = 0.35$, 0.50, 0.65). Note that the intercept on the ordinate is 0.5, equal to n, and that the theoretical relation is very close to linear for these δ values. Further discussion in text.

ditism, this model also allows us to ask how this self-fertility affects selection for or against hermaphroditism, contrasted to dioecy. Since a linear tradeoff between m and f forms the hermaphrodite-dioecy boundary with self-incompatibility (Fig. 14.1), it is useful to ask now this is altered with self-fertility. For this purpose, let $m = r, f = 1 - r$. The ESS r^* (equation 14.8) is $r^*/(1 - r^*) = x/y$. Note that $r^* < \frac{1}{2}$ since $x/y < 1$. Will this population be stable to a rare female phenotype? The total fitness (W_h) for a hermaphrodite individual is $W_h = [2(1 - S) + 2S(1 - \delta)]c$ where c is the number of seeds produced by an individual. The first term in this equation, $2(1 - S)c$, is the outcrossed seeds set by each hermaphrodite, $(1 - S)c$, plus the seeds that each individual will fertilize through pollen, also $(1 - S)c$. On average, each hermaphrodite will fertilize (via pollen) one other individual's outcrossed seed set. Thus the first term is twice $(1 - S)c$. The second term in the equation, $2S(1 - \delta)c$, is the number of selfed progeny (Sc) times their fitness $(1 - \delta)$. Since each contains a double dose of the mother's genes, the quantity is multiplied by two. This equation may be simplified to:

$$W_h = 2(1 - \delta S)c. \tag{14.9}$$

A female will have fitness W_f, equal to the number of seeds it can produce. This will be the same seed set as the hermaphrodite $(= c)$ plus the seeds produced from the resource freed from male function. For every unit of resource the hermaphrodite gives to seeds, it also gives $r^*/(1 - r^*)$ to male function. If the female can recover all of this, its fitness will be

$$W_f = \left(1 + \frac{r^*}{1 - r^*}\right)c;$$

since $r^*/(1 - r^*) = x/y$, we have

$$W_f = \left(1 + \frac{1 - S}{1 + S(1 - 2\delta)}\right)c. \tag{14.10}$$

Finally, let us form the ratio W_f/W_h which after some algebra is shown to equal

$$W_f/W_h = \frac{1}{1 + S(1 - 2\delta)}. \tag{14.11}$$

As the Charlesworths (1981) noted, this ratio is only greater than one if $\delta > \frac{1}{2}$ (high inbreeding depression); otherwise it is always $(\delta < \frac{1}{2})$ less than one. Indeed, if we plot equation 14.11 versus S (selfing rate), as in Figure 14.8, the relative fitness of the female declines with S for $\delta < \frac{1}{2}$ and increases for $\delta > \frac{1}{2}$. That is, a positive selfing rate makes hermaphroditism even more stable if $\delta < \frac{1}{2}$, but less stable if $\delta > \frac{1}{2}$. The value $\delta = \frac{1}{2}$ appears to be a sort of boundary. What meaning can be attached to the value $\delta = \frac{1}{2}$? In order to answer this (at least tentatively), we need to ask the further question of why there is any self-fertilization in the first place. Why might $S > 0$?

233

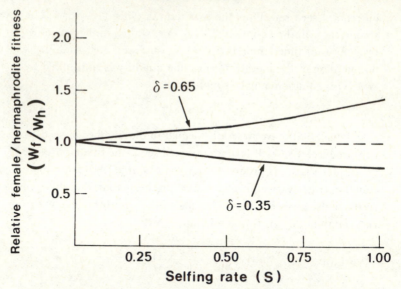

FIGURE 14.8. The fitness of a rare female mutant relative to the total fitness of a typical hermaphrodite individual, as a function of the selfing rate (S) for two levels of inbreeding depression ($\delta = 0.35, 0.65$) (equation 14.11). Offspring produced via selfing have survival to adulthood of $1 - \delta$ relative to outcrossed offspring. This graph assumes a linear fitness set for male versus female fitness. High inbreeding depression ($\delta = 0.65$) makes the female more fit than the hermaphrodite, low inbreeding depression ($\delta = 0.35$) the reverse. Thus, positive levels of self-fertilization will make hermaphroditism either more stable ($\delta = 0.35$), or less stable ($\delta = 0.65$) depending upon the level of inbreeding depression. Further discussion in text.

The question of selection for or against inbreeding in general, and self-fertilization in particular, is very complex, and the population genetics rapidly becomes unmanageable (review in Jain, 1976). The approach adopted here follows the simple phenotypic models (of selection for selfing) proposed by Maynard Smith (1978) and Lloyd (1979a). Like the Charlesworths, these authors take the main effect of selfing to be the production of less viable offspring. From their models, it seems that some positive level of selfing ($S > 0$) may exist for any of three reasons.

(1) Under low population density, an individual who cannot get another's sperm could self-fertilize. Such an ability would be

useful whenever reproduction was limited in this way. This idea goes back at least to Darwin (1877). This selfing advantage applies only to hermaphrodites (although a dioecious female might be able to produce apomictic diploid eggs) and would be selected for even if the selfed offspring had greatly reduced viability (i.e., better to self than not reproduce at all).

(2) Self-fertilization may be of selective advantage; hermaphroditism is then a means by which this is realized. If a gene arises in an outcrossed hermaphrodite which causes self-fertilization with no decreased offspring fitness, the gene is of automatic selective advantage. If the pollen used in such fertilization is of negligible quantity (i.e., selfing does not affect reproduction via outcrossed pollen), the gene of interest will be *doubly* represented in the selfed-seeds, with no loss of representation in the outcrossed. All else being equal, the gene will be selected for (first demonstrated by Fisher, 1941a). If the selfed offspring have reduced fitness, the selective advantage of the gene depends upon the strength of inbreeding depression. Since it is doubly represented in selfed offspring, it follows that it will be selected for if the inbred offspring have greater than half the viability of typically outbred offspring (i.e., if $\delta < \frac{1}{2}$). If the inbred fitness is less than half, then strict outbreeding is selected for. This model is a very simple one and assumes that the only difference is that some offspring are selfed. In fact, selfing is often accompanied by modification in floral structure (i.e., reduction of advertisement for pollinators—Darwin, 1877), and selfed seeds may be considerably cheaper than outcrossed (Waller, 1979; Schemske, 1978). Still, the model illustrates the basic point; selfing is often advantageous.

This discussion is for the initial spread of a rare gene for selfing; in the simple model such a gene will go to fixation. Lloyd (1979a) and Maynard Smith (1978) have discussed several situations which favor a polymorphism, an equilibrium at some intermediate level of selfing. They both note that various plant species show the entire range from totally outcrossed to totally selfed, and propose that the range represents various equilibria. This is important—under this model a level of selfing is maintained by selection, and selfed offspring have a fitness greater than or equal to half that of the outcrossed offspring. It is also possible that the inbreeding depression (δ) is itself a function of the frequency of the two types of offspring (i.e., depression is not simply a physiological effect; the value depends critically upon the competitive relationships in the environment—see Lloyd, 1980c, for more complete discussion of factors such as this). If selfed viability declines with selfing frequency, it may be reduced to a half ($\delta = \frac{1}{2}$), resulting in a polymorphism.

(3) Finally, if the inbreeding depression is large ($\delta > \frac{1}{2}$), selfing is selected against; however, constraints of anatomy or physiology may make it difficult for a hermaphrodite to avoid some selfing.

Of these three forms of selfing, the last two would seem to play a critical role in selection for or against hermaphroditism. If selfing is itself selected for, $\delta < \frac{1}{2}$. *But,* this form of selfing makes hermaphroditism even more stable, as shown in Figure 14.8. However, if selfing is disadvantageous ($\delta > \frac{1}{2}$), but difficult for the hermaphrodite to avoid, then dioecy may be the means by which an individual avoids the production of offspring with low fitness (also shown in Fig. 14.8). Since a female (or a male) does not self, dioecy becomes an outbreeding mechanism. However, I stress that in this situation, the hermaphrodite would be likewise selected to outcross only.

I summarize this section as follows. Self-fertility makes hermaphroditism more stable or less stable (contrasted to dioecy) depending upon the level of inbreeding depression for the selfed offspring (Fig. 14.8) and the reasons for the selfing in the first place. If selfing is selectively advantageous ($\delta < \frac{1}{2}$), selfed hermaphroditism is even more stable. If selfing is selected against ($\delta > \frac{1}{2}$), but difficult for the hermaphrodite to avoid, it is less stable.

Two final things to note. (1) Throughout this discussion I have considered the fate of a rare female morph. Because selfing removes some seeds from pollen competition, a rare male morph faces an even more difficult time (Charlesworth and Charlesworth, 1979c, 1981). (2) It is obvious that the two types of selfing play similar roles with other, nonlinear tradeoffs for f and m (discussed in Charlesworth and Charlesworth, 1981). For example, if the female gain curve is linear (i.e., $f = 1 - r$) and the inbreeding depression level (δ) is equal to a half, hermaphroditism is stable if the male gain curve saturates (i.e., $m = r^n$ where $n < 1$), just as in the outbreeding case (Fig. 14.3).

CHAPTER FIFTEEN

Hermaphroditism in Animals

This chapter briefly reviews the distribution of hermaphroditism in animals. The review is exploratory since the position I take is that while there are certainly life history patterns in the distribution of animal hermaphroditism, the selective forces involved in those patterns are as yet poorly understood. I then discuss two case histories: barnacles and a coral reef fish. With these I ask some more precise questions and test some particular hypotheses.

The distribution of hermaphroditism in animals has been reviewed by Ghiselin (1969, 1974). Several patterns have emerged. There is often a correlation between hermaphroditism and the brooding habit: e.g., anemones, some bivalves, and Echinoderms. Hermaphroditism is often associated with a sessile or sedentary adult habit: e.g., attached barnacles, attached Tunicates, Pulmonate and Opisthobranch snails and slugs, many sponges, attached Endoprocts, and attached Ectoprocts. However, many groups with equally sedentary adults are dioecious: e.g., most Cnidaria, Brachiopods, bivalves, Prosobranch snails, and Echinoderms (especially Crinoids and Echinoids). Conversely, hermaphroditism is the rule in some groups which are neither sedentary, nor seem to have typically low densities: e.g., Ctenophores, Turbellarians (flatworms), Annelids (earthworms and leeches), and Chaetognaths. Hermaphroditism is also often associated with a parasitic or commensal mode of life: e.g., nestling bivalves, Crustaceans, flukes and tapeworms. Finally, hermaphroditism is widely scattered through typically dioecious groups: e.g., polychaete annelids (*Ophryotrocha,* Akesson, 1973) and fish (see Table 12.1).

Ghiselin (1969, 1974), Maynard Smith (1978), Warner (1978), and Charnov (1979c) have attempted to discuss some of

238

these patterns from the sex allocation viewpoint. The major problem is that since virtually no one has studied these animals from the standpoint of selection for or against hermaphroditism, it is almost impossible to use the present broad-scale data to test hypotheses fully. For example, brooding may be implicated with hermaphroditism for any one of several reasons: (1) brood space is a limiting factor in female function; (2) brooding often goes along with some type of copulation, and there are limitations on male reproductive success (the male gain curve saturates—Charnov 1979c); (3) brooding implies that offspring receive nutrition from the mother—thus the resource is gathered and given to them some time after sperm is transferred. This resource is thus not available for male function; (4) brooding is often associated with release of offspring as small adults with no long-range dispersal. The siblings compete with each other, making the female gain curve saturate; (5) finally, retention of offspring may facilitate selfing, if the individual fails to get sperm.

These hypotheses (plus others) can be tested in particular cases either by showing that the assumption is simply incorrect (e.g., selfing is not possible) or by calculating the consequences of the hypothesis in terms of sex allocation. For example, if brood space limits female function, greater than half the reproductive resources should be given to male function (Fig. 14.4); but if male reproductive success saturates, less than half should thus be allocated.

What is important is that we work out the consequences of the various sex allocation hypotheses and then ask just what observations, comparisons, or experiments will allow us to distinguish among various alternatives. For example, the brooding habit may favor hermaphroditism only in some circumstances. Sometimes it may go along with dioecy. Our theory should be able to specify each of these conditions. The parasitic mode of life is often associated with hermaphroditism in bivalves, while free-living sedentary bivalves are dioecious. However, this pattern is reversed in barnacles (Table 15.1). Why?

A key observation for sex allocation hypotheses will often be the proportion of resource devoted to male versus female function. Such data tell us about the symmetry of the male/female gain curves (under outcrossing) or strongly suggest the degree of selfing (LMC). For example, Ghirardelli's (1968) diagram of the Chaetognath *Spadella cephaloptera* shows large ovaries and testes, which would seem to rule out typical selfing. Since a strong female skew in sex allocation is predicted with high selfing levels *or* outbreeding combined with particular male/female gain curves, it is useful to have independent indices for the level of selfing. Since selfing alters genotype frequencies away from those expected under outcrossing, various genetic techniques have been used to estimate selfing rates, particularly in plants (see Jain, 1976, Schoen, 1980, for higher plants). Selfing has been studied using marker genes (Ikeda, 1937, Williamson, 1959, for terrestrial slugs, reviewed in Runham and Hunter, 1970), electrophoretic estimates of genetic variability (e.g. McCracken and Selander, 1980, for terrestrial slugs and review of earlier snail work), and isolation experiments (Brown, 1981, for freshwater snails). McCracken and Selander (1980) looked at several loci in fourteen taxonomic species of terrestrial slugs. Four species were selfers, nine were predominately outcrossed. One "species" (*Arion subuscus*) had both selfing and outcrossing forms. At present there are no data on relative male/female allocation for these groups.

The presence of genetic markers (e.g., color genes) should make possible both selfing and fatherhood studies. Estimating the numbers of fathers for a brood, the outcome of sperm competition between individuals, becomes important in measuring "male" fitness. Some species are also more easily reared in the lab (e.g., earthworms, whose culture is of much economic importance— Edwards and Lofty, 1977; Gaddie and Douglas, 1975, 1977). C. S. Richards (per. comm.) has done extensive studies with the genetics of *Biomphalaria glabrata,* a snail which is a host for *Schistosoma mansoni* (also 1973, 1976). Some lines have been maintained in the lab for as long as twenty generations (generation time approx. 6 weeks) with selfing. In crossing experiments with compatible stocks, cross-fertilized eggs are produced for 2–3 weeks by which time selfed progeny have begun to appear. Reversion to selfing is complete by about 6 weeks. This sort of organism may prove very useful in sex allocation studies.

I recognize that the perspective provided above is without a strong role for history, particularly historical constraints. It may be that some present-day species have a sex habit which benefited their ancestors and which has not yet altered for the changed habitat or life-history conditions of today (if conditions have indeed changed). It may also be that there exist physiological or developmental barriers to change, factors which are difficult to overcome (Warner, 1978). In these respects plants may be more suitable material, since evidence for present-day genetic variability in sex habit (for some groups) is widespread. Within animals, the sex habit seems more definite. I suggest that closely related groups which contain both hermaphroditic and dioecious species (e.g., *Ophryotrocha, Hydra,* barnacles) may provide the most useful comparative material.

The role of history (and other constraints) is difficult to assess. Certainly, hermaphroditism in animals shows a phylogenetic bias, typically found throughout a large systematic group. However, habitat and life-history patterns may also follow taxonomic lines (e.g., all slugs are sluggish). At least one "constraint" hypothesis suggests itself. It may be easier to change from hermaphroditic to dioecious than the reverse. A hermaphrodite need only suppress the development or use of one sex function; suppression early in development may automatically free resources for the other sex function. Under dioecy, an individual becoming a hermaphrodite must build and operate the other sex function. Until the other function works, selection must operate against diverting resources there. That is, dioecy $\rightarrow$ hermaphroditism requires larger and more difficult initial steps than the reverse. This suggests that simplicity of reproductive function (e.g., male and female reproduction requires simply transporting gametes to the outside at the appropriate time) should characterize genera or families with both sex types, lineages which show much historical alteration of sex type. At present, I know of no data on this hypothesis.

241

HERMAPHRODITISM IN BARNACLES: A TEST CASE

In this section I would like to pose some simple questions about sex type in Cirripedia (barnacles). In Table 15.1 I have summarized the general distribution of sex types. Note three things: (1) All male barnacles are tiny, and are usually found in close association with much larger females or hermaphrodites. (2) Dioecy is generally characteristic of burrowing (Tomlinson, 1953, 1969), parasitic, and deep-sea forms. (3) In the order Thoracica (the common acorn, wart, or goose barnacles) hermaphroditism is the rule with scattered cases of associated small males (called complemental or dwarf males by Darwin [1854], who first discovered them).

Some of the most useful comparisons should be between dioecy and hermaphroditism within the parasitic forms, and especially within the free-living Lepadomorph families Scalpellidae and Iblidae. Not being in a position to provide such a comparison, I will pose the more general question: why are typical, free-living barnacles so often hermaphroditic (or have associated tiny males)?

Acorn barnacles are some of the most common creatures of the seashore, and have been widely used for studies of interspecific competition, habitat selection by planktonic larva, and life histories (Wethey, 1979; Barnes and Barnes, 1968; Crisp, 1954; Hurley, 1973; Lewis, 1975) (e.g., clutch size variation, mortality patterns). Some species produce a single large brood a year (e.g., *Balanus balanoides*—Stubbings, 1975; Wethey, 1979), while others produce a sequence of broods throughout a season (reviewed in Hines, 1978, 1979). The classic work on the ecological significance of barnacle life histories is that of Crisp and Patel (1979 for review and list of their earlier studies). Barnacles are completely immobile as adults. The description I like best is that barnacles are small shrimp, standing on their heads in rock houses, kicking food into their mouths with their feet.

Clegg (1955), Walker (1977, 1980), and Barnes et al. (1977) have described copulation and fertilization. Almost all hermaph-

242

TABLE 15.1. Barnacle breeding systems (from Newman et al., 1969; W. Newman, per. comm.)

Order	Habitat/lifeform	Sex type
1. Acrothoracia	free-living, burrow in calcarous substrates (e.g., mollusc shells)	dioecious; dwarf males on or in the burrows of large females
2. Rhizocephala	parasitic mostly in decapod crustaceans	mostly dioecious; dwarf males parasitic inside large females
3. Ascothoracica	parasitic on coelenterates and echinoderms	dioecious, with dwarf males; protandric hermaphrodites; or hermaphroditic
4. Thoracica	free-living or commensals (e.g., on whales) = common barnacle form	
Suborder 4.1 Lepadomorpha	(goose barnacles)	mostly hermaphroditic but among families Scalpellidae and Iblidae we also find dioecy (with dwarf males) and androdioecy (small males— Darwin's complemental males, associated with much larger hermaphrodites)
4.2 Balanomorpha	(acorn barnacles)	almost all are hermaphroditic, although small complemental males are present in some species of *Balanus* (see McLaughlin and Henry, 1972)
4.3 Verrucomorpha	(wart barnacles)	all hermaphroditic

roditic barnacles have a well-developed penis. An individual, receptive as a female, most likely signals in some way to "her" neighbors (suggested by Walley, 1967), although initial searching by a "male" seems to involve somewhat random penis movement. Once the "female" is found, the "male" deposits sperm (in quantities that appear to be much more than needed to fertilize all the eggs) in the "female's" mantle cavity. More than one individual may copulate with a single "female." Copulation (more precisely, pseudocopulation) is not mutual at the same time. Copulation may require several insertions of the penis, interrupted by withdrawal (e.g., *B. balanoides* 6–8 insertions over 30–90 minutes—Barnes et al., 1977). After copulation, the "female's" mantle cavity may be literally filled with sperm. Sperm competition between individuals may be particularly intense given the time scale of fertilization opportunities. The eggs are laid (within minutes after copulation) in two elastic sacs, secreted by the oviducal gland. The sperm are apparently activated by secretions from this same gland (Walley et al., 1971). In order to fertilize the eggs, the sperm must pass into the sac. The first sperms apparently pass through special places (craters as viewed by SEM), and the holes they leave may be used by other sperm (Walker, 1977, 1980). All of this takes at most a few hours. After fertilization, excess sperm are ejected from the mantle cavity. The eggs are brooded (in the sacs) within the mantle cavity for up to several months, depending upon the number of broods per year. The eggs are oxygenated by the adult's respiratory current but there is no parent-offspring nutrient transfer. The sacs eventually break apart and the barnacle releases a free swimming planktonic larva. After some time in the plankton, the cyprid larva settles to begin growth to the adult form (reviewed for *B. balanoides* in Stubbings, 1975). It has probably traveled far from its parent and sibs by this time.

Even this simplified and brief description of barnacle mating suggests several implications for sex allocation.

(1) Self-fertilization by mistake is very unlikely.

(2) Offspring probably do not compete with sibs for space to develop.

(3) There is no maternal transfer of food to offspring.

(4) It also seems unlikely that brood space limits brood size, but this is tested by the calculation of resources into male versus female function.

I think that there are two hypotheses most likely to account for hermaphroditism here: selfing and saturation for the male gain curve.

Selfing in barnacles has been studied only by observation of isolated individuals. If they produce no viable eggs, selfing is eliminated; viable eggs implicate facultative selfing. Barnes and Crisp (1956) and Crisp (1954) have discussed or presented original data for seven barnacle species. Three could produce viable offspring in isolation (one of these showed lowered viability among those offspring), while four did not. No barnacle is known to be a typical selfer. The four species who did not self probably are obligate outcrossers. While scanty, these data suggest to me that typical selfing probably does not play a major role in barnacle hermaphroditism.

Based on the above description of barnacle mating, I would like to propose a simple model for sex allocation, under the assumption of outcrossing (Charnov, 1980), and make some testable predictions. The hypothesis being developed is that hermaphroditism results from saturation of the male gain relation.

Define as follows: (1) All individuals are the same size—each has R resources to divide among sperm and eggs. (2) The penis has already been built and is sufficient to deliver sperm to K other individuals. (3) The species is annual, one brood is produced, and breeding is synchronous. (4) At the time eggs are fertilized, an individual A receives sperm from K others. The fraction of A's eggs which are fertilized by any specified mate depends only upon the number of sperm given by that mate, compared to all the sperm present. (5) The amount of sperm or eggs produced is directly proportional to the resource (fraction of R) invested.

245

Now, consider a large population of barnacles, each of which allocates a proportion r of its total resources, R, to sperm. We introduce into this population a mutant that allocates $\hat{r}$ proportion of R to sperm. The question is whether this individual will contribute genes to more or fewer eggs, compared to a typical member of the population (i.e., one who allocates r). The fitness or number of eggs (W_t) for our mutant is:

$$W_t \propto \text{eggs it produces} + \text{eggs it fertilizes};$$

$$W_t \propto R(1 - \hat{r}) + KR(1 - r)\left(\frac{\hat{r}}{\hat{r} + (K - 1)r}\right). \quad (15.1)$$

The second term in W_t is simply the eggs produced by the mutant's mates, $KR(1 - r)$, times the relative number of sperm the mutant contributes to those matings. To find the ESS r^*, we look at $\partial W_t/\partial \hat{r}$ when $\hat{r} = r$:

$$\partial W_t/\partial \hat{r} \propto -R + KR(1 - r)\left(\frac{(K - 1)r}{(r + (K - 1)r)^2}\right),$$

or

$$\partial W_t/\partial \hat{r} \propto \frac{(1 - r)}{r}\left(\frac{K - 1}{K}\right) - 1.$$

If r is very small, $\partial W/\partial \hat{r} > 0$ and selection favors mutants who make $\hat{r}$ slightly larger than r. If r is too large, the reverse obtains. The only r^* which makes $\partial W/\partial \hat{r} = 0$ is

$$\frac{1 - r^*}{r^*}\left(\frac{K - 1}{K}\right) = 1, \text{ or } r^* = \frac{K - 1}{2K - 1}. \quad (15.2)$$

Thus, we predict that the proportion of reproductive resources (R) devoted to male function (sperm) should increase as the mating group size ($K + 1$) increases. Since the model assumes that all eggs are fertilized, regardless of the actual quantity of sperm delivered, it predicts that an individual with a single partner ($K = 1$) should produce no sperm. Biologically this means that an individual should produce the small quantity of sperm necessary to fertilize its partner's eggs. As the mating group ($K + 1$) size gets larger, r^* approaches one-half.

In equation 15.1, the female gain curve is linear, while the male gain curve saturates, because of the limitations of male mating opportunities imposed by the finite size of the mating group ($= K + 1$) and the inability of any one individual (as a male) to monopolize mating with the others. This situation favors hermaphroditism provided the fixed cost (resource invested in the penis) is small, along with the number of mates, K. Are these conditions met? Hines (1978, 1979) studied three species of intertidal barnacles in California. The total yearly clutch weight ranged from about 4 to almost 12 times the animals' total body weight. The penis is a very small part of the body. If these figures are representative (this is a remarkable quantity of resource to be putting into reproduction), then the cost of a penis is extremely small, relative to the total reproductive resource.

As K becomes smaller, hermaphroditism becomes more stable, since the saturation rate for male reproductive success is steeper. How large is K, and why is it not larger? In an important unpublished study, Wong (1967) observed mating in two west coast North American species of *Balanus* (*B. glandula, B. tintinnabulum*). In *B. tintinnabulum*, the recipient individual closes its operculum after a single penis is inserted, holding the penis tight. After sperm accumulate in the shaft of the penis, the recipient opens the operculum to let the sperm enter. Here K always equals 1. In *B. glandula* the matings involved 1–4 donors with 4 rather uncommon. In their discussion of *B. balanoides,* Barnes et al. (1977) reported that mating involved up to 6 "males." One was the most common, with 2–3 fairly common. Higher values were fairly rare. Walker (1980) reported similar results for *B. balanoides* and contrasted this species with *Balanus hameri,* where a "female" receives sperm from only one "male". D. J. Crisp (per. comm.) suggests that the mating group for *Chthamalus fragilis* is of size 7–10, while the group size for *Elminius modestus* is generally 4–7. He notes that there is a correlation with barnacle size, the smallest species having the largest mating groups.

These are the only data I know of which estimate K. Unfortunately, there are no estimates for the proportion of resources put into male function. It would be very useful to contrast *B. tintinnabulum* and *B. hameri* ($K = 1$) with the other species. It would also be interesting to look for geographic variation in K within a species. In these *Balanus* examples, K is small enough ($<$ 3-4) to strongly favor hermaphroditism. In *Chthamalus* and *Elminius*, the larger mating group size would seem to make hermaphroditism less stable; but if there is little fixed cost for male reproduction, the male gain relation will still saturate for these group sizes. These species should be allocating relatively more of their reproductive resources to male function, contrasted to the *Balanus* species.

These examples raise the question of selection on K, or the penis size itself. In thinking about selection on the male role, we must keep in mind that the recipient individual may control the acceptance of sperm (witness *B. tintinnabulum*). There would seem no reason for "her" to provide receptivity information beyond a distance which results in adequate numbers of sperm for "her" eggs. Likewise, "she" will not benefit from the male-male (sperm) competition—indeed, such competition could well result in losses to "her" (e.g., polyspermy, attraction of predators). "She" may also be at risk while open during copulation; again, once enough sperm are received "she" ceases to gain. From the male viewpoint, several factors select against increasing the group size: (1) resources to build a larger penis are unavailable for other functions (but the penis seems so cheap?); (2) the penis may be at predation risk during copulation; (3) there may be severe sensory limitations on the ability to find receptive "females" over larger distances. These are hypothetical, yet plausible factors which may explain why K is often small. Some of them are testable via behavioral or physiological measurements (e.g., the distances over which "males" can detect ripe "females"). Of course, a key measurement is the resource allocation to male versus female function.

Let me now propose two alterations in the basic model (equation 15.1). These are to alter the male gain relation, and to relax the assumption that all individuals are the same size. Equation 15.1 assumes that eggs via male function depend upon the relative volume (or numbers) of sperm. Since the sperm must pass through the surface of the bubble sac to get to the eggs (i.e., sperm and eggs are not simply mixed up) male success may scale less than proportionally to numbers. I suggest this because the volume of sperm are projected onto the two-dimensional surface of the egg sac. Suppose that we substitute

$$\frac{\hat{r}^x}{\hat{r}^x + (K-1)r^x}$$

for the comparable term in (15.1). The exponent x allows male gain to increase at a slower rate ($x < 1$) than sperm number. The ESS now becomes:

$$r^* = \frac{x(K-1)}{(x+1)K - x}.$$

Surprisingly, for x in the range 0.75 to 1, the affect on r^* is very small. However, $x < 1$ greatly increases the stability of hermaphroditism by even further limiting opportunities for male gain.

It is straightforward to consider a barnacle population with a multiple of size (R) classes present. However, the equations are complex, and I discuss only the qualitative results of a model which includes large individuals and very small ones. In general, members of the two size classes will have different mating group sizes (small barnacles will be able to mate with fewer). The model also assumes that small barnacles could be females, and that the other barnacles would provide sperm for their eggs. Provided small barnacles can reach others and that the penis is of negligible cost, the model predicts that small barnacles should emphasize male function. While being small decreases both male and female reproductive success (RS), the relative decrease is smaller for male RS. The model is very similar to the LMC model for superparasitism and sex ratio proposed by Holmes (1970, 1972) and Werren (1980a,b, 1982).

249

Note that this prediction is for small barnacles in the midst of larger ones, not small barnacles per se. This relativity aspect suggests a test. We may contrast small in the midst of other small, versus small with large. There are some data on the sexuality of small barnacles which suggest that the hermaphroditism of barnacles is often somewhat protandrous, with individuals beginning life as males and later being fully hermaphroditic (D. J. Crisp and W. Newman, per. comm.—further discussion below; Walker, 1980 for *B. hameri*). Newman (1980) suggested that this, in fact, preadapts barnacles for becoming dwarf (or complemental) males.

Darwin (1854) called the tiny males associated with female barnacles *dwarf* and used the term *complemental* for those males associated with hermaphrodites. The male-female association is often rather remarkable, the male occupying a special place designed to hold him on the female/hermaphrodite individual. In at least one case, being a male may be genetically determined (Gomez, 1975). What might select for this association? Since a tiny barnacle is not much of a food competitor, the female/hermaphrodite would benefit by having a ready supply of sperm. What is in it for the small male? Ghiselin (1974) and Newman (1980) suggest that low population density might help here, since if the small male does not have to compete (for eggs) with larger individuals, it would enhance its fitness by forming the association (and perhaps not competing for food or space resources with the larger individual, who would be its mate). In this case, we might expect the hermaphrodite to become a functional female since there is no one to mate with. Newman (1980) has discussed the genus *Scillaelepas* where the hermaphrodite's penis is rudimentary and the group is effectively dioecious.

If these selective forces thus lead to dioecy, when might we expect true complemental males? I suggest that extreme space limitation (for example, crowded populations or species where the acceptable habitat is very limited) which selects for some larva to settle upon other individuals might set the stage (also Ghiselin, 1974). If crowding severely limits the chances to grow big, some individuals might elect to settle where they cannot grow—always being small, they will live and die as males. In this case, lifetime maleness is expected to be facultative, depending upon the place of settlement.

W. Newman (per. comm.) states that this situation character-izes several species on the Southwest coast of the U.S. The small barnacles are males, and in crowded populations most will not grow large (unless disturbance or death opens up space for them). For all practical purposes, they will live and die as complemental males. In crowded barnacle populations we predict that the large barnacles will not be greatly modified to accept the small ones, since here the large ones will not lack sperm. Anatomical modifi-cation of large barnacles to accept small ones should characterize species where there is space limitation (limited habitat) *and* low population density. Here, the large barnacles also benefit from having the small males close. Interestingly, if this is true, it suggests that selfing is often selected against in barnacles—individuals in sparse populations could self rather than accept close association with small males.

It should be clear from even this preliminary discussion of barnacle mating systems that there are many possibilities here for testing sex allocation theory. A few minutes spent on the intertidal are enough to convince one that the density, size relations, etc. of a common barnacle species vary on the scale of inches. I cannot help but wonder if the individual barnacles are also sensitive to their breeding opportunities over this spatial scale. Can an individual adjust its male/female allocation to the immediate surroundings?

A CORAL REEF FISH, THE BLACK HAMLET
(HYPOPLECTRUS NIGRICANS)

Fischer (1980, 1981) provides a detailed study of breeding in a coral-reef-living hermaphroditic fish, the Black Hamlet (*Hypo-plectrus nigricans*). The species is a diurnal planktivore which defends feeding territories. Reproduction is aseasonal with the spawning of planktonic eggs taking place at the edge of the reef shortly before sunset. Before going to the edge of the reef, the fish form pairs. Spawning is very synchronous, with most spawns within one hour of sunset. Egg release takes place during 4–5 bouts within each spawning period. The individuals of a pair reverse roles between bouts, first one acting as male, then the other. This alternation of sex roles means that an individual releases eggs to be fertilized, and then requires eggs for it to fertilize before it provides further eggs to the partner. This role reversal (*egg trading*) effectively limits the opportunities for one member of the pair to fertilize the other's eggs, then to depart in search of other "females." The synchronization of breeding also limits opportunities for increased male fitness. Following 70 fish for a complete spawning period showed that 39 had only one partner, 24 had two and only 7 had three partners. Various experiments showed that the species did not self fertilize.

Fischer (1981) derived equation 15.2, but decided it was not applicable to the fish since the local populations were rather large (K large?). Contrary to Fischer's (1981) interpretation, I believe that K refers to the size of the mating groups and not to a local population. In effect, $K \sim 1$, since each individual gets but a single mate. As predicted by theory, only a small fraction ($\sim$ 10% by volume or biomass) of the gonad is devoted to sperm. The mating group size is kept small by the egg-trading behavior.

I can summarize this chapter with the suggestion that progress in understanding hermaphroditism in animals would seem to follow mostly from the testing of alternative hypotheses on the selective forces involved. The *resource allocation model* (Chapter Fourteen) points toward some particular factors (e.g., male gain relation). What we now need are critical data.

CHAPTER SIXTEEN

Sex Types
in Higher Plants

This chapter briefly reviews our knowledge of the distribution of sex types in higher plants and looks at evidence for genetic effects on gender expression. For hermaphroditic (cosexual) plants, I suggest some key factors involved in selection for the allocation to male versus female function, and propose several alternative hypotheses to explain why hermaphroditism is so common in higher plants. Finally, the chapter looks at data bearing on the predicted negative relation between selfing and allocation to male function (the LMC hypothesis).

DISTRIBUTION

The distribution of gender in higher plants is complex because even at a simple morphological level, we can talk of the sex of a flower (stamens and pistils, or only one), the sex of an individual (combinations of flower types), or the sexual distribution of a population (various flower and individual types). Darwin (1877) classified flowering plants according to this scheme. In Darwin's view, monoecy, for example, would refer to a population consisting of individuals, each of which produces both male and female flowers. Androdioecy would refer to a population with male individuals and hermaphroditic individuals (probably with perfect flowers). The classification refers to the presence of a morphological type. It does not specify anything particular about the *functional gender* (Lloyd, 1980b, 1979b), the extent to which an individual passes genes to the next generation via pollen or seeds.

253

Using this scheme, Yampolsky and Yampolsky (1922) surveyed published data for about 10^5 angiosperm species. A summary of their data, along with a definition of terms, is shown in Table 16.1. Perfect-flowered species make up almost 75% of the flowering plants. In contrast dioecy and monoecy are rather uncommon (~ 5% each). However, populations consisting of mixtures of two or more sex types (including dioecy) make up almost 25% of the species. Bawa (1980) suggested that this classification may not be as revealing as it first seems, even though these results are widely cited. He noted that recent research with previously little-studied tropical floras has turned up many more instances of dioecy, often functional dioecy with perfect flowers (or in taxonomic groups previously described as having perfect flowers). He also noted that even under the old scheme, the distribution of functional sex (discussed below) is really not known for the species which consist of mixtures of two or more types.

TABLE 16.1. Sex type in angiosperms (based on flower morphology).

Sex type	Proportion of species*
Hermaphrodite (perfect flowered)	0.72
Monoecious	0.05
Dioecious	0.04
Andromonoecious	0.017
Gynomonoecious	0.028
Hermaphrodite + one other sex type	0.07
Monoecious + males and females	0.036
Other mixtures	~ 0.039

*Survey of 121,492 angiosperm species, data from Yampolsky and Yampolsky (1922).

Definitions:
Hermaphrodite: male and female elements in the same flower.
Monoecious: male and female flowers distinct but on the same plant.
Dioecious: male and female flowers on separate plants.
Andromonoecious: plant with hermaphrodite and male flowers.
Gynomonoecious: plant with hermaphrodite and female flowers.

In a long series of papers Lloyd (1972b, 1980a,b, 1979b,c; Primack and Lloyd, 1980; Lloyd and Myall, 1976) has developed the concept of *functional gender*. He notes that it is uncommon in plants for individuals to be functionally entirely male or female. Sexual type is simply not that rigid. In many so-called dioecious species, males may set some seed and females produce some pollen. He also notes that flower type may itself be a very imperfect predictor of functional gender. In *Cirsium arvense* Lloyd and Myall (1976) showed that the hermaphroditic florets were in fact acting as males or females (e.g., the female's anthers produced no pollen). He proposed that in general, plant species or populations would fall into two broad categories. In the first, the population would consist of two kinds of plants—one type would pass most of its genes to the next generation via seed, the other type would do so via pollen. These we should call females and males, respectively. The second kind of population would be (more or less) monomorphic, with discrete functional types absent. While in such populations there might be great variability in the extent to which individuals succeed as pollen or seed parents, the absence of a clear dimorphism suggests that we label the individuals *cosexual* (since the average individual passes genes equally via male and female function). Lloyd (1980b) has proposed numerical indices which are useful in discussing functional gender.

Two questions immediately present themselves. First, within cosexual populations, what determines the variability of pollen versus seed parentage? Some of the species discussed in the works of Lloyd show a broad range (some individuals are pure males and females), while others show a very narrow range. Second, there are many possible ways to be cosexual (e.g., perfect flowers versus monoecy); what selective forces determine the form of monomorphism? Lloyd (1979b), and Bawa and Beach (1981) have discussed in great detail some advantages of various flower types and arrangements among plants, again in terms of effects on the opportunities to gain fitness via pollen versus seeds (or vice versa). I refer the reader to these discussions. Bawa and Lloyd's suggestions come down to an acknowledgment that we have as yet only a sketchy idea of the distribution of functional gender among angiosperms. While the categories of Table 16.1 are useful, their limitations must be recognized.

In contrast to the large diversity of sexual types in angiosperms, gymnosperms are fairly simple. As reviewed by Givnish (1980), all are wind pollinated and almost all species are either dioecious or monoecious (relative numbers shown in Table 17.4). In monoecious species the flower types are usually spatially segregated. This suggests that, combined with the simplicity of pollen donation and reception (no animal vectors), an individual may itself be patchy with respect to opportunities for male and female function (with some places relatively better for giving off pollen). The simplicity of flower types correlates well with the absence of animal pollination. Dioecy is discussed in Chapter Seventeen.

GENES FOR SEXUALITY IN HIGHER PLANTS?

There is a vast literature documenting genetic effects on sexuality in higher plants, particularly in species of agricultural importance. Older reviews are Allen (1940) and Westergaard (1958). The most useful recent review is the book by Frankel and Galun (1977). For details on the family Cucurbitaceae (cucumber, melons, squash) see Robinson et al. (1976) and the papers by Kubicki (1969a,b,c). Many instances of genes with large, qualitative effects (e.g., complete male sterility) are known, as well as genes affecting the quantitative allocation of resource to male versus female function. This latter are particularly well documented in the family Cucurbitaceae. Velich and Satyko (1974) studied 24 monoecious and andromonoecious cultivars of melon. There was much variation in the sex ratio (ratio of male flowers to female flowers) and they could select for femaleness—fewer male flowers. Omar and Graham (1974) looked at sex ratio (flower ratio) in monoecious cucumber. They cited five earlier studies showing genetic control over sex ratio (and eight studies showing that sex expression was modifiable by environmental factors such as fertilizer or soil moisture). They estimated "broad sense heritability" for the sex ratio at 0.96, a remarkably high value. Beginning with a parental generation sex ratio of 30 male flowers per female flower, and selecting individuals with a mean ratio of 14:1, they altered the sex ratio to about 12:1 in a single generation!

Since female function includes resources put into seeds, while male function is more simply the male flower, most monoecious plants show a large excess of male over female flowers. However, I know of virtually no study (except Lloyd, 1972b; Lemen, 1980) which relates variation in this ratio to sex allocation theory. Since agricultural yield often depends upon seed characters, much artificial selection has been devoted to altering seed size, seed content, and the total reproductive effort the plant devotes to seed.

Artificial selection may also alter the allocation to male function, bleeding it (so to speak) to increase harvestable seed. After all, no one eats cucumber pollen! In effect this selection alters the male/female fitness set. However, in the face of artificial selection for seed characters there is always selection acting on sex allocation. I suggest that a careful review of the plant breeding literature (e.g., cereal crops), will turn up cases where artificial selection for seed characters additionally altered male characters. For example, selection for more resource being transferred from soma to seeds (i.e., increased reproductive effort) should likewise result in selection for more resource into pollen. Selection for larger seeds should result in relatively fewer female flowers in monoecious species.

COSEXUAL PLANTS

Male reproductive function consists of attracting pollinators (or pollen donation) and the success of that pollen in contributing genes to seeds (e.g., getting pollen transferred to another individual, having that pollen outcompete other pollen for fertilization of ovules, and having those ovules incorporated into seeds and fruits—Charnov, 1979c). Pollen success may depend partly upon

257

the number of pollen grains, their size, and their resource for growth once on the stigma. Female reproductive success depends upon receiving pollen, allocating resource to seeds and fruit, and having the fruit disperse and/or escape predators. This view is simplistic, but it begins to suggest how the degree of success through male or female function depends upon various characters and tradeoffs.

Let me propose two key questions for sex allocation, and then discuss some of the reasons why hermaphroditism (cosexuality) may be so common in plants.

(1) *Does availability of pollen limit seed set,* or *is seed set more related to the resources allocated to seeds?* Under what conditions does pollen limit seed set? Sexual selection theory in dioecious species is based on the general assumption that females are not limited in egg production by the availability of sperm but by the female's opportunities to garner resources to make eggs. Male reproductive success is thus limited by access to females and their eggs, although male control over critical resources (e.g., oviposition sites) may be the form of male competition. This is termed *Bateman's principle* and has been discussed and extended by several other authors (Trivers, 1972; Orians, 1969). Bateman (1948) suggested that it should also apply to plants. Two recent authors have extended it to hermaphroditic organisms, including plants (Willson, 1979; Charnov, 1979c). Lloyd and Webb (1977) have discussed sexual dimorphism in dioecious plants from the viewpoint of the differing ways males and females gain reproductive success.

To rephrase the question—in what ways do floral and other reproductive characters of cosexual plants evolve with the major selective force being male reproductive success (fitness gains through the donation of pollen)? If pollen does not in general limit seed set, opportunities arise for reproductive characters to be shaped primarily by male function (although I note here that seed dispersal, a female function, may well select for aspects of floral display). This sexual selection view has been discussed in some specific cases by Bawa (1980), Bawa and Beach (1981), Casper

258

and Charnov (1982), and Willson (1979). Part of the question involves the realization that some forms of the male gain relation result in the instability of hermaphroditism itself and selection for dioecy (Willson, 1979; Charnov, 1979c; Charnov et al., 1976; Bawa, 1980; Beach, 1981). Many temporal and spatial (e.g., within-plant) aspects of male/female function in hermaphroditic plants have been classically viewed as devices by which an individual avoids (or controls the amount of) self-fertilization. Sexual selection, primarily gains through male function, provides an interesting alternative hypothesis (of course, both may be involved).

Let me provide a possible example. In *Delphinium nelsoni,* a montane wild flower with an upright inflorescence, the flowers are strongly protandrous. Older flowers on the lower part are female receptive, while the younger ones above can as yet only donate pollen. As the lower ones set seed, those just above become female receptive, turning off male function. New flowers arise at the top. Pyke (1978) showed that the plant has a gradient of nectar reward from bottom to top. More nectar is provided in the lower flowers. Thus, bees arrive at the bottom, move upward, and finally leave to visit another plant. This would appear to be an effective outcrossing mechanism; bees with foreign pollen first visit female flowers, then male, then they leave. But what about male-male (pollen) competition? The order of visitation seems tailor-made for sexual selection. The "female receptive" flowers remove foreign pollen (to set seed and *simply to remove it*), while the male flowers cover the bee with new pollen and send them off. One wonders if the female flowers have any special devices for extra-effective pollen removal.

(2) *A second key question would seem to be the extent to which male and female function are seasonally (temporally) displaced.* Suppose that a tree blooms in the spring, relying upon resources stored from the past season's growth. Pollen is given off and fertilizations result. After a short time there are no more ovules for pollen to compete for since the earlier pollen has already fertilized them. Photosynthate produced after this period is used to fill the

259

seeds. It is unavailable for male function *that year* because it simply does not yet exist when male function happens. To be available for male function it would have to be stored until the next year. Some of it obviously is, but storage and movement costs now play a large role in its availability for male function. Pollen and seed function often differ temporally (e.g., seed set fails because of drought *after* flowering). Lloyd (1979b) has discussed some of these possibilities, noting that predictability of fruiting opportunities may often be low at the time of flower formation. *Opportunities and costs for the production, movement, use, and storage of reproductive resources may play important roles in sex allocation.* Likewise, sex allocation may greatly influence the resource flow patterns within the plant.

Why are plants so often hermaphroditic (cosexual)? Let me suggest several hypotheses, with the suggestion that we do not yet know their relative importance. However, most of these suggestions are testable.

(1) Hermaphroditism allows self-fertilization which is adjusted to an intermediate optimum.
(2) It allows facultative selfing.
(3) Pollen is a primary attractant for pollinating agents; a female would simply not be visited.
(4) Pollen limits seed set and the visit of a pollinating agent achieves gains for both genders. Both genders share the flower resource, or cost of attraction, which makes the fitness set convex.
(5) Temporal displacement of availability of resource for the two sex functions means that female resource is simply not available for male function.
(6) Seed set is resource limited; pollen (the male gain curve) fitness saturates because of limitations in mate availability (e.g., the barnacle model) or saturation of pollen vectors.
(7) Seed set is resource limited, but limited fruit dispersal results in sib competition and thus a law of diminishing returns through seeds.

260

(8) Male and female function may depend upon (be limited by) different resources (e.g., protein versus carbohydrate).

These factors either relate to the shapes of the male/female gain curves or the effect of selfing. Of course, the factors may well interact (e.g., diminishing returns through both seeds and pollen). It is assumed here that the avoidance of selfing (type 2) is not a major factor—see dioecy discussion, Chapter Seventeen.

SEX ALLOCATION AND THE SELFING RATE

While some recent studies have begun to look at the resource allocation to male versus female function in cosexual plants (Lovett Doust, 1980; Lovett Doust and Harper, 1980), clear interpretation is difficult without additional information on the breeding systems. This pioneering work is important, however, since it represents the first steps toward an understanding of the selective forces on male/female allocation in these plants. Here I restrict attention to one particular sex allocation hypothesis.

There is one sex allocation hypothesis (for cosexual species) for which plant data exist, namely the LMC prediction that relative allocation to male function shows decline as the selfing rate increases (Chapter Fourteen). Complete selfing (cleistogamy) should select for very little male function (as first pointed out by Darwin, 1877), while total outcrossing with symmetric male/female gain curves should favor about equal allocation to each function (qualifications depending upon shapes of male/female gain curves). I discuss here four patterns which bear on this hypothesis.

Lemen (1980) studied sex allocation in several species of wind-pollinated annual herbs. In the genus *Amaranthus* both monoecious and dioecious species were studied. The monoecious species were highly selfed. He defined relative allocation to male function as:

$$C \left(\frac{\text{total anther volume on the plant}}{\text{total seed weight}} \right).$$

Note that the ratio is volume of male parts to seed weight. The factor C was a conversion factor used to equate male volume to seed weight. To estimate C, he argued as follows. Assume that males and females of the same size in the dioecious species allocate the same quantity of resource to reproduction. If we match males and females by size, we can measure the total volume of anthers for the male and the total seed set for the female. Suppose that the anther volume was A, the seed set B. Under the equal allocation assumption, A anther volume is *equivalent* in resource content to B seeds. Applying this conversion factor to the monoecious species allows us to use total anther volume and seed weight to estimate the resource allocated to anthers versus seeds.

Applying this method to the highly selfed monoecious species (six species in five genera, including *Amaranthus*) produced the estimate that typically < 5% of an individual's resource was being spent on male function. Further evidence for this small male allocation was that for plants of the same size, both monoecious and dioecious females (in different *Amaranthus* species) were setting about the same amount of seed. However, when Lemen calculated the same allocation for outcrossed *Lolium perenne* (perfect-flowered, self-incompatible, still wind-pollinated), the result was that near-equal resource was given to male and female function. I think that these data are particularly important. Wind pollination is strongly suggestive of an approximately linear male gain curve (not strongly saturating). If the female gain curve is similarly near linear, we would predict that total outcrossing would favor near-equal allocation to male versus female function.

In a series of papers, Cruden (1976, 1977) has proposed that the ratio of pollen grains to ovules in a plant population is a reasonable indicator of a species' breeding system (i.e., degree of selfing). This will be termed the pollen ovule ratio, or P/O. In addition, botanists have known for a long time that selfing is often indicated by floral structure (Lloyd, 1979a, for review); typical selfers often have a much-reduced floral structure. By using these and other indices of selfing rate, Cruden (1977) divided dozens of angiosperm species into five selfing categories: cleistogamy, selfed but open flowers, mostly selfed, mostly outcrossed, obligate out-crossed. While this last category includes some dioecious species, their inclusion will hardly alter our conclusions. The mean P/O ratios were respectively 4.7, 27.7, 168.5, 797, 5859—an apparently massive shift toward male function under progressively more outcrossing.

Cruden (1977) has explained these data in a very different way from the LMC hypothesis. He assumes that pollen will be produced in just the quantities needed to maximize seed set in the population and that the gradient (selfing to outcrossed) is really one of increasing difficulty in getting pollen to set seeds. His notion of *efficiency* of the pollination system relates entirely to the problem of getting pollen to set seeds. Inefficient systems (out-crossed, wind-pollinated) need more pollen to do this. By contrast to sex ratio in dioecious species, it would be as if male production were considered a means by which females in the population got mated, with the suggestion that the sex ratio would be adjusted so that "just enough" males were around. Clearly, except for complete sib-mated LMC, neither theory nor the data support this view for the sex ratio.

Except for complete selfing, Cruden's perspective is not supported by LMC theory. Rather it is the opportunities for an individual to gain reproductive success, through male or female function, which drive the allocation ratio. Pollen does not exist so as to ensure seed set, but as an *equivalent* (*to seeds*) *means toward fitness gain.* Under total outcrossing, the allocation ratio is driven by the male/female gain curves (Chapter Fourteen). We might then expect pollen to be produced in excess of that necessary to ensure seed set in the population (just as females in dioecious species should rarely be limited in their reproduction by the availability of males to fertilize their eggs).

The P/O ratio is, of course, not strictly equivalent to the relative male/female allocation; at the very least, seed and pollen size must also be considered. For example: let $1 - r$ = proportion of resource (R) given to seeds (and assume for simplicity that ovule number = seed numbers). Let each seed cost C_2 and each

263

pollen grain C_1 units of resource. It follows that:

number of pollen grains, $P = rR/C_1$,

number of seeds, $\qquad O = (1 - r)R/C_2,$ or

$$\log (P/O) = \log \left(\frac{r}{1 - r}\right) + \log C_2 - \log C_1. \qquad (16.1)$$

This very simple hypothesis relates P/O to three factors, one of which (seed size, C_2) would seem to play no role in Cruden's (1977) hypothesis. Why should seed size be intimately related to the difficulties of pollination? If we allow the r in equation 16.1 to be the r^* in the sex allocation theory (the ESS value, forgetting other aspects of gender investment), then as a first approximation r^* might be considered as a constant *within* one of Cruden's breeding systems (e.g., mostly outcrossed). In a recent paper Cruden and Miller-Ward (1981) looked at P/O ratios in nineteen species of cross-pollinated plants, each of which had bees as the major pollen vector. They interpreted the variation in P/O ratios for these species in terms of the efficiency of pollen transfer (maximum seed set hypothesis), and produced a complex analysis of how this might work. Here, I propose that the variation is simply due to variation in size of a pollen grain (C_1); unfortunately there are no seed data. In Figure 16.1, I have graphed $\log(P/O)$ versus log(volume of a pollen grain). If r is a constant related to this breeding system ($= r^*$), and if seed size shows no systematic variation with pollen size, we expect a linear relation with slope -1 (equation 16.1). Indeed, the relation is linear (correlation coefficient $= 0.84$, sample size $= 19$). The appropriate slope is probably the slope of the functional regression (Ricker, 1973) since both variables are estimated with error. This value is -1.42. This is a bit too small, but still close to -1, considering the imprecision in the analysis (i.e., does cost of a grain scale with volume? what about other aspects of male investment?). As is often the case, the variation in pollen size itself remains unexplained. In reference to Figure 16.1, I suggest that for fixed pollen

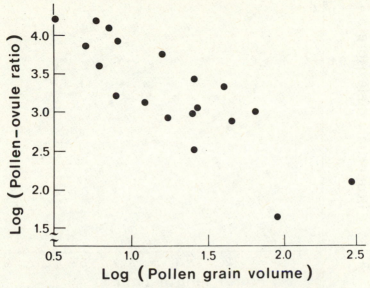

FIGURE 16.1. Variation in the pollen-ovule ratio, related to pollen grain size, for nineteen species of outcrossed bee-pollinated plants. If the proportion of resources devoted to male function is a constant for this breeding system (the ESS r^*), we expect a linear relationship on a log-log plot, with a slope of minus one (equation 16.1). Indeed the relation is linear (correlation coef. = -0.84), with a slope somewhat lower (-1.42) than one. (Data from Cruden and Miller-Ward, 1981.)

size, species with higher P/O ratios will show relatively larger seeds.

As the third example of testing the LMC hypothesis, consider the work of Lloyd (1972a,b) on the genus *Cotula* (Compositae). There are about 80 species, with gender expression as follows: dioecy ~10; monoecy ~24; gynomonoecy ~35; perfect flowers ~10. In the species tested there were no physiological barriers to selfing. In the monoecious species, a floral head has both male and female florets. Floret length was an approximate indicator of the level of selfing—shorter florets meaning more selfing. In Figure 16.2 I have graphed the average proportion male florets versus floret length for each of 17 monoecious species. As first noted by

265

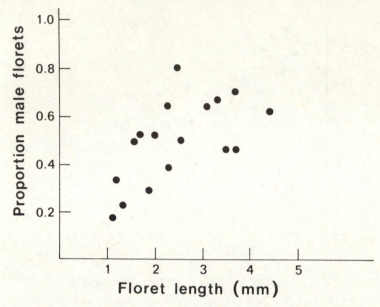

FIGURE 16.2. Local mate competition and sex ratio (flower ratio) in monoecious composites of the genus *Cotula*. Each floral head has both male and female florets. Floret length is a rough indicator of the degree of selfing; longer florets meaning more outcrossing (= less selfing). The relative allocation to male function increases with level of outcrossing, for the seventeen species studied. (Data from Lloyd, 1972b.)

Lloyd (1972b), there is a significant linear regression (correlation coefficient = 0.61, sample size = 17), although visual inspection of the data suggests (with the exception of one point) a relation with an asymptote at about 60% male flowers. Perhaps some of the scatter is related to variation among the species in seed size. This positive relation is predicted by LMC theory.

The fourth (and final) example bearing on LMC theory is the work of Schoen (1981) on several Californian populations of the spring annual *Gila achilleifolia* (Polemoniacae). Using electrophoretic procedures, he estimated the selfing rates (proportion of the seeds produced by selfing) in several populations. Somewhat surprisingly, they varied from 0.04 to 0.85. Selfing rates (*S*) in this species are strongly correlated with the degree of temporal separation between maturation of the anthers and the start of receptivity of the stigma within a flower. This characteristic (temporal separation) is under genetic control, suggesting that the variation in S among populations reflects adjustment by selection. If the selfing rate in each population is adjusted to an intermediate equilibrium, we might expect the fitness of selfed offspring to be near one-half (compared to outcrossed offspring),

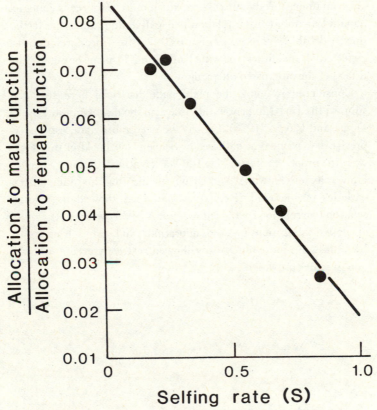

FIGURE 16.3. Resource allocation to male versus female function related to the selfing rate (S), for several populations of *Gilia achilleifolia*. For levels of inbreeding depression (δ) in the range 0.35–0.65, we expect a negative, linear relationship (as in Fig. 14.7). The observed data are very close to the theoretically expected results. Further discussion in text. (Data from Schoen, 1981; see for measurement details).

under the simple assumption that there is frequency dependence in fitness of selfed offspring as a function of the selfing rate.

Schoen (1981) also estimaed the allocation to male versus female function (using several definitions of what constitutes male function—the qualitative conclusions discussed below are not altered by his alternative procedures). In Figure 16.3, I have graphed relative male allocation, $(r^*/[1 - r^*]$ according to theory, Fig. 14.7) versus the selfing rate S. There are two things to note: (1) even under mostly outcrossing, much more resource is going to female function; (2) the relation is negative and almost perfectly linear. With reference to Figure 14.7, the linear relation is expected if the fitness of selfed offspring is near one-half the fitness of the outcrossed offspring.

Considered in total, the plant data discussed here strongly support the LMC interpretation (see also the discussion in Lovett Doust and Cavers, 1981). Clearly we need more data, especially precise data of the type gathered by Schoen (1981). After this book was in proof, Professor H.-I. Oka (National Chung Hsing University of Taiwan) pointed out to me that his data on 35 varieties of the wild rice, *Oryza perennis,* showed a striking relation (correlation coefficient $= -79$, $N = 35$) between the *ratio* of pollen allocation to seed allocation, and the selfing rate. Varieties with more outcrossing showed relatively greater allocation to male function.

CHAPTER SEVENTEEN

Two Plant Sex Types: Heterostyly and Dioecy

This chapter looks at sex allocation for two special systems in higher plants, dioecy and heterostyly.

Heterostyly is a reproductive polymorphism whereby a plant population consists of two (distyly) or three (tristyly) morphs, characterized by different style and stamen lengths (Darwin, 1877). In distyly the morph with a long style and short stamens is called a pin and the reciprocal a thrum. Botanists have classically viewed this polymorphism as an outcrossing mechanism, since in most situations pins and thrums can only cross-fertilize (Vuilleumier, 1967). Outcrossing probably plays an important role in the origin of heterostyly, and the Charlesworths (1979a, b) have discussed some detailed population genetic models for its establishment in previously hermaphroditic species.

Here I propose to view heterostyly from the perspective of sex allocation theory. Casper and Charnov (1982) and Beach and Bawa (1980) (also Bawa, 1980) have suggested that the heterostylous morphs are most usefully viewed in terms of their abilities (sometimes differing) to gain reproductive success through male (pollen) versus female (seed) function. My discussion is drawn from Casper and Charnov (1982). I first consider distyly, then, briefly, tristyly.

In distyly, the pin and thrum morphological characters and incompatibility system are closely linked in a supergene so that (for example) ss individuals are pin while Ss individuals are thrum. Obligatory cross mating (ss × Ss) will produce half of each morph. This is not at all necessary, however, since the morph ratio would seem to be easily altered through discrimination either for or against certain pollen (e.g., ss seed parents accepting mostly S pollen) or selective abortion of ovules. The adult morph ratio is often near equality in nature (Ganders, 1979).

I suggest that this is not due to the ss, Ss mating system (although this may be a proximate cause) but because equality among the zygotes is the ESS favored by selection acting on autosomal genes (genes not linked to the S-s locus). Suppose that the pin morph produces F_p seeds and M_p pollen grains, while the thrum morph produces F_t and M_t. Consider a rare mutant at an autosomal locus which produces $\hat{q}$ proportion of pins among its progeny, while the wild type produces q pins. The fitness (W_t) for the mutant individual in a large population of size N is

$$\text{fitness} = \begin{pmatrix} \text{reproduction} \\ \text{through seeds} \\ \text{of pin progeny} \end{pmatrix} + \begin{pmatrix} \text{reproduction} \\ \text{through seeds} \\ \text{of thrum progeny} \end{pmatrix}$$

$$+ \begin{pmatrix} \text{reproduction} \\ \text{through pollen} \\ \text{of thrum progeny} \end{pmatrix} + \begin{pmatrix} \text{reproduction} \\ \text{through pollen} \\ \text{of pin progeny} \end{pmatrix}$$

$$W_t = \hat{q} \cdot F_p + (1 - \hat{q}) F_t + \left[\frac{(1 - \hat{q}) M_t}{(1 - q) N \cdot M_t} \right] (q \cdot N \cdot F_p)$$

$$+ \left(\frac{\hat{q} \cdot M_p}{q \cdot N \cdot M_p} \right) [(1 - q) N \cdot F_t]. \quad (17.1)$$

By setting $\partial W_t / \partial \hat{q} = 0$ and solving for q, we find the ESS to be $q^* = \frac{1}{2}$. Note that this ESS is independent of the F and M values—thus $q^* = \frac{1}{2}$ even if pins and thrums suffer differential mortality to adulthood or produce different quantities of seeds or pollen. The calculation in equation 17.1 is for a large, random-mated population, and the result of equality among the zygotes is comparable to models for the evolution of primary sex ratio in dioecious species. By analogy to sex ratio models, we would expect the ESS to deviate from equality under several circumstances, particularly in certain forms of population structure (e.g., local mate competition) or when seeds carrying the pin and thrum genotypes receive different quantities of resources from the parent. Also the ESS would likely differ from a half if the cross-mating were not complete—if, for example, pin pollen sometimes fertilized pin ovules.

While equation 17.1 considers the ESS proportion of pins versus thrums, there are two additional sex allocation problems here, namely, the allocation to pollen versus seeds within each of the two morphs. Consider a mutant autosomal gene which, when present in a pin, alters its resource allocation from (F_p, M_p) to $(\hat{F}_p, \hat{M}_p)$. In a large, random-mated population, such a mutant individual will have fitness W_p:

$$W_p = \hat{F}_p + \left(\frac{\hat{M}_p}{\frac{1}{2} \cdot N \cdot M_p}\right) (\frac{1}{2} \cdot N \cdot F_t), \quad \text{or}$$

$$W_p = \hat{F}_p + F_t \cdot \left(\frac{\hat{M}_p}{M_p}\right). \tag{17.2}$$

The analogous fitness for a rare thrum mutant $(\hat{F}_t, \hat{M}_t)$ is, of course,

$$W_t = \hat{F}_t + F_p \cdot \left(\frac{\hat{M}_t}{M_t}\right). \tag{17.3}$$

The ESS (F_t, F_p, M_t, M_p) are values such that the mutants cannot increase W_p, W_t by altering their values ("." variables) away from the population values. An example is illustrated in Figure 17.1. I note here two things. First, the formalism is presented in terms of numbers of pollen and seeds; it is easily generalized to the relative abilities to reproduce through pollen and seeds, of which number is only one component. It generalizes, for example, to the ability of each morph to dispense pollen. Secondly, some shapes (e.g., linear) for the pollen-seed tradeoff relations (Fig. 17.1) select for one morph to be male (no F), the other to be female (no M). Dioecy is favored. Beach and Bawa (1980) reviewed instances where dioecy has apparently evolved

271

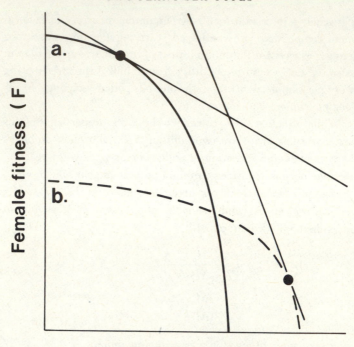

Male fitness (M)

FIGURE 17.1. Hypothetical fitness sets for pins (*a*) and thrums (*b*) in a distylous population. I have made the thrums better at being male, as suggested by Beach and Bawa, 1980. Also illustrated are the ESS allocations to male versus female function within each morph, per equations 17.2 and 17.3. (Redrawn from Casper and Charnov, 1982.)

from heterostyly (see also Baker, 1966; Opler et al., 1975). In every case, the thrum (short style) has become the male. They suggest that the initial step toward dioecy is an alteration in the pollination system which results in greater pollen flow from thrums to pins. In terms of Figure 17.1, the suggestion is that the male/female tradeoff within thrums is altered by the change in pollination system.

In tristylous species three morphs (characterized by style and stamen lengths) coexist. This is more complicated than the above system since the morphs may not only produce different quantities

272

of pollen versus seeds, but they may also show various mating relations with each other. Probably the simplest situation is where each morph can mate equally well with the other two; however, more complex arrangements are also known (Weller, 1976). In the simple case, provided that the morphs show different male/female fitnesses, the ESS will not in general be equal numbers of each morph. Unlike distyly, the fitnesses here do not cancel out of the ESS answer.

Since heterostylous species have not been studied from the perspective of sexual selection and sex allocation, data are not available to test the model directly. In some heterostylous species, the morphs apparently invest equally in pollen and seeds, and populations exhibit consistently equal morph ratios; but there are exceptions. I present examples which may be particularly relevant to the above model (Casper and Charnov, 1982).

The floral morphs of several distylous species specialize in their reproductive effort through male and female function (Lloyd, 1979c). One morph may be more male either by producing more pollen or by maturing fewer seeds per flower. An increased abortion of fruits or flowers following anther dehiscence could also increase maleness. Such flowers would have served their male function before "failing" to mature fruit.

Extreme examples of gender differentiation occur in heterostylous species that are functionally dioecious or nearly so. The short style morphs of *Cordia inermis*, *C. collococca*, and *C. panamensis* produce few or no seeds, while the reciprocal morphs have aborted anthers or inviable pollen (Opler et al., 1975). The greater seed production in the thrum morph of all six distylous species of *Primula* is considered a characteristic of the dimorphism (Darwin, 1877; Dowrick, 1956). Artificial pollination produces greater seed set in pins of *Oldenlandis umbellata* and *Hedyotis nigricans* (Bahadur, 1970a,b). Darwin (1877) considered the midstyle form of the tristylous species *Lythrum salicaria* "more feminine," while the short style form produces the fewest, smallest seeds. Conversely, the midstyle form of tristylous *Oxalis suksdorfii* produces very few seeds (Ornduff, 1964).

273

Differences in the relative amounts of resources allocated to pollen production between morphs are less evident. The pin morph of most distylous species produces more pollen, but this difference may be balanced by larger pollen grains of thrums (Ganders, 1979; Dulberger, 1974). Perhaps a better estimate of resource allocation to male function is anther size. Darwin (1877) lists five species, *Hottonia palustris, Limnanthemum indicum, Pulmonaria augustifolia, Linum flavum,* and *Forstythia suspensa,* in which anthers are of unequal size in the two morphs. Thrum anthers are also larger in the heterostylous species of *Lithospermum* and *Amsinckia* (Ganders, 1979; Johnston, 1952).

The morph ratios obtained by censusing natural populations of heterostylous species are necessarily proportions of flowering adults. Particularly for perennials, this may reflect differences in survivorship, and vegetative reproduction. These factors cannot be separated in the available data. Several species already discussed, however, do not always exhibit equal representation of morphs. The three *Cordia* spp. have greatly skewed morph ratios, and unequal morph ratios in many populations of *Primula vulgaris* and *Lythrum salicaria* have historically attracted considerable attention (Bodmer, 1960; Christy, 1922; Crosby, 1949; Fisher, 1941b, 1944; Haldane, 1936, 1938; Halkka and Halkka, 1974; Heuch, 1979a,b; Ornduff, 1979; Schoch-Bodmer, 1938).

Hedyotis caerula, interestingly, shows significantly more pins in 25 of 33 samples, representing 17 sites. The distributions of two morphs within populations of this species and of *H. nigricans* are not always random in space (Levin, 1974; Ornduff, 1980). Pollen production per flower and seed production per fruit are approximately equal in the two morphs, but in one of the two populations for which such data were gathered, pins matured fruit in only 43% of initiated flowers while thrums exhibited 68% fruit set (Ornduff, 1980). At least in this locality, pins are more male.

For self-compatible heterostylous species, the morph ratios in the progeny of naturally pollinated individuals have been used as measures of intramorphic pollination (Ganders, 1975). While self-compatible species do not meet the assumptions of the simple

274

model, I would expect sexual selection to operate in these species as well. Under the assumption that seed parents can discriminate against gametes carrying certain genotypes, I would not predict the frequency of morphs in the progeny to be determined solely or directly by the amount of intramorphic pollination. Instead, the ratio of pins to thrums should follow an ESS under autosomal control. The relative degree of successful intramorphic matings in the two morphs is only one factor influencing the ESS. Evidence for control of progeny morph ratios is found, in fact, in the self-compatible distylous *Amsinckia grandiflora* (Weller and Ornduff, 1977). In this species, naturally pollinated thrums produce excess pins. An artificial thrum (Ss) × thrum (Ss) cross also yields significantly more pins than expected. Since the thrum genotype is heterozygous and pins are homozygous recessive, one possible explanation is that unfertilized embryo sacs or embryos carrying the thrum allele are selectively eliminated. Because this species consistently matures fewer than its full complement of ovules in each flower (Ornduff, 1976), such an abortion mechanism could easily be operating.

DIOECY

There are several recent reviews of the taxonomic, geographic, and life history distribution of dioecy in higher plants (Bawa, 1980; Givnish, 1980; Freeman, Harper, and Ostler, 1980; Thomson and Barrett, 1981). This section briefly reviews data and theory. In general three explanations have been put forward to explain the occurrence of dioecy.

(1) Dioecy is an outbreeding mechanism, a means by which *an individual* avoids self-fertilization and thus avoids the production of less viable offspring (see many references cited in Thomson and Barrett, 1981). Many recent population genetic models incorporate the effects of selfing and inbreeding depression (in showing selection for dioecy, or at least a pure sex in a hermaphroditic population—Charlesworth and Charlesworth 1978a,b, 1979c; Lloyd 1974a,b, 1975a, 1976, 1979a,b).

(2) Dioecy is favored where ecological and life history conditions make sexual specialization (as males and females) of selective advantage. The conditions influence the opportunities for an individual to reproduce via male or female function. In the approach of this book, this means that we should look at the shapes of the male and female gain curves (Chapter Fourteen, Fig. 14.3). In its simplest form this hypothesis allows no role for selfing and its avoidance. Papers suggesting this hypothesis (in various forms, with various degrees of rigor) include Charnov et al., 1976; Charnov, 1979c; Bawa, 1980; Beach and Bawa, 1980; Bawa and Beach, 1981; Beach, 1981; Willson, 1979; and Givnish, 1980. Although most of these authors realize that the avoidance of selfing is potentially an important factor, the emphasis is clearly on the opportunities (inherent in the ecology) for specialization in male and female roles (i.e., the male/female gain relations).

Hypotheses (1) and (2) are, of course, not really distinct, and many authors (e.g., Darwin, Lewis, Lloyd, B. and D. Charlesworth) have clearly seen that the act of becoming a pure sex in a hermaphroditic population would free resources for use by that sex (from the sex given up). Thus, Darwin (1877) discussed the increased seed set shown by females in various gynodioecious plant species. However, the blending of sex allocation theory (in the sense of opportunities for fitness gain through male and female function) with self-fertility is recent (Charlesworth and Charlesworth, 1981), and more clearly specifies the nature of the interaction between hermaphroditic selfing and selection for dioecy (discussed in Chapter Fourteen).

(3) The third hypothesis is a variant of number 2 (ecology), but is sufficiently different to be considered separately. In the usual hermaphrodite-dioecy theory (Chapter Fourteen), the dioecious morphs are assumed to have fixed sex expression. Indeed, when we ask if dioecy is vulnerable to invasion by a hermaphrodite, we commonly let the sex ratio of the dioecious species be fixed at equality. However, under the environmental conditions discussed in the chapter on sex choice (Chapter Thirteen), selection might favor maleness or femaleness as a function of particular environ-

mental conditions (e.g., turn into male in a dry patch, female in wet). Freeman et al. (1980a,b; see also Charnov and Bull, 1977) suggested that dioecy with sex choice might be favored in these sorts of environments. It is not immediately obvious just when dioecy would be favored over hermaphroditism with emphasis on one or the other sex function related to environmental conditions. However, it may be more a matter of definition: will we call a species with relatively extreme sexual specialization dioecious? Under Lloyd's concept of functional gender (Chapter Sixteen), such a species would be considered dioecious.

Along with these three hypotheses, there have been two general approaches to thinking about the transition from hermaphroditism to dioecy. The first is more intuitive and simply asks if hermaphroditism is stable to a pure sex type (e.g., work of Charnov, Willson, Beach, Bawa, Givnish). If hermaphroditism is not stable (e.g., as shown by the shapes of male/female gain curves), it is assumed that selection will push toward dioecy (or at least a mixed population).

The second approach looks in detail at the stages of transition to dioecy. This is best represented by the work of the Charlesworths (1978–1981). By way of example, there are several possible pathways from hermaphroditism to dioecy:

(1) via monoecy (e.g., Lloyd, 1972a,b for *Cotula*);
(2) via gynodioecy from perfect flowers (many authors);
(3) via androdioecy;
(4) via heterostyly (Lloyd, 1979c; Beach and Bawa, 1980; Casper and Charnov, 1982);
(5) via gradual reduction of pollen and seed function in perfect flowered or monoecious species (disruptive selection).

Each of these may place different constraints on the transition process, as in the following example. In a perfect flowered species, a rare female mutant is selected for, resulting in a gynodioecious population. Its frequency is given by equation 2.1 of Chapter Two (Lloyd, 1975a, 1976). Genes which turn off female function in the hermaphrodite may now be selected for. However, depending upon the dominance of the initial male sterile (= female) gene, selection on these new genes may be affected by particular linkage relations (i.e., linkage to the male sterile locus). If the "linkage constraint" is only partially met, the population may not go fully to dioecy, yet the modifier will still often be selected for. The reduction of female function after establishment of gynodioecy will thus often be gradual; and species showing this pathway often have males who still set some seed (Lloyd, 1980a). The linkage constraint is such that when dioecy is achieved, sex will often be determined by sex chromosomes, with male heterogamety. Indeed this is a very common pattern of sex determination in dioecious plants (Westergaard, 1958). I refer the reader to the Charlesworths' (1978–1981) discussion of modeling the details of the transition. Here, I will concentrate on the more intuitive approach, and the ecological and life history correlates of dioecy.

Self-incompatibility systems are widely distributed throughout the angiosperms (Lewis, 1979), with some estimates that almost 50% of all angiosperms are self-incompatible (Thomson and Barrett, 1981). As discussed by Baker (1959, 1967), a notable feature of the systematic distribution of dioecy and self-incompatibility is their strong negative correlation within taxonomically related groups (reviewed in Thomson and Barrett, 1981). Dioecy is, with few exceptions, absent from groups which have well-developed self-incompatibility systems. The inference is that the groups without such systems have a selfing problem; Baker (1967) has suggested that the establishment of incompatibility alleles as a means of limiting selfing may simply be more difficult than dioecy. While this correlation is striking, I cannot help but wonder if it must follow that dioecy equals outcrossing advantage. For example, the hypothesis requires that selfing be selected against but difficult to avoid, rather than that selfing be selected for and adjusted to some intermediate level (Chapter Fourteen). This would appear to be a testable prediction—both that selfing is hard to avoid and that inbred offspring are of very low viability. It is also not entirely clear why production of selfed offspring should be such a problem—why, for example, abortion of selfed ovules cannot be used to shift maternal resources toward outcrossed seeds. However, at present, I think we must admit that the avoidance of selfing has played some role (perhaps a very important role) in selection for dioecy.

Bawa (1980) and Freeman et al. (1980b) have reviewed the ecology of dioecy in angiosperms. Dioecy (morphological definition in Table 16.1) is rare overall (<5%) but is commonly associated with a few particular conditions. For example, it is much more common among large woody plants (20–30%—Table 17.1). Dioecy is also more common on certain islands (New Zealand 12%, Hawaii 28%—Bawa, 1980, for references).

Bawa (1980) also notes that, at least in the tropics, there is a strong correlation between dioecy and certain modes of pollination and seed dispersal. Almost all animal-pollinated, dioecious species use insects, and most of these are pollinated by small, opportunistic bees (Table 17.2). In contrast to this, in the temperate zones dioecy is often associated with wind pollination (Freeman et al., 1980b). Bawa (1980) further notes that tropical forest dioecy shows a strong correlation with mode of fruit dispersal. As summarized in Table 17.3, it is most often associated with animal

TABLE 17.1. Frequency of dioecious species in different life forms of angiosperms (from Bawa, 1980; see for original references).

| Life form | Dioecious species (%) | | | | |
	North Carolina	Barro Colorado Island	California†	U.K.*	Hawaii/Malayan Rain Forest/ Costa Rica**
Trees	12	21	20–33	20–30	~25
Shrubs	14	11	0–23		
Vines	16	11	—		
Herbs	1	2	4–9		

*From Baker (1959).
**References in Freeman, Harper, and Ostler (1980).
†Freeman et al. (1980b), in a much more detailed classification (for California), show a very similar pattern.

TABLE 17.2. Correlation between dioecy and pollination systems in a dry forest in Costa Rica (from Bawa, 1980; see for details of classification of pollination systems).

Pollination systems	Percentage of tree species	
	Hermaphroditic/ Monoecious (N = 94)	Dioecious (N = 28)
Medium-large bee*	25	1
Small bee or opportunistic**	26	80
Beetle	14	3
Fly	1	2
Wasp	3	2
Moth	19	9
Butterfly	1	0
Hummingbird	3	0
Bat	8	0
Wind	0	3

*Mostly Anthophoridae, some Xylocopids.
**Mostly Halictidae, Megachilidae and/or Meliponini (Apidae).

dispersal. He states, "In dioecious tropical trees and shrubs, the fruits are single or few-seeded; in the vast majority of species the seeds are dispersed by birds." He proposes the idea that animal dispersal here means a disproportionate increase in female fitness with resources shifted into seeds (further discussion below). In addition, he cites an unpublished idea of Beach's (see also Beach, 1981) that a large male flower display could well result in large fitness increases through pollen donation (bowed upward male gain curve). Beach (1981) and Bawa and Beach (1981) have discussed in much detail the notion that the pollination system might play a large role in the evolution of sexual type (as proposed in Charnov, 1979c). If they are correct, this would seem to discount the role of selfing (and its avoidance), as models with substantial selfing rates discount the value of pollen donation, since fewer ovules are free for pollen competition (Chapter Fourteen).

TABLE 17.3. Correlation between breeding systems and modes of dispersal for angiosperms (from Bawa, 1980).

| Locality/taxonomic group | Breeding system | Number of Species* | | |
		Animal dispersed	Wind dispersed	χ^2
1. Tropical lowland dry deciduous forest	Dioecious	30	3	5.8†
(Palo Verde, Costa Rica)	Hermaphroditic and monoecious	60	26	
2. Tropical lowland wet evergreen forest	Dioecious	66	0	8.4†
(La Selva, Costa Rica)**	Hermaphroditic and monoecious	222	29	
3. Meliaceae	Dioecious	16	0	13.5†
	Hermaphroditic and monoecious	9	12	

*For Meliaceae read number of genera. Also, in Meliaceae, genera containing both dioecious and hermaphroditic and/or monoecious species are excluded from the analysis, but the number of such genera is only 12.
**Tentative figures for dioecious species, the number of which may increase; however, all the wind-dispersed species are known to be hermaphroditic and/or monoecious.
†Prob. <0.05.

Although all gymnosperms are wind pollinated there are two modes of seed dispersal. One is the presence of wooden or leathery cones which have wind- or gravity-dispersed seeds. The other is the presence of animal-dispersed fruits. Givnish (1980) has shown an almost perfect correlation between dispersal mode and dioecy versus monoecy (Table 17.4). Almost all cone-bearing species are monoecious, and animal-dispersed species are dioecious. He notes that this correlation is partly taxonomic, with most families having only one form. This correlation with taxonomy makes his use of a chi-square analysis suspect, as we have no idea of the sample size for the statistical test. However, the pattern seems real and important enough to justify a closer look. Further, the family Cupressaceae contains species with either winged seeds or wing-

TABLE 17.4. Correlation between breeding system and dispersal syndrome in gymnosperms (data from Givnish, 1980).

Number of species that are:	Monoecious	Dioecious
Wind dispersed	339	18
Animal dispersed	45	402

less seeds (presumably animal dispersed), and the correlation also holds here. Givnish's suggestion as to why the correlation exists is twofold (and identical to Bawa's): (1) wind pollination makes the male gain curve fairly linear—it is not strongly saturating; (2) animal dispersal means that a larger seed crop attracts a disproportionate number of animals and results in a bowed upward female gain curve. In the absence of these dispersal agents (i.e., wind-dispersed seeds) there is much sib competition for space/ light and the female gain curve saturates, favoring hermaphroditism (here monoecy).

These suppositions can be tested experimentally. For example, each tree must operate as a separate dispersal unit in (2). If the trees do not act as independent dispersal units, the female gain curve may not be bowed upward. If an unusually large seed crop results in relatively more dispersal, there is still one potential problem with the hypothesis. Seed crop size may increase with the shunting of resource from male to female function, but it will also increase with tree size itself. This could well mean that larger (older?) trees are relatively better at being female, and could select for a form of sequential hermaphroditism rather than dioecy. While not developed in detail here (but see barnacle discussion) age- or size-structured models for hermaphroditism open up all sorts of possibilities for degrees of sex reversal within simultaneous hermaphroditism.

I have discussed these ecological patterns because they (plus the dioecy-incompatibility systems correlation) are the data which theory must explain. While the avoidance of selfing is strongly implicated, the patterns seem less easily explained by this alone. Maybe both factors are deeply involved and the question reduces to "how much of each?" Surely the dispersal and pollination mechanisms will have implications for the avoidance of selfing, as well as influencing the chances to play male/female roles. For instance, being large and woody may make it difficult to get pollen carried away (Maynard Smith, 1978). The correlation of dioecy with dispersal may follow because long-distance dispersal *allows* dioecy to be used as an outbreeding mechanism. If selfing is selected against, then it seems likely that mating between siblings would also be disadvantageous. Self-incompatibility alleles may also function well to stop matings between close relatives (e.g., sibs; Lewis, 1979, proposed this as an important role for them). If dispersal is close to the parent plant, dioecy will not stop sibs from mating. However, long-distance dispersal will stop sibling mating, and may allow dioecy to be used as an outcrossing device.

I think that the ecological correlations compel us to look closely at dioecy, in both its aspects: outcrossing and sexual specialization (including sex choice). And this includes alternative hypotheses for the systematic distribution of dioecy (e.g., is selfing in those groups of the right form—that is, difficult to avoid). The current meshing of work on inbreeding and its avoidance (or regulation) with sex allocation ideas holds promise for a much more comprehensive understanding of the selective forces involved in plant reproduction and breeding systems.*

---

*Several recent papers by Bawa, Givnish, Lloyd, Willson, and Cox in *The American Naturalist* (1982) explore some of the dioecy vs. hermaphroditism issues raised here, as well as other questions about plant dioecy.

CONCLUSION:

Thoughts for the Future

In the last sixteen chapters, I have reviewed the beginnings of a theory of sex allocation—a natural selection perspective on the biological question of the allocation of resources (time and energy) to male versus female reproductive function. Blending together population genetics, physiology, and ecology has produced a theory which has withstood its first encounters with nature fairly well. The generality of the theory is suggested by the oft-encountered Shaw-Mohler equation, or its corollary, the product theorem. While I find these results encouraging, they are probably best considered to be just a beginning. This last chapter is neither a conclusion nor a summing up. Rather, it briefly discusses eight areas or problems which I think are of particular importance.

(1) *Relativity Principle.* In many places in the previous chapters, situations were discussed where particular individuals (or individuals in particular circumstances) were selected to alter their sex allocation. To list a few examples: (i) *small* hermaphroditic barnacles, in the midst of larger ones, were predicted to be more male; (ii) parasitoid wasps ovipositing in *small* hosts should produce mostly sons; (iii) plants in a *dry* patch should be more male; (iv) *smaller* individuals in a protandrous shrimp population are males; (v) female mammals in *good* physiological condition should produce mostly daughters; (vi) *older* mothers should overproduce the sex which imposes the higher parental mortality; (vii) for iteroparous species, a season of *exceptional* mortality on young males should be followed by overproduction of sons.

Of course, all of the above statements follow only for particular life histories, as developed in the previous chapters. However, for present purposes I note that each statement is about sex allocation altering in response to a variable (in italics in the list), where that

284

variable has *no absolute meaning,* and can only be measured in a relative sense. If theory predicts that older or bigger mothers should produce sons, what is older or bigger depends upon the age/size distribution of mothers, and many change from place to place (or time to time). The *relativity principle* for sex allocation is useful as a device for testing, for example, that a sex ratio shift is an adaptation, rather than (say) a mere physiological effect. If, for example, a certain maternal nutritional level is shown to affect sex ratio, then the same level may lead to different sex ratios in populations with different average nutritional levels. Here the comparison holds physiology constant but alters the predicted sex ratio response to the specified physiology. If the sex ratio shift is seen, it seems difficult to argue for a mere physiological constraint.

(2) *Facultative Sexuality.* In all of the above cases, theory says that the direction of shift of resources is toward that sex function which shows relatively larger reproductive gains (Charnov and Bull, 1977). For example, in terms of sex ratio, if both the sons and the daughters of a female (of a certain type) turn out to be below average in reproductive potential, the sex ratio should shift toward the sex which suffers the least, compared to the average member of its sex.

(3) *Spatially Structured Models.* Both local mate competition and local resource competition are models which involve explicit consideration of spatial movement on the part of individuals. They are very simple models. The population genetics of spatial models is often very difficult. LMC theory allows local mating but then has the inseminated daughters randomly dispersed into new groups. While Hamilton (1979), and Bulmer and Taylor (1980a,b) have considered situations where the daughters (or seeds in a hermaphrodite) are less than randomly dispersed (i.e., kin may associate), we really know very little about sex allocation evolution here. Our intuition (Clark, 1978), and some preliminary calculations (Bulmer and Taylor, 1980a,b) suggest that the ratio should be skewed toward the sex which "traveled further" (i.e., suffered less sibling competition). However, it must be

285

admitted that there has been little formal work on the problem. Much more is needed before we can look for critical acceptance of these tentative generalizations.

(4) *Control of Sex Allocation.* Control here implies both the form of inheritance, and the proximate mechanisms. Various genetical elements (cytoplasmic particles, sex chromosomes, autosomes) often disagree over the equilibrium allocation. In addition, participants in social interaction may likewise disagree. This latter is particularly true for the haplodiploid, eusocial insects. In building an evolutionary model and solving for an ESS, one either assumes a perspective (e.g., autosomal control, queen control) or explicitly models the interaction. Interaction models (e.g., queen versus worker) can be very complicated, and as yet we have little biological guidance for what to put into the models. On the other hand, where one can argue for a particular perspective, such as autosomal control, the ESS's are often rather simple. The autosomal perspective (or equivalent assumption for haplodiploidy) underlies much of this book. Without losing sight of possible complications, this assumption appears to be the only generally defensible one at present.

In the realm of proximate mechanisms for sex ratio, it seems clear that haplodiploidy provides an easy means for short-term alteration, while sex chromosomes greatly limit short-term options. A mammal might practice sex-specific abortion or infanticide, but these mechanisms impose added costs on the alteration of sex allocation over a short time scale. Here, the response selected for must include the gains and losses imposed by the control mechanisms itself. At present we have little knowledge of such costs and benefits, so they are difficult to include in the theory. In addition to these costs and benefits, information, in the sense of the appropriate response to an environmental challenge, appears in many theoretical predictions. If a female deer knows that young males have suffered extraordinary mortality, then she should overproduce sons for a while. In the absence of the information, the ESS sex ratio is equality, even though the mortality event happened. In the host size model for wasp sex ratio, the ESS would be equality in all hosts if the wasp could not measure host size, so that in the model a single sex ratio was used in all hosts. The information available to a participant plays an important role in the response to be favored. It would be very interesting to construct selection models for the control processes themselves. Bull (1983) reviews selection theory applied to the mechanisms of sex determination under dioecy.

(5) *Role of History in the Evolution of Sex Allocation.* With the exception of two brief discussions under hermaphroditism, this book allowed no real role for history in the theory. I raise the issue of the role of history and historical constraints in the evolution of sex allocation, but cannot provide any particular insight. Probably a key question is the ease with which sex type may be altered. "Ease" is used here in the sense of the development and inheritance of sex expression. How difficult is it to change a hermaphrodite into a male? Or to change from sex determination by chromosomes to environmental sex determination? This second question is discussed in Bull (1982, 1983). If linkage constraints within the genome (Charlesworth and Charlesworth, 1978a), or embryogenic (developmental) constraints are difficult to meet, then history may be very important. If sex expression is often as easy to alter as the genetic evidence indicates for cucumbers (and relatives), then history may play a minor role.

One hypothesis about the role of constraints on the alteration of sex type was discussed in Chapters 9 and 15. There it was suggested that the transition from hermaphroditism to dioecy may often be much easier (at least in animals) than the reverse. From this it follows that hermaphroditic (simultaneous or sequential) species should often be found to support sex allocation predictions, while some dioecious species may well show characters which would indicate that hermaphroditism would be favored. That is, constraints to the alteration of sex type should show up in errors associated with dioecy, but not hermaphroditism.

(6) *Coevolution and Sex Allocation.* Beginning with the hypothesis that a convex fitness set favors hermaphroditism, we are immediately led to ask just what biological factors control the

287

shape of the fitness set. As particularly discussed for plants, pollination and fruit (seed) dispersal are often involved. But these factors involve other species, and lead to the idea that coevolved relations between species are probably very important in selection for or against various sex types. If food habits (planktivore versus bottom grazer) of reef fish greatly influence social structure, then the selective advantage of sex change is tied to the occupation of particular feeding niches. Then, interspecific competition for food may be important in sex types. These examples suggest that we might profitably consider multispecies evolutionary models where the variables of interest are the sex types. Indeed, there may exist community-level laws for frequency of sex types. Could it be that a certain kind of terrestrial community can contain only up to $X\%$ dioecious species among the plants? All other fitness sets are then constrained to be convex. If these speculations seem vague, it is because no one has yet looked for community-level patterns for sex types (but see Bawa, 1980 and Freeman et al., 1980b, for higher plants and dioecy).

(7) *Macroevolution and Sex Types.* Many questions of higher plant macroevolution are discussed in terms of the advantages of ovule protection, pollination efficiency (in the Cruden, 1977, sense), and seed size and dispersal. I know of no discussions of a role for male reproductive success. Perhaps if the availability of pollen does not generally limit seed set (Bateman's principle), then pollination relationships have commonly evolved with the major selective force being male fitness. Charnov (1979c) suggested several other aspects of plant macroevolution which might be reinterpreted in terms of male fitness, or mating differences between male and female function.

(8) *New Systems.* This book has discussed many data on sex allocation, both to test hypotheses and to suggest directions which might provide good future tests. It is clear that progress in the field depends upon choice of appropriate systems for study. To echo an infamous biologist, who shall remain nameless: "Given an arbitrarily chosen biological system, you can't measure anything of interest." This book has had little to say about some systems which

may be very useful. Algae, some of which are easily cultured (e.g., *Volvox*, which shows both hermaphroditism and dioecy), are not even mentioned. Mating types in yeast, fungi, and other micro-organisms are likewise omitted. The reason for such omissions is that I personally know very little about these creatures. It may well be that within the groups omitted will fall the ideal organism for testing and extending some of the basic ideas discussed here.

Population Genetics
of Sex Ratio

This appendix will derive sex ratio results in four models, illustrating some basic math techniques.

(1) Suppose we have an outcrossed, haplodiploid wasp with discrete generations. The population is homozygous at a locus of interest (AA, A), which controls the production of sons and daughters by a female. Each AA female produces m sons and f daughters, the offspring counted at adulthood. We introduce into this population a mutant (a), where its female bearers rear some other combination of sons and daughters (say, $\hat{m}, \hat{f}$). While the a gene is rare, we need only consider the dynamics of the heterozygote females (Aa) and a males to know if the gene is being selected for or against. Let the frequencies of a among the adult males be ϵ_1 and Aa among the adult females be ϵ_2. While both are rare, they each mate effectively only with the more common homozygote (i.e., $Aa \times A$, $a \times AA$). The following are the mating types and their offspring production.

Mating type	Frequency of mating	Offspring production
(1) $AA \times A$	$(1 - \epsilon_1)(1 - \epsilon_2) \sim 1$	m, f all are a, aa
(2) $Aa \times A$	$(1 - \epsilon_1) \epsilon_2 \sim \epsilon_2$	$\hat{m}/2\, Aa, \hat{f}/2\, a$
(3) $AA \times a$	$(1 - \epsilon_2) \epsilon_1 \sim \epsilon_1$	$f\, Aa$

I have ignored the AA, A contributed via $Aa \times A$ or $AA \times a$ matings—they will be very few compared to those produced via $AA \times A$ matings.

The frequency of Aa among the adults in one generation is ϵ_2'

and is given by

$$\epsilon_2' \sim \frac{\#Aa}{\#AA} \sim \epsilon_1 + \frac{\hat{f}}{2f} \cdot \epsilon_2. \tag{A1}$$

Likewise, the frequency of a in one generation (ϵ_1') is

$$\epsilon_1' \sim \frac{\#a}{\#A} \sim \frac{\hat{m}}{2m} \cdot \epsilon_2. \tag{A2}$$

Writing these in the form of matrix multiplication,

$$\begin{pmatrix} 0 & \dfrac{\hat{m}}{2m} \\[2ex] 1 & \dfrac{\hat{f}}{2f} \end{pmatrix} \begin{pmatrix} \epsilon_1 \\[1ex] \epsilon_2 \end{pmatrix} \sim \begin{pmatrix} \epsilon_1' \\[1ex] \epsilon_2' \end{pmatrix}. \tag{A3}$$

The characteristic equation of (A3) is

$$\lambda^2 - \frac{\lambda \hat{f}}{2f} - \frac{\hat{m}}{2m} = 0. \tag{A4}$$

The λ of interest is the dominant eigenvalue (which will be positive and real) of A4. If $\lambda > 1$, the a allele is being selected for; if $\lambda < 1$ it is being selected against. $\lambda < 1$ provided

$$\frac{\hat{m}}{m} + \frac{\hat{f}}{f} < 2, \tag{A5}$$

which of course is the Shaw-Mohler equation.

A similar argument for a diploid produces a characteristic equation of the form

$$\lambda^2 - \lambda \left(\frac{f + \hat{f}}{2f} \right) + \frac{1}{4} \left(\frac{\hat{f}}{f} - \frac{\hat{m}}{m} \right) = 0. \tag{A6}$$

For $\lambda < 1$, (A6) also reduces to (A5).

(2) In this case, the population has overlapping generations. A single offspring is born each year and begins reproducing at age 1. Consider a population of outcrossed diploids, homozygous at a locus of interest (AA) which controls sex ratio. Suppose further that the yearly survivorship of a mother depends upon whether

she rears a son or a daughter. Define:

$n(T) = ♀\ AA$ at time T

$n^*(T) = ♂\ AA$ at time T

P_m = yearly survivorship for adult $♂$

S_m = survival of a newborn $♂$ to age 1

S_f = survival of a newborn $♀$ to age 1

P_1 = mom's yearly survival if she has a son that year

P_2 = mom's yearly survival if she has a daughter that year

$r = ♂$ proportion of newborns

It follows that:

$$n(T + 1) = n(T)[r \cdot P_1 + (1 - r)P_2 + (1 - r)\,S_f],$$

$$n^*(T + 1) = n^*(T) \cdot P_m + n(T) \cdot r \cdot S_m. \tag{A7}$$

Such a population will have a yearly rate of increase (λ_1) of

$$\lambda_1 = r \cdot P_1 + (1 - r)(P_2 + S_f). \tag{A8}$$

If we introduce into this population a mutant, dominant allele (a) which alters its life history paramters to $(\hat{r}, \hat{S}_m, \hat{S}_f, \hat{P}_1, \hat{P}_2)$, the mutant is selected only if its yearly rate of increase (λ) is $>\lambda_1$. While the mutant is rare, we need only consider the dynamics of the heterozygote ($Aa\ ♂,\ Aa\ ♀$). While rare they mate only with the common homozygote, and half the offspring are Aa. Let $\hat{n}(T) = Aa\ ♀$ at time T; $\hat{n}^*(T) = Aa\ ♂$ at time T. We then have

$$\hat{n}(T + 1) \sim \hat{n}(T)[\hat{r} \cdot \hat{P}_1 + (1 - \hat{r})\hat{P}_2 + (1 - \hat{r})\,\hat{S}_f/2]$$
$$+ \phi \cdot n(T)(1 - r)\,S_f/2. \tag{A9}$$

The second term is the Aa born to homozygote mothers (AA)—ϕ is the fraction of all $AA\ ♀$ who mate with $Aa\ ♂$. This will be $\sim \hat{n}^*(T)/n^*(T)$. Thus the second term may be written as

$$\left(\frac{n(T)}{n^*(T)}\right)\left(\frac{\hat{n}^*(T)(1 - r)}{2}\,S_f\right). \tag{A10}$$

The first term in this expression is a *time independent constant* if the AA population is in stable age distribution. If in (A7) we set $n^*(T + 1) = \lambda_1 \cdot n^*\,(T)$, we get

292

$$\lambda_1 \cdot n^*(T) = n^*(T) \cdot P_m + n(T) \cdot r \cdot S_m.$$

Dividing through by $n^*(T)$ and setting $n(T)/n^*(T) = \overline{R}$, we get

$$\overline{R} = \frac{\lambda_1 - P_m}{r \cdot S_m},$$

which may be substituted into (A10). If we repeat the argument for males ($\hat{n}^*[T + 1]$), we may write the two equations as

$$\hat{n}(T + 1) \sim \hat{n}(T)[\hat{r} \cdot \hat{P}_1 + (1 - \hat{r})(P_2 + S_f/2)]$$
$$+ \hat{n}^*(T)[\overline{R} \cdot (1 - r) S_f/2],$$

$$\hat{n}^*(T + 1) \sim \hat{n}(T)(\hat{r} \cdot \hat{S}_m/2)$$
$$+ \hat{n}^*(T)(P_m + \overline{R} \cdot r \cdot S_m/2), \quad \text{(A11)}$$

or

$$\begin{pmatrix} \hat{r} \cdot \hat{P}_1 + (1 - \hat{r})(\hat{P}_2 + \hat{S}_f/2) & \overline{R}(1 - r) S_f/2 \\ \hat{r} \cdot \hat{S}_m/2 & P_m + \overline{R} \cdot r \cdot S_m/2 \end{pmatrix} \begin{pmatrix} \hat{n}(T) \\ \hat{n}^*(T) \end{pmatrix} \sim$$
$$\begin{pmatrix} \hat{n}(T + 1) \\ \hat{n}^*(T + 1) \end{pmatrix}. \quad \text{(A12)}$$

The characteristic equation of (A12) is

$$\lambda^2 - \lambda (a_{11} + a_{22}) + a_{11} \cdot a_{22} - a_{12} \cdot a_{21} = 0, \quad \text{(A13)}$$

where a_{ij} refers to row i and column j.

If the "$\sim$" variables are set equal to their respective population (homozygote) values (i.e., drop the $\sim$), $\lambda = \lambda_1$ since the mutant is indistinguishable from the homozygote. Thus, for some set of population values to be an equilibrium, it must be that $\lambda < \lambda_1$ for all "$\sim$" variables *not* equal to the population values. For "$\sim$" variables near the population values, this is the requirement that, considering a mutant who affects only the sex ratio (for example),

$$\frac{\partial \lambda}{\partial \hat{r}} = 0 \text{ when } \lambda = \lambda_1, \hat{r} = r.$$

This reduces to (from A13)

$$-\lambda \cdot \left[\frac{\partial(a_{11} + a_{22})}{\partial \hat{r}}\right] + \frac{\partial(a_{11}a_{22})}{\partial \hat{r}} - \frac{\partial(a_{12}a_{21})}{\partial \hat{r}} = 0 \quad \text{(A14)}$$

when $\lambda = \lambda_1$, $\hat{r} = r$.

After much algebra we get the ESS r^*:

$$r^* = \frac{1}{2}\left(\frac{S_f}{S_f + P_2 - P_1}\right). \quad \text{(A15)}$$

If we assume tradeoffs between the survival of the mother and the offspring (e.g., S_f is inversely related to P_2, and the same for the "$\sim$" variables), we can look at the equilibrium for r^*, S_f, and S_m all at once. The value of r^* is given by (A15), and S_f and S_m satisfy the following optimality principles:

(A16) Equilibrium (S_f, P_2) maximizes K_1 which is equal to

$$K_1 = P_2 + S_f/2;$$

(A17) Equilibrium (S_m, P_1) maximizes K_2 where

$$K_2 = S_m/(K_1 - P_1).$$

Of course, these results assume maternal control of the sex ratio and the investment in offspring. Vesting control in the offspring (or the father) will produce different answers, as parent and offspring (or mother and father) are in conflict (Trivers, 1974).

(3) This section will sketch a method for derivation of equilibrium sex ratios for spatially structured populations (as given in Taylor and Bulmer, 1980; Charnov, 1978). Consider a haplodiploid species homozygous at a locus of interest (AA, A) which controls sex ratio. Introduce into this population a recessive mutant, where its female bearers produce another sex ratio, $\hat{r}$ (i.e., AA-r, Aa-r, aa-$\hat{r}$). If each female mates once, there will be six family types (see next page). All except $AA \times A$ will be very rare.

Type	Sex ratio produced	Frequency
1. $AA \times A$	r	$1 - \epsilon_1 - \epsilon_2 - \epsilon_3 - \epsilon_4 - \epsilon_5 \sim 1$
2. $AA \times a$	r	ϵ_1
3. $Aa \times A$	r	ϵ_2
4. $Aa \times a$	r	ϵ_3
5. $aa \times A$	$\hat{r}$	ϵ_4
6. $aa \times a$	$\hat{r}$	ϵ_5

Now, suppose that these families (or mated females) associate into groups of size n at random. Suppose further that the females produce sons and daughters and that all mating is confined within the group. The newly fertilized females then disperse to form groups for the next generation. This is Hamilton's (1967, 1979) population structure, termed "local mate competition." Note that while the ϵ are very small, families which carry the mutant gene (a) will never associate in the same group—that is, $n - 1$ members of the group will be $AA \times A$ families and the nth member will be one of the mutant families (except for groups of all $AA \times A$). To calculate the fraction of these groups which contain a mutant, consider for a moment that there are only two family types with frequencies as follows.

$$AA \times A \quad 1 - \epsilon \quad (\epsilon \sim 0)$$

$$AA \times a \quad \epsilon$$

If we draw from an infinite population a sample of n families, the samples will contain $0, 1, 2, \ldots n$ $AA \times a$. The fraction of the groups with k $AA \times a$ is simply given by the binomial probability law:

$$\text{Prob.} (k) = \binom{n}{k} \epsilon^k (1 - \epsilon)^{n-k}, \quad k = 0, 1, 2, \ldots n.$$

Groups with more than one $AA \times a$ will occur with frequency of order ϵ^2 (or smaller) and are too rare to be counted. Thus families with 0 mutants will be of frequency

295

$$\text{Prob.}(0) = (1 - \epsilon)^n \sim 1 \qquad (\text{with } \epsilon \sim 0),$$

and those with one mutant,

$$\text{Prob. } (1) = n(1 - \epsilon)^{n-1}\epsilon \sim n\epsilon \qquad (\text{with } \epsilon \sim 0).$$

With five mutant families, the same argument goes through. Groups with no mutant ($n - AA \times A$) have frequency ~ 1 while groups with one mutant family (plus $AA \times A$) are present with frequency $n\epsilon_i$ ($i = 1, \ldots 5$). If we form these groups and look at the offspring production, letting the males produced compete for the females, it is clear that we can simply count up the family types (mated females) one generation hence.

As before ϵ' may be calculated as (say, for example) $\epsilon_1' \sim (AA \times a)/(AA \times A)$. Thus we get a set of five equations ($\epsilon_i' = ?$, $i = 1 \ldots 5$) which can be written as matrix multiplication, or

$$M\epsilon = \epsilon' \qquad (M = 5 \times 5 \text{ matrix}).$$

If the dominant eigenvalue of M (call it λ) is <1, the mutant gene is being selected against. λ will be in terms of r, $\hat{r}$, and n. As before, if $\hat{r} = r, \lambda = 1$; so an equilibrium requires that $\lambda < 1$ for all $\hat{r} \neq r$. For $\hat{r}$ near r, this means that $\partial\lambda/\partial\hat{r} = 0$ when $\hat{r} = r$. Some tedious algebra may be involved in getting an equation for λ (but see Taylor and Bulmer, 1980), but once obtained, it is straightforward to set $\partial\lambda/\partial\hat{r} = 0$ and $\hat{r} = r$ and then to solve for r^*. This process is aided if the mutant is recessive, since fewer terms will have an $\hat{r}$. Experience with other models of this type suggests that the equilibrium is the same as for dominant or partially dominant genes. Of course, once one has M, a computer may be used to find the equilibrium numerically. Hamilton (1979) discusses another method for finding the ESS.

(4) This section will develop a sex ratio model for worker control of sex ratio in eusocial hymenoptera. Assume a haplodiploid population homozygous (AA, A) at a locus controlling sex ratio. The queen is mated once and while she produces the male and female reproductives, the workers (her daughters) *control* the

production. Suppose that a typical AA worker rears m male reproductives and f female. Introduce into this population a mutant where its bearers (i.e., workers) rear some other female combination $(= \hat{m}, \hat{f})$. Let $\epsilon_1 =$ adult frequency of a among males; $\epsilon_2 =$ frequency of Aa among females. While the a gene is rare, there are effectively only three colony types.

Colony type	Frequency	Worker genotypes
(1) $AA \times a$	$(1 - \epsilon_1)(1 - \epsilon_2) \sim 1$	all AA
(2) $Aa \times a$	$(1 - \epsilon_1) \epsilon_2 \sim \epsilon_2$	½ Aa, ½ AA
(3) $AA \times A$	$(1 - \epsilon_2) \epsilon_1 \sim \epsilon_1$	all Aa

In the next generation there will be approximately the following adult types (let each colony have C workers):

$$\left. \begin{array}{l} Aa \sim Cf \\[2mm] A \sim Cm \end{array} \right\} \text{ all from } aa \times a \text{ colonies,}$$

$$Aa \sim \epsilon_1 C\hat{f} + C \epsilon_2 \left(\frac{f + \hat{f}}{4} \right),$$

$$a \sim \epsilon_2 C \left(\frac{m + \hat{m}}{4m} \right),$$

or letting ϵ_1' and ϵ_2' be the genotype frequencies in the next generation:

$$\epsilon_1' \sim \frac{\#Aa}{\#A} \sim \epsilon_2 \left(\frac{m + \hat{m}}{4m} \right),$$

$$\epsilon_2' \sim \frac{\#Aa}{\#AA} \sim \epsilon_1 \frac{\hat{f}}{f} + \epsilon_2 \left(\frac{f + \hat{f}}{4f} \right).$$

The characteristic equation of this set $(\epsilon_1', \epsilon_2')$ of equations is

$$\lambda^2 - \lambda \left(\frac{f + \hat{f}}{4f} \right) - \left(\frac{\hat{f}}{f} \right) \left(\frac{m + \hat{m}}{4m} \right) = 0.$$

Assume that m, f, (or $\hat{m}, \hat{f}$) are inversely related. To find the equilibrium m, f we impose the conditions that $\partial\lambda/\partial\hat{f} = 0$ when $\hat{m} = m, \hat{f} = f$. These conditions do not reduce to a Shaw-Mohler equation, yet the equilibrium can still be shown to maximize a male-female product. In this case the product is

$$\text{maximize } m \cdot f^3.$$

Note that the coefficient 3 indicates that female reproductives are in some way three times as valuable (to workers) as males. Intuitively this follows, since the workers are three times as related to their sisters as to their brothers (3/4 versus 1/4).

Similar population genetic methods have been used to derive ESS results under sex reversal, simultaneous hermaphroditism, and many other sex ratio situations (Charnov 1978, 1979a; Leigh, Charnov, and Warner 1976).

Literature Cited

Abramson, N. J. and P. K. Tomlinson. 1972. An application of yield models to a California ocean shrimp population. *Fish. Bull.* 70:1021–1041.

Akesson, B. 1973. Reproduction and larval morphology of five *Ophryotrocha* species (Polychaeta, Dorvilleidae). *Zool. Scripta* 2:145–155.

———. 1976. Morphology and life cycle of *Ophryotrocha diadema*, a new polychaete species from California. *Ophelia* 15:23–35.

———. 1977. Crossbreeding and geographic races: experiments with the polychaete genus *Ophryotrocha. Mikrofauna Meeresboden* 61:11–18.

Alexander, R. D. and P. W. Sherman. 1977. Local mate competition and parental investment in social insects. *Science* 196:494–500.

Alexander, R. D. and D. W. Tinkle, eds. 1981. *Natural Selection and Social Behavior.* Chiron Press, N.Y.

Allen, C. E. 1940. The genotypic basis of sex-expression in angiosperms. *Bot. Rev.* 6:227–300.

Allen, G. R. 1972. *Anemone Fishes.* T.F.H. Publ., Neptune City, N.J.

Allen, J. A. 1959. On the biology of *Pandalus borealis* Kroyer, with reference to a population of the Northumberland coast. *J. Mar. Biol. Assn. U.K.* 38:189–220.

———. 1963. Observations on the biology of *Pandalus montagui* (Crustacea: Decapoda). *J. Mar. Biol. Assn. U.K.* 43:665–682.

Amano, H. and D. A. Chant. 1978. Some factors affecting reproduction and sex ratios in two species of predacious mites, *Phytoseiulus persimilis* and *Amblyseius andersoni* (Acarina: Phytoseiidae). *Can. J. Zool.* 56:1593–1607.

Anderson, F. S. 1961. Effect of density on animal sex ratio. *Oikos* 12:1–15.

Andrews, J. D. 1977. Pelecypoda: Ostreida. *In*: Giese, A. C. and J. S. Pearse (eds.), *Reproduction of Marine Invertebrates*, Vol. 5. Academic Press, N.Y., pp. 293–342.

Aoto, T. 1952. Sexual phases in the prawn, *Pandalus kessleri* (Czerniavski), with special reference to the reversal of sex. *J. Fac. Sci., Hokkaido Univ. Ser. VI, Zool.* 11:1–20.

Appolonio, S. and E. E. Dunton, Jr. 1969. The northern shrimp *Pandalus borealis,* in the Gulf of Main [Manuscript]. Available from: Department of Sea and Shore Fisheries, Augusta, Maine.

Arthur, A. P. and H. G. Wylie. 1959. Effects of host size on the sex ratio, development time and size of *Pimpla turionellae* (Hymenoptera: Ichneumonidae). *Entomophaga* 4:297–301.

Assem, J. van den. 1970. Courtship and mating in *Lariophagus distinguendus. Neth. J. Zool.* 20:329–352.

———. 1971. Some experiments on sex ratio and sex regulation in the Pteromalid *Lariophagus distinguendus. Neth. J. Zool.* 21:373–402.

———. 1979. Grote vrouwen, kleine mannetjes: een zaak van belegging en rendement. *In:* H. Klomp and J. Wiebes (eds.), *Sluipwespen in relatie tot hun gastheren.* Pudoc, Wageningen, pp. 64–96.

Atz, J. W. 1964. Intersexuality in fishes. *In:* Armstrong, C. N. and A. J. Marshall (eds.), *Intersexuality in Vertebrates Including Man.* Academic Press, N.Y., pp. 145–232.

———. 1965. Hermaphroditic fish. *Science* 150:789–796.

Bacci, G. 1952. Diverso comportamento sessuale delle *Ophryotrocha puerilis* di Napoli e di Plymouth. *Boll. Soc. It. Biol. Sper.* 28:1293.

———. 1955. Controllo genetico della inversione sessuale in individui isolati di *Ophryotrocha. Caryologia* (Suppl.):966–968.

———. 1965. *Sex Determination.* Pergamon, Elmsford, N.Y.

———. 1978. Genetics of sex determination in *Ophryotrocha*

(Annelida, Polychaeta). *In:* Battaglia, B. and J. Beardmore (eds.), *Marine Organisms.* Plenum Press, N.Y.

Bacci, G. and O. Bortesi. 1961. Pure males and females from hermaphroditic strains of *Ophryotrocha puerilis. Experientia* 17:229.

Bacci, G. and M. LaGreca. 1953. Genetic and morphological evidence for subspecific differences between Naples and Plymouth populations of *Ophryotrocha puerilis. Nature* 171:1115.

Bahadur, Bir. 1970a. Heterostyly in *Hedyotis nigricans* (Lam.) Fosb. *J. Genetics* 60:175–177.

_____.1970b. Homostyly and heterostyly in *Oldenlandia umbellata* L. *J. Genetics* 60:192–198.

Baker, H. G. 1959. Reproduction methods as factors in speciation in flowering plants. *Cold Spring Harbor Symp. Quant. Biol.* 24:177–191.

_____. 1966. The evolution, functioning and breakdown of heteromorphic incompatibility systems. *Evolution* 20:349–368.

_____. 1967. Support for Baker's Law—as a rule. *Evolution* 21:853–856.

Bakke, A. 1968. Field and laboratory studies on sex ratio in *Ips acuminatus* (Coleoptera: Scolytidae) in Norway. *Can. Ent.* 100:640–648.

Ballantine, W. J. 1961. The population dynamics of *Patella vulgata* and other limpets. Ph.D. Thesis, Queen Mary College, London University.

Barker, P., Freeman, D. C. and K. T. Harper. 1982. Sexual flexibility in *Acer grandidentatum. Forest Sci.* (in press).

Barnes, H. 1962. The composition of the seminal plasma of *Balanus balanus. J. Exp. Biol.* 39:345–351.

Barnes, H. and D. J. Crisp. 1956. Evidence for self-fertilization in certain species of barnacles. *J. Mar. Biol. Assn. U.K.* 35:631–639.

Barnes, H. and M. Barnes. 1968. Egg numbers, metabolic efficiency of egg production and fecundity: local and regional variations in a number of common cirripedes. *J. Exp. Mar. Biol. Ecol.* 2:135–153.

Barnes, H., Barnes, M. and W. Klepal. 1977. Studies on the reproduction of Cirripedes. I. Introduction: copulation, release of oocytes, and formation of the lamellae. *J. Exp. Mar. Biol. Ecol.* 27:195–218.

Bartels, J. M. and G. N. Lanier. 1974. Emergence and mating in *Scolytus multistriatus* (Coleoptera: Scolytidae). *Ann. Ent. Soc. Amer.* 67:365–369.

Bateman, A. J. 1948. Intra-sexual selection in *Drosophila. Heredity* 2:349–368.

Bawa, K. S. 1980. Evolution of dioecy in flowering plants. *Ann. Rev. Ecol. Syst.* 11:15–39.

Bawa, K. S. and P. A. Opler. 1975. Dioecism in tropical forest trees. *Evolution* 29:167–179.

Bawa, K. S. and J. H. Beach. 1981. Evolution of sexual systems in flowering plants. *Ann. Mo. Bot. Gard.* 68:259–275.

Beach, J. H. 1981. Pollinator foraging and the evolution of dioecy. *Amer. Natur.* 118:572–577.

Beach, J. H. and K. S. Bawa. 1980. Role of pollinators in the evolution of dioecy from distyly. *Evolution* 34:1138–1143.

Beard, B. H. 1981. The sunflower crop. *Scientific Amer.* 244:150–162.

Beard, R. L. 1964. Pathogenic stinging of housefly pupae by *Nasonia vitripennis* (Walker). *J. Insect Pathol.* 6:107.

Beatty, R. A., Lim, M.-C. and V. J. Coulter. 1975. A quantitative study of the second meiotic metaphase in male mice (*Mus musculus*). *Cyto. and Cell. Genet.* 15:256–275.

Beaver, R. A. 1977. Bark and Ambrosia beetles in tropical forests. *Proc. Symp. Forest Pests and Diseases in S.E. Asia. Biotropica special pub.* 2:133–147.

Bellrose, F. C., Scott, T. G., Hawkins, A. S. and J. B. Low. 1961. Sex ratios and age ratios in North American ducks. *Bull. Ill. Nat. Hist. Survey* 27.

Bengtsson, B.-O. 1977. Evolution of sex ratio in the wood lemming. *In:* F. B. Christiansen and T. M. Fenchel (eds.),

Measuring Selection in Natural Populations. Springer-Verlag, Berlin, pp. 333–343.

Bergard, J. 1972. Environmental and physiological control of sex determination and differentiation. *Ann. Rev. Ent.* 17:57–74.

Berkeley, A. A. 1930. The post-embryonic development of the common Pandalids of British Columbia. *Contrib. Canad. Biol.* 10:79–163.

Berry, P. A. 1939. Biology and habits of *Ephialtes turionellae*, a pupal parasite of the European pine shoot moth. *J. Econ. Ent.* 32:717–721.

Beverton, R. J. H. 1963. Maturation, growth and mortality of clupeid and engraulid stocks in relation to fishing. *Rapp. P.-V. Reun., Cons. Int. Explor. Mer.* 154:44–67.

Beverton, R. J. H. and S. J. Holt. 1957. On the dynamics of exploited fish populations. *Fish. Invest. Ser. II. Mar. Fish. G. B., Minist. Agric. Fish. Food* 19.

———. 1959. A review of the lifespan and mortality rates of fish in nature, and their relation to growth and other physiological characteristics. *Ciba Found. Colloq. Aging* 5:142–77.

Bierzychudek, P. 1981a. Pollinator limitation of plant reproductive effort. *Amer. Natur.* 117:838–840.

———. 1981b. The demography of jack-in-the-pulpit, a forest perennial that changes sex. Ph.D. Diss., Cornell University, Ithaca, N.Y.

Blackmore, D. T. 1969. Studies of *Patella vulgata*. I. Growth, reproduction and zonal distribution. *J. Exp. Mar. Biol. Ecol.* 3:200–213.

Bodmer, W. F. 1960. The genetics of homostyly in populations of *Primula vulgans. Phil. Trans. Roy. Soc. London (B)* 242:517–549.

Bodmer, W. F. and A. W. F. Edwards. 1960. Natural selection and the sex ratio. *Ann. Hum. Genet.* 24:239–244.

Bouletreau, M. 1976. Effect of photoperiod experienced by the adults on the sex ratio of the progeny in *Pteromalus puparum* (Hymenoptera: Chalcididae). *Ent. Exp. Appl.* 19:197–204.

Branch, G. M. 1971. The ecology of *Patella* Linnaeus from the

Cape Peninsula, South Africa. I. Zonation, movements and feeding. *Zool. Afr.* 6:1–38.

_____. 1974a. The ecology of *Patella* Linnaeus from the Cape Peninsula, South Africa. II. Reproductive cycles. *Trans. Roy. Soc. S. Afr.* 41:111–160.

_____. 1974b. The ecology of *Patella* Linnaeus from the Cape Peninsula, South Africa. III. Growth rates. *Trans. Roy. Soc. S. Afr.* 41:161–193.

_____. 1975a. Notes on the ecology of *Patella concolor* and *Cellana capensis,* and the effects of human consumption on limpet populations. *Zool. Afr.* 10:75–85.

_____. 1975b. Intraspecific competition in *Patella cochlear* Born. *J. Anim. Ecol.* 44:263–282.

_____. 1975c. Mechanisms reducing competition in limpets: migration, differentiation and territorial behaviour. *J. Anim. Ecol.* 44:575–600.

_____. 1975d. Ecology of *Patella* from the Cape Peninsula, South Africa. IV. Desiccation. *Mar. Biol.* 32:179–188.

_____. 1976. Interspecific competition experienced by South African *Patella* species. *J. Anim. Ecol.* 45:507–529.

Bridgeman, M. R. and B. R. Kerry. 1980. The sex ratios of cyst-nematodes produced by adding single second-stage juveniles to host roots. *Nematologica* 26:209–213.

Brown, K. M. 1981. The evolution of breeding systems in monoecious fresh water snails. In manuscript.

Brunson, M. H. 1934. The fluctuation of the population of *Tiphia popilliavora* (Rohwer) in the field and its possible causes. *J. Econ. Ent.* 27:514–518.

_____. 1937. The influence of the instars of host larvae on the sex of progeny of *Tiphia popilliavora. Science* 86:197.

_____. 1939. Influence of Japanese beetle instar on the sex and population of the parasite *Tiphia popilliavora. J. Agric. Res.* 57:379–386.

Buckman, N. S. and J. C. Ogden. 1973. Territorial behavior of the striped parrotfish *Scarus croicensis* Block (Scaridae). *Ecology* 54:1377–1382.

Bull, J. J. 1979. An advantage for the evolution of male haploidy and systems with similar genetic transmission. *Heredity* 43:361–381.

_____. 1980. Sex determination in reptiles. *Quart. Rev. Biol.* 55:3–21.

_____. 1981a. Sex ratio evolution when fitness varies. *Heredity* 46:9–26.

_____. 1981b. Evolution of environmental sex determination from genotypic sex determination. *Heredity* 47:173–184.

_____. 1983. *The Evolution of Sex Chromosomes and Sex Determination.* Book in preparation.

Bull, J. J. and E. L. Charnov. 1977. Changes in the heterogametic mechanism of sex determination. *Heredity* 39:1–14.

Bull, J. J. and R. C. Vogt. 1979. Temperature-dependent sex determination in reptiles. *Science* 206:1186–1188.

_____. 1981. Temperature-sensitive periods of sex determination in emydid turtles. *J. Exp. Zool.* 218:435–440.

Bull, J. J. and M. G. Bulmer. 1981. The evolution of XY females in mammals. *Heredity* 47:347–365.

Bull, J. J., Vogt, R. C. and C. J. McCoy. 1982a. Sex determining temperatures in turtles: a geographic comparison. *Evolution* 36:326–332.

Bull, J. J., Vogt, R. C. and M. G. Bulmer. 1982b. Heritability of sex ratio in turtles with environmental sex determination. *Evolution* 36:333–341.

Bulmer, M. G. and P. D. Taylor. 1980a. Sex ratio under the haystack model. *J. Theor. Biol.* 86:83–89.

_____. 1980b. Dispersal and the sex ratio. *Nature* 284:448–449.

Bulmer, M. G. and J. J. Bull. 1982. Models of polygenic sex determination and sex ratio evolution. *Evolution* 36:13–26.

Butler, T. H. 1964. Growth, reproduction, and distribution of pandalid shrimps in British Columbia. *J. Fish. Res. Board. Can.* 21(6):1403–1452.

Canham, R. P. 1970. Sex ratios and survival in fluctuating populations of the deer mouse, *Peromyscus maniculatus borealis. Can. J. Zool.* 48:809–811.

Carothers, A. D. 1980. Population dynamics and the evolution of sex-determination in lemmings. *Genet. Res.* 36:199–209.

Carpenter, A. 1978. Protandry in the freshwater shrimp, *Paratya curvirostris* (Heller, 1862) (Decapoda:Atyidae), with a review of the phenomenon and its significance in the Decapoda. *J. Roy. Soc. New Zealand* 3:343–358.

Casida, L. E. 1971. Observations on the symposium and panel discussion. *In:* Kiddy, C. A. and Hafs, H. D. (eds.), *Sex ratio at birth—prospects for control.* Symp. pub. by Amer. Soc. Anim. Science, pp. 98–104.

Cassidy, J. D. 1975. The parasitoid wasps. *Habrobracon* and *Mormoniella. In:* R. C. King (ed.), *Handbook of Genetics,* Vol. 3. Plenum Press. pp. 173–203.

Casper, B. B. and E. L. Charnov. 1982. Sex allocation in heterostylous plants. *J. Theor. Biol.* 96:143–149.

Chabora, P. C. and D. Pimentel. 1966. Effect of host (*Musca domestica* L.) age on the Pteromalid parasite (*Nasonia vitripennis* Walker). *Can. Ent.* 98:1226–1231.

Chailakhyan, M. Kh. 1979. Genetic and hormonal regulation of growth, flowering, and sex expression in plants. *Am. J. Bot.* 66:717–736.

Chan. S. T. H. 1970. Natural sex reversal in vertebrates. *Phil. Trans. Roy. Soc. London (B),* 259:59–71.

Chan, S. T. H., Wai-sum, O. and W. D. Hui. 1975. The gonadal and adenohypophysial functions on natural sex reversal. *In:* Reinboth, R. (ed.), *Intersexuality in the Animal Kingdom.* Springer-Verlag, Berlin, pp. 201–221.

Chanter, D. O. and D. F. Owen. 1972. The inheritance and population genetics of sex ratio in the butterfly *Acraea encedon. J. Zool. Lond.* 166:363–383.

Charlesworth, B. 1977. Population genetics, demography and the sex ratio. *In:* F. B. Christiansen and T. M. Fenchel (eds.), *Measuring Selection in Natural Populations.* Springer-Verlag, Berlin, pp. 345–363.

———. 1978. Model for evolution of Y chromosomes and dosage compensation. *Proc. Natl. Acad. Sci.* 75:5618–5622.

Charlesworth, B. and D. Charlesworth. 1978a. A model for the evolution of dioecy and gynodioecy. *Amer. Natur.* 112:975–997.

Charlesworth, D. and B. Charlesworth. 1978b. Population genetics of partial male-sterility and the evolution of monoecy and dioecy. *Heredity* 41:137–153.

Charlesworth, D. and B. Charlesworth. 1979a. A model for the evolution of distyly. *Amer. Natur.* 114:467–498.

Charlesworth, B. and D. Charlesworth. 1979b. The maintenance and breakdown of distyly. *Amer. Natur.* 114:499–513.

Charlesworth, D. and B. Charlesworth. 1979c. The evolutionary genetics of sexual systems in flowering plants. *Proc. Roy. Soc. London (B)* 205:513–530.

Charlesworth, D. and B. Charlesworth. 1981. Allocation of resources to male and female functions in hermaphrodites. *Biol. J. Linn. Soc.* 14:57–74.

Charniaux-Cotton, H. 1960. Sex determination. *In:* Waterman, T. H. (ed.), *The Physiology of Crustacea.* Vol. 1. Academic Press, N.Y., pp. 411–447.

Charnov, E. L. 1975. Sex ratio selection in an age structured population. *Evolution* 29:366–368.

_____. 1978. Sex ratio selection in eusocial hymenoptera. *Amer. Natur.* 112:317–326.

_____. 1979a. The genetical evolution of patterns of sexuality: Darwinian fitness. *Amer. Natur.* 113:465–480.

_____. 1979b. Natural selection and sex change in Pandalid shrimp: test of a life history theory. *Amer. Natur.* 113:715–734.

_____. 1979c. Simultaneous hermaphroditism and sexual selection. *Proc. Natl. Acad. Sci.* 76:2480–2484.

_____. 1980. Sex allocation and local mate competition in barnacles. *Mar. Biol. Letters* 1:269–272.

_____. 1981. Sex reversal in *Pandalus borealis:* effect of a shrimp fishery? *Mar. Biol. Letters* 2:53–57.

_____. 1983. Alternative life-histories in protogynous fish: A general ESS theory (submitted to *Marine Biology*).

Charnov, E. L. and J. J. Bull. 1977. When is sex environmentally determined? *Nature* 266:828–830.

Charnov, E. L., J. Maynard Smith and J. Bull. 1976. Why be an hermaphrodite? *Nature* 263:125–126.

Charnov, E. L., Gotshall, D. and J. Robinson. 1978. Sex ratio: adaptive response to population fluctuations in Pandalid shrimp. *Science* 200:204–206.

Charnov, E. L., Los-den Hartogh, R. L., Jones, W. T. and J. van den Assem. 1981. Sex ratio evolution in a variable environment. *Nature* 289:27–33.

Chen, C. P., Hsieh, H. L. and K. H. Chang. 1980. Some aspects of sex change and reproductive biology of the grouper, *Epinephelus diacanthus*. *Bull. Inst. Zool., Acad. Sinica* 19:11–17.

Chewyreuv, I. 1913. Le rôle des femelles dans la détermination du sexe de leur descendance dans le groupe des Ichneumonides. *C. R. Soc. Biol. Paris* 74:695–699.

Choat, J. H., and D. R. Robertson. 1975. Protogynous hermaphroditism in fishes of the family Scaridae. *In:* Reinboth, R. (ed.), *Intersexuality in the Animal Kingdom*. Springer-Verlag Berlin, pp. 263–283.

Christie, J. R. 1929. Some observations of sex in the Mermithidae. *J. Exp. Zool.* 53:59–76.

Christophers, S. R. 1960. *Aedes aegypti (L.), The Yellow-fever Mosquito; Its Life History, Bionomics and Structure*. Cambridge University Press.

Christy, R. M. 1922. The pollination of British Primulas. *J. Linn. Soc. (Bot.)* 46:105–139.

Clark, A. B. 1978. Sex ratio and local resource competition in a prosimian primate. *Science* 201:163–165.

Clausen, C. D. 1939. The effect of host size upon the sex ratio of Hymenopterous parasites and its relation to methods of rearing and colonization. *J. N.Y. Ent. Soc.* 47:1–9.

Clegg, D. J. 1955. Reproduction in the Cirripedia with special reference to *Balanus balanoides*. M.Sc. Thesis, University of Wales.

Clutton-Brock, T. H. and S. D. Albon. 1982. Parental investment in male and female offspring in mammals. *In: Current Problems in Sociobiology,* Cambridge Univ. Press, pp. 223–248.

Clutton-Brock, T. H., Albon, S. D. and F. E. Guinness. 1981. Parental investment in male and female offspring in polygynous mammals. *Nature* 289:487–489.

Coe, W. R. 1935. Sexual phases in *Crepidula. J. Exp. Zool.* 72:455–477.

_____. 1938a. Conditions influencing change of sex in mollusks of the genus *Crepidula. J. Exp. Zool.* 77:401–424.

_____. 1938b. Influence of association on the sexual phases of gastropods having protandric consecutive sexuality. *Biol. Bull.* 75:274–285.

_____. 1941. Sexual phases in wood-boring mollusks. *Biol. Bull.* 81:168–176.

_____. 1943. Sexual differentiation in molluscs. I. Pelecypods. *Quart. Rev. Biol.* 18:154–164.

_____. 1944. Sexual differentiation in mollusks. II. Gastropods, Amphineurans, Scaphopods, and Cephalopods. *Quart. Rev. Biol.* 19:85–97.

_____. 1948. Variations in the expression of sexuality in the normally protandric gastropod *Crepidula plana* Say. *J. Exp. Zool.* 108:155–169.

_____. 1953. Influences of association, isolation, and nutrition on the sexuality of snails of the genus *Crepidula. J. Exp. Zool.* 122:5–19.

Collier, A., Ray, S. and W. B. Wilson. 1956. Some effects of specific organic compounds on marine organisms. *Science* 124:220.

Colwell, R. K. 1981. Group selection is implicated in the evolution of female-biased sex ratios. *Nature* 290:401–404.

Correns, C. 1928. *Hanb. Vererbursw.* 2:1–138.

Crisp, D. J. 1954. The breeding of *Balanus porcatus* (DaCosta) in the Irish Sea. *J. Mar. Biol. Assn. U.K.* 33:473–494.

Crisp, D. J. and B. Patel. 1969. Environmental control of the breeding of three boreo-arctic cirripedes. *Mar. Biol.* 2:283–295.

Crosby, J. L. 1949. Selection of an unfavorable gene-complex. *Evolution* 3:212–230.

Crow, J. F. and M. Kimura. 1970. *An Introduction to Population Genetics Theory.* Harper and Row, N.Y.

Cruden, R. W. 1976. Fecundity as a function of nectar production and pollen-ovule ratios. *In:* J. Burley and B. T. Styles (eds.), *Variation, Breeding and Conservation of Tropical Forest Trees.* Academic Press, pp. 171–178.

———. 1977. Pollen-ovule ratios: a conservative indicator of breeding systems in flowering plants. *Evolution* 31:32–46.

Cruden, R. W. and S. Miller-Ward. 1981. Pollen-ovule ratio, pollen size, and the ratio of stigmatic area to the pollen-bearing area of the pollinator: an hypothesis. *Evolution* 35:964–974.

Curtsinger, J. W. and M. W. Feldman. 1980. Experimental and theoretical analysis of the "sex-ratio" polymorphism in *Drosophila pseudoobscura. Genetics* 94:445–466.

Darwin, C. 1854. *A monograph on the sub-class Cirripedia.* The Ray Society, London.

———. 1871. *The Descent of Man and Selection in Relation to Sex.* John Murray, London.

———. 1877. *The Different Forms of Flowers on Plants of the Same Species.* John Murray, London.

Das, S. M. and G. Sesheppa. 1948. A contribution to the biology of *Patella:* on population distribution and sex proportions in *Patella vulgata* Linnaeus at Cullercoats, England. *Proc. Zool. Soc. Lond.* 117:653–662.

Dawson, E. R. 1917. *The Causation of Sex in Man.* Paul B. Hoeber, N.Y.

Den Ouden, H. 1960. A note on parthenogenesis and sex determination in *Heterodera rostochiensis. Nematologica* 5:215–216.

Dhondt, A. A. 1968. The sex ratio of nestling Great Tits. *Bird Study* 17:282–286.

Dobzhansky, T. and C. Epling. 1944. Contributions to the genetics, taxonomy, and ecology of *Drosophila pseudoobscura* and its relatives. *Carnegie Inst. Washington Publ.* 554:1–183.

Dodd, J. M. 1956. Studies on the biology of limpets. III. Hermaphroditism in the three British species of *Patella*. *J. Mar. Biol. Assn. U.K.* 35:327–340.

Dodson, C. H. 1962. Pollination and variation in the subtribe Catasetinae (Orchidaceae). *Ann. Mo. Bot. Gard.* 49:35–36.

Dowrick, V. P. J. 1956. Heterostyly and homostyly in *Primula obconica*. *Heredity* 10:219–236.

Dulberger, R. 1974. Structural dimorphism of stigmatic papillae in distylous *Linum* species. *Am. J. Bot.* 61:238–243.

Dyer, J. G. 1975. Sex ratio and arrenotokous reproduction in Phytoseiid mites (Acarina: Mesostigmata). Ph.D. Thesis, Rutgers University.

Dyer, J. G. and F. C. Swift. 1979. Sex ratio in field populations of Phytoseiid mites (Acarina: Phytoseiidae). *Ann. Ent. Soc. Amer.* 72:149–154.

Dzhaparidze, L. I. 1963. *Sex in plants*. Akademiya Nauk Gruzinskoi SSR. Institut Botaniki. Translated from Russian for NSF.

Edwards, A.W.F. 1962. Genetics and the human sex ratio. *Adv. Genet.* 11:239–272.

———. 1970. The search for genetic variability of the sex ratio. *J. Biosoc. Sci. Suppl.* 2:55–60.

Edwards, C. A. and J. R. Lofty. 1977. *Biology of Earthworms*. Halsted Press, N.Y.

Edwards, R. L. 1954. The host finding and oviposition behavior of *Mormoniella vitripennis* (Walker) (Hym.: Pteromalidae), a parasite of muscoid flies. *Behavior* 7:88–112.

Ellenby, C. 1954. Environmental determination of the sex ratio of a plant parasitic nematode. *Nature* 174:1016–1017.

Endler, J. A. 1978. A predator's view of animal color patterns. *Evol. Biol.* 11:319–364.

311

————. 1980. Natural selection on color patterns in *Poecilia reticulata*. *Evolution* 34:76–91.

————. 1982. Convergent and divergent effects of natural selection on color patterns in two fish faunas. *Evolution* 36:178–188.

Evans, F. C. 1949. A population study of house mice following a period of local abundance. *J. Mamm.* 30:351–363.

Ezenwa, A. O. and N. E. Carter. 1975. Influence of multiple infections on sex ratios of Mermithid parasites of Blackflies. *Environ. Ent.* 4:142–144.

F.A.O. world scientific conference on the biology and culture of shrimps and prawns. 1968–1970. *F.A.O. Fish. Rep.* 57(Parts 1–4).

Falconer, D. S. 1954. Selection for sex ratio in mice and *Drosophila*. *Amer. Natur.* 88:385–397.

Fechheimer, N. S. and R. A. Beatty. 1974. Chromosome abnormalities and sex ratio in rabbit blastocysts. *J. Repr. and Fert.* 37:331–341.

Ferguson, M.W.J. and T. Joanen. 1982. Temperature of egg incubation determines sex in *Alligator mississippiensis*. *Nature* 296:850–853.

Fiala, K. L. 1979. Natural selection and the sex ratio in the red-winged blackbird. Ph.D. Thesis, University of Michigan, Ann Arbor.

————. 1981. Reproductive cost and the sex ratio in red-winged blackbirds. *In:* Alexander, R. D. and D. W. Tinkle (eds.), *Natural Selection and Social Behavior: Recent Research and New Theory.* Chiron Press, N.Y.

Filipponi, A. and G. Petrelli. 1975. Laboratory studies on the autecology of three species of the glaber group (Acarina, Mesostigmata). *Riv. Parasitt.* 36:295–308.

Fischer, E. A. 1980. The relationship between mating system and simultaneous hermaphroditism in the coral reef fish *Hypoplectrus nigricans* (Serranidae). *J. Anim. Behav.* 28:620–634.

————. 1981. Sexual allocation in a simultaneously hermaphroditic coral reef fish. *Amer. Natur.* 117:64–82.

Fischer-Piette, E. 1948. Sur les éléments de prospérité des *Patelles* et sur leur spécificité. *J. Conchyl.* 88:45–96.

Fishelson, L. 1970. Protogynous sex reversal in the fish *Anthias squamipinnis* (Teleostei, Anthiidae) regulated by the presence or absence of a male fish. *Nature* 227:90–91.

———. 1975. Ecology and physiology of sex reversal in *Anthias squamipinnis* (Peters) (Teleostei: Anthiidae) *In:* Reinboth, R. (ed.), *Intersexuality in the Animal Kingdom.* Springer-Verlag, Berlin, pp. 284–299.

Fisher, R. A. 1930. *The Genetical Theory of Natural Selection.* Oxford University Press.

———. 1941a. Average excess and average effect of a gene substitution. *Ann. Eugen.* 11:53–63.

———. 1941b. The theoretical consequences of polyploid inheritance of the mid style form of *Lythrum salicaria. Ann. Eugen.* 11:31–38.

———. 1944. Allowance for double reduction in the calculation of genotype frequencies with polysomic inheritance. *Ann. Eugen.* 12:169–171.

Flanders, S. E. 1946. Control of sex and sex-limited polymorphism in the Hymenoptera. *Quart. Rev. Biol.* 21:135–143.

———. 1956. The mechanisms of sex-ratio regulation in the (parasitic) Hymenoptera. *Insectes Sociaux* 3:325–334.

———. 1959. Differential host relations of the sexes in parasitic Hymenoptera. *Ent. Exp. Appl.* 2:123–142.

———. 1965. On the sexuality and sex ratios of hymenopterous populations. *Amer. Natur.* 99:489–494.

Fordham, R. A. 1971. Field populations of deermice with supplemental food. *Ecology* 52:138–146.

Foster, W. H. and D.M.G. McSherry. 1980. A search for genetic variation in the sex ratio at hatching. *British Poultry Science* 21:131–134.

Fox, W. W. 1972. Dynamics of exploited Pandalid shrimps and an evaluation of management models. Ph.D. Thesis, University of Washington, Seattle.

Frankel, R. and E. Galun. 1977. *Pollination Mechanisms, Reproduction and Plant Breeding.* Springer-Verlag, Berlin.

Fredga, K., Gropp, A., Winking, H. and F. Frank. 1976. Fertile XX- and XY-type females in the wood lemming *Myopus schisticolor. Nature* 261:225–227.

Fredga, K., Gropp, A., Winking, H. and F. Frank. 1977. A hypothesis explaining the exceptional sex ratio in the wood lemming (*Myopus schisticolor*). *Hereditas* 85:101–104.

Freeman, D. C. and E. D. McArthur. 1981. The infuence of environment on the sex ratios of six species of plants within the genus *Atriplex* (submitted to *Ecology*).

———. 1982. A comparison of water stress between males and females of six species of desert shrubs. *Forest Sci.* (in press).

Freeman, D. C., Klikoff, L. G. and K. T. Harper. 1976. Differential resource utilization by the sexes of dioecious plants. *Science* 193:597–599.

Freeman, D. C., Harper, K. T. and E. L. Charnov. 1980a. Sex change in plants: old and new observations, and new hypotheses. *Oecologia* 47:222–232.

Freeman, D. C., Harper, K. T. and W. K. Ostler. 1980b. Ecology of plant dioecy in the Intermountain region of Western North America and California. *Oecologia* 44:410–417.

Freeman, D. C., McArthur, E. D., Harper, K. T. and C. Blauer. 1981. The influence of environment on the floral sex ratio of monoecious plants. *Evolution* 35:194–197.

Fretter, V. and A. Graham. 1962. *British Prosobranch molluscs; their functional anatomy and ecology.* The Ray Society, London.

Fricke, H. W. 1974. Oko-ethologie des monogamen Anemonenfisches *Amphiprion bicinctus* (Freiwasseruntersuchung aus dem Roten Meer). *Z. Tierpsychol.* 36:429–512.

———. 1979. Mating system, resource defense and sex change in the anemone fish *Amphiprion akallopisos. Z. Tierpsychol.* 50:313–326.

Fricke, H. and S. Fricke. 1977. Monogamy and sex change by

aggressive dominance in coral reef fish. *Nature* 266:830–832.

Gaddie, R. E. and D. E. Douglas. 1975. *Earthworms for Ecology and Profit*, Vol. 1. Bookworm Pub. Co., Ontario, Calif.

Gaddie, R. E. and D. E. Douglas. 1977. *Earthworms for Ecology and Profit*, Vol. 2. Bookworm Pub. Co., Ontario, Calif.

Galtsoff, P. S. 1964. The American oyster *Crassostrea virginica* Gmelin. *Fish. Bull.* 64:1–480.

Ganders, F. R. 1975. Mating patterns in self-compatible distylous populations of *Amsinckia* (Boraginaceae). *Can. J. Bot.* 53:773–779.

———. 1979. The biology of heterostyly. *New Zeal. J. Bot.* 17:607–635.

Geibel, J. J. and R.F.G. Heinmann. 1976. Assessment of ocean shrimp management in California resulting from a widely fluctuating recruitment. *Calif. Fish Game* 62:255–273.

Geiringer, E. 1961. Effect of ACTH on sex ratio of the albino rat. *Proc. Soc. Exp. Biol. and Med.* 106:752–754.

Geiser, S. W. 1924. Sex ratios and spermatogenesis in the top-minnow, *Gambusia holbrooki*. *Biol. Bull.* 47:175–212.

Ghirardelli, E. 1968. Some aspects of the biology of chaetognaths. *Adv. Mar. Biol.* 6:271–375.

Ghiselin, M. T. 1969. The evolution of hermaphroditism among animals. *Quart. Rev. Biol.* 44:189–208.

———. 1974. *The Economy of Nature and the Evolution of Sex.* University of California Press, Berkeley.

Giese, A. C. and J. S. Pearse, eds. 1974–1979. *Reproduction of Marine Invertebrates,* Vols. 1–5, Academic Press, N.Y.

Givnish, T. J. 1980. Ecological constraints on the evolution of breeding systems in seed plants: dioecy and dispersal in gymnosperms. *Evolution* 34:959–972.

Gomez, E. D. 1975. Sex determination in *Balanus (Conopea) galeatus* (L.) (Cirripedia: Thoracica). *Crustaceana* 28:105–107.

Gotshall, D. W. 1972. Population size, mortality rates and growth

315

rates of Northern California ocean shrimp, *Pandalus jordani* 1965–1968. *Calif. Fish. Bull.* 155:1–47.

Gould, H. N. 1917a. Studies on sex in the hermaphrodite mollusk *Crepidula plana*. 1. History of the sexual cycle. *J. Exp. Zool.* 23:1–68.

———. 1917b. Studies on sex in the hermaphrodite mollusk *Crepidula plana*. 2. Influence of the environment on sex. *J. Exp. Zool.* 23:225–250.

———. 1919. Studies on sex in the hermaphrodite mollusk *Crepidula plana*. 3. Transference of the male producing stimulus through sea water. *J. Exp. Zool.* 29:113–120.

———. 1952. Studies on sex in the hermaphrodite mollusk *Crepidula plana*. 4. Internal and external factors influencing growth and sex development. *J. Exp. Zool.* 119:93–163.

Gould, S. J. 1980. Is a new and general theory of evolution emerging? *Paleobiology* 6:119–130.

Green, R. F. 1982. Optimal foraging and sex ratio in parasitic wasps. *J. Theor. Biol.* 95:43–48.

Gregg, K. B. 1973. Studies on the control of sex expression in the genera *Cycnoches* and *Catasetum*, subtribe Catasetinae, Orchidaceae. Ph.D. Diss., University of Miami, Coral Gables, Florida.

———. 1975. The effect of light intensity on sex expression in species of *Cycnoches* and *Catasetum* (Orchidaceae). *Selbyana* 1:101–113.

———. 1978. Ethylene physiology, sunlight intensity, and sex in the orchid genera *Catasetum* and *Cycnoches*. In manuscript.

———. 1978. The interaction of light intensity, plant size and nutrition in sex expression in *Cycnoches* (Orchidaceae). *Selbyana* 2:212–223.

Haldane, J.B.S. 1936. Some natural populations of *Lythrum salicaria*. *J. Genetics* 32:393–397.

———. 1938. Heterostylism in natural populations of the primrose, *Primula acaulis*. *Biometrika* 30:196–198.

Halkka, O. and L. Halkka. 1974. Polymorphic balance in small island populations of *Lythrum salicaria*. *Ann. Bot. Fennici* 11:267–270.

Hamilton, W. D. 1964. The genetical evolution of social behavior. *J. Theor. Biol.* 7:1–52.

———. 1967. Extraordinary sex ratios. *Science* 156:477–488.

———. 1979. Wingless and fighting males in fig wasps and other insects. *In:* M. S. Blum and N. A. Blum (eds.), *Reproductive Competition and Sexual Selection in Insects*. Academic Press, N.Y.

Harlos, J., Brost, R. A. and T. D. Galloway. 1980. Observations on a nematode parasite of *Aedes vexans* (Diptera: Culicidae) in Manitoba. *Can. J. Zool.* 58:215–220.

Hartl, D. L. 1971. Some aspects of natural selection in arrhenotokous populations. *Amer. Zool.* 11:309–325.

Hartl, D. L. and S. W. Brown. 1970. The origin of male haploid genetic systems and their expected sex ratio. *Theor. Pop. Biol.* 1:165–190.

Hartmann, M. 1956. *Die Sexualitat,* 2nd ed. Fischer, Stuttgart.

Haynes, E. B. and R. Wigley. 1969. Biology of the northern shrimp, *Pandalus borealis,* Gulf of Maine. *Trans. Amer. Fish. Soc.* 98:60–76.

Heath, D. J. 1977. Simultaneous hermaphroditism: cost and benefit. *J. Theor. Biol.* 64:363–373.

———. 1979. Brooding and the evolution of hermaphroditism. *J. Theor. Biol.* 81:151–155.

Helle, W. 1967. Fertilization in the two-spotted spider mite (*Tetranychus urticae:* Acari). *Ent. Exp. Appl.* 10:103–110.

Hendler, G. and D. R. Franz. 1971. Population dynamics and life history of *Crepidula convexa* Say (Gastropoda: Prosobranchia) in Delaware Bay. *Biol. Bull.* 141:514–526.

Herlin-Houtteville, P. and P. E. Lubet. 1975. The sexuality of pelecypod molluscs. *In:* Reinboth, R. (ed.), *Intersexuality in the Animal Kingdom*. Springer-Verlag, Berlin, pp. 179–187.

Hertwig, R. 1912. Ueber den derzeitigen stand des sexualproblems. *Biol. Zbl.* 21:1–146.

LITERATURE CITED

Heslop-Harrison, J. 1957. The experimental modification of sex expression in flowering plants. *Biol. Rev.* 32:38–90.

——. 1972. Sexuality of angiosperms. *In:* Stewart, F. C. (ed.), *Plant Physiology*, Vol. 6C. Academic Press, N.Y., pp. 133–290.

Heuch, I. 1978. Maintenance of butterfly populations with all-female broods under recurrent extinction and recolonization. *J. Theor. Biol.* 75:115–122.

——. 1979a. The effect of partial self-fertilization of type frequencies in heterostylous plants. *Ann. Bot.* 44:611–616.

——. 1979b. Equilibrium populations of heterostylous plants. *Theor. Pop. Biol.* 15:43–57.

Hickey, W. A. 1970. Factors influencing the distortion of sex ratio in *Aedes aegypti*. *J. Med. Ent.* 7:727–735.

Hickey, W. A. and G. B. Craig. 1966a. Distortion of sex ratio in populations of *Aedes aegypti*. *Can. J. Genet. Cytol.* 8:260–278.

Hickey, W. A. and G. B. Craig. 1966b. Genetic distortion of sex ratio in a mosquito, *Aedes aegypti*. *Genetics* 53:1177–1196.

Hildebrand, S. F. 1927. Sex ratio in *Gambusia*. *Biol. Bull.* 53:390–404.

Hilgard, G. H. 1960. A study of reproduction in the intertidal barnacle, *Mitella polymerus* in Monterey Bay, California. *Biol. Bull.* 119:169–188.

Hines, A. H. 1978. Reproduction in three species of intertidal barnacles from central California. *Biol. Bull.* 154:262–281.

——. 1979. The comparative reproductive ecology of three species of intertidal barnacles. *In:* S. E. Stancyk (ed.), *Reproductive Ecology of Marine Invertebrates.* University of South Carolina Press, Columbia, pp. 213–233.

Hjort, J. and J. T. Ruud. 1938. Deep-sea prawn fisheries and their problems. *Hvalradfts. Skr.* 17:1–144.

Hoagland, K. E. 1975. Reproductive strategies and evolution in the genus *Crepidula* (Gastropoda: Calyptraeidae). Ph.D. Diss., Harvard University.

——. 1977. Systematic review of fossil and Recent *Crepidula*

318

and discussion of evolution of the Calyptraeidae. *Malacologia* 16:353–420.

———. 1978. Protandry and the evolution of environmentally-mediated sex change: a study of the Mollusca. *Malacologia* 17:365–391.

Hoelscher, C. E. and S. B. Vinson. 1971. The sex ratio of a hymenopterous parasitoid *Campoletis perdistinctus* as affected by photoperiod, mating and temperature. *Ann. Ent. Soc. Amer.* 64:1373–1376.

Hohenboken, W. D. 1981. Possibilities for genetic manipulation of sex ratio in livestock. *J. Anim. Sci.* 52:265–277.

Holdaway, F. T. and H. F. Smith. 1933. A relation between size of host puparia and sex ratio of *Alysia manducator*. *Aust. J. Exp. Biol. and Med.* 10:247–259.

Holmes, H. B. 1970. Alteration of sex ratio in the parasitic wasp, *Nasonia vitripennis*. Ph.D. Diss., University of Massachusetts, Amherst.

———. 1972. Genetic evidence for fewer progeny and a higher percent males when *Nasonia vitripennis* oviposits in previously parasitized hosts. *Entomophaga* 17:79–88.

Hominick, W. M. and H. E. Welch. 1971. Synchronization of life cycles of three mermithids (Nematoda) with their chironomid (Diptera) hosts and some observations on the pathology of the infections. *Can. J. Zool.* 49:975–982.

Hopping, G. R. 1962. The sex ratio of *Ips tridens* Mannerheim (Coleoptera: Scolytidae). *Can. Ent.* 94:506.

———. 1964. The breeding evidence indicating two genetic types of females in *Ips tridens* (Mannerheim) (Coleoptera: Scolytidae). *Can. Ent.* 96:117–118.

Horsted, S. A. and E. Smidt. 1956. The deep sea prawn (*Pandalus borealis* Kr.) in Greenland waters. *Medd. Dan. Fisk.-Havunders* 1:118.

Howe, H. F. 1977. Sex-ratio adjustment in the common grackle. *Science* 198:744–746.

Hurley, A. C. 1973. Fecundity of the acorn barnacle *Balanus pacificus:* a fugitive species. *Limnol. Oceanogr.* 18:386–393.

LITERATURE CITED

Hutt, F. B. 1949. *Genetics of the Fowl*. McGraw-Hill, N.Y.

Huxley, J. S. 1920. Note on an alternating preponderance of males and females in fish, and its possible significance. *J. Genetics* 10:265–276.

Ikeda, K. 1937. Cytogenetic studies on the self-fertilization of *Philomycus bilineatus*. *J. Sci. Hiroshima Univ.* B5:66–123.

Ikeda, H. 1970. The cytoplasmically-inherited "sex-ratio" condition in natural and experimental populations of *Drosophila bifasciata*. *Genetics* 65:311–333.

Ishiki, H. 1936. Sex changes in the slipper limpets, *Crepidula aculaeata* and *Crepidula walshi*. *J. Sci. Hiroshima Univ. Series B, Div. 1*, 4:91–99.

Ivanov, B. G. 1969. The biology and distribution of the northern shrimp (*Pandalus borealis* Kr.) in the Bering Sea and the Gulf of Alaska. *F.A.O. Fish. Rep.* 57:800–810.

Jain, S. K. 1976. The evolution of inbreeding in plants. *Ann. Rev. Ecol. Syst.* 7:469–495.

James, H. C. 1937. Sex ratios and the status of the male in Pseudococcinae (Hem. Coccidae). *Bull. Ent. Res.* 28:429–461.

James, W. H. 1975. The distributions of the combinations of the sexes in mammalian litters. *Genet. Res.* 26:45–53.

Jensen, A.J.C. 1965. *Pandalus borealis* in the Skagerrak (length, growth and changes in the stock and fishery yield). *Rapp. P.-V. Reun., Cons. Int. Explor. Mer.* 156:109–111.

———. 1967. The *Pandalus borealis* in the North Sea and Skagerrak. *Mar. Biol. Assn. India, Proc. Symp. on Crustacea*, Part IV:1317–1319.

Jensen, J. P. 1958. The relation between body size and number of eggs in marine Malacostraca. *Medd. Dan. Fisk.-Havunders* 2:1–25.

Johnson, A. A. 1955. Life history studies on *Hydromeris contorta*, a nematode parasite of *Chironomus plumosus*. Ph.D. Thesis, University of Illinois.

Johnson, C. 1977. Evolution of sex ratios in the isopod, *Venezillo evergladensis*. *Evolution* 31:603–610.

320

Johnson, R. N. and D. R. Viglierchio. 1969. Sugar beet nematode (*Heterodera schachtii*) reared on axenic *Beta vulgaris* root explants. *Nematologica* 15:144–152.

Johnston, I. M. 1952. Studies in the Boraginaceae. XXIII. A survey of the genus *Lithospermum*. *J. Arnold Arboretum* 33:299–363.

Kalela, O. 1971. Seasonal trends in the sex ratio of the grey-sided vole, *Clethrionomys rufocanus*. *Ann. Zool. Fenn.* 8:452–455.

Kalela, O. and T. Oksala. 1966. Sex ratio in the wood lemming, *Myopus schisticolor* (Lilljeb.), in nature and in captivity. *Ann. Univ. Turkuensis, Ser. AII.* 37:1–24.

Kallman, K. 1973. The sex-determining mechanism of the platy-fish, *Xiphophorus maculatus*. *In:* Schröder, J. H. (ed.), *Genetics and Mutagenesis of Fish*. Springer-Verlag, N.Y., pp. 19–28.

————. 1975. The platyfish, *Xiphophorus maculatus*. *In:* King, R. C. (ed.), *Handbook of Genetics, Vol. 4, Vertebrates of Genetic Interest*. Plenum Press, N.Y., pp. 81–132.

Kethley, J. 1971. Population regulation in quill mites (Acarina: Syringophilidae). *Ecology* 52:1113–1118.

Kiddy, C. A. and H. D. Hafs, eds. 1971. *Sex ratio at birth—prospects for control*. Symp. pub. by Amer. Soc. Anim. Science.

King, H. D. 1918. Studies on inbreeding III. The effects of inbreeding, with selection on the sex ratio of the albino rat. *J. Exp. Zool.* 27:1–35.

King, P. E. and C. R. Hopkins. 1963. Length of life of the sexes in *Nasonia vitripennis* (Walker) (Hymenoptera: Pteromalidae) under conditions of starvation. *J. Exp. Biol.* 40:751–761.

Kirkpatrick, R. L. and D. A. Wilbur. 1965. The development and habits of the granary weevil, *Sitophilus granarius* within the kernel of wheat. *J. Econ. Ent.* 58:979–985.

Kishi, Y. 1970. Difference in the sex ratio of the pine bark weevil parasite, *Dolichomitus sp.* (Hymenoptera: Ichneumonidae), emerging from different host species. *Appl. Ent. Zool.* 5:126–132.

Kochetova, N. I. 1977. Factors determining the sex ratio in some entomophagous hymenoptera. *Entomol. Rev.* 56:1–5.

Koliopanos, C. N. and A. C. Triantaphyllou. 1972. Effect of infection density on sex ratio of *Heterodera glycines. Nematologica* 18:131–137.

Kolman, W. 1960. The mechanism of natural selection for the sex ratio. *Amer. Natur.* 94:373–377.

Krebs, C. J., Gaines, M., Keller, B., Myers, J. and R. Tamarin. 1973. Population cycles in small rodents. *Science* 179:35–41.

Krebs, J. R. and N. B. Davies, eds. 1978. *Behavioral Ecology.* Sinauer, Sunderland, Mass.

Krombein, K. V. 1967. *Trap-nesting Wasps and Bees.* Smithsonian Press, Washington, D.C.

Kubicki, B. 1969a. Investigations on sex determination in cucumber (*Cucumis sativus*) (parts 3–8). *Genetica Polonica* 10:5–144.

_____. 1969b. Sex determination in muskmelon (*Cucumis melo*). *Genetica Polonica* 10:145–166.

_____. 1969c. Comparative studies on sex determination in cucumber (*Cucumis sativus*) and muskmelon (*Cucumis melo*). *Genetica Polonica* 10:167–184.

Kubo, I. 1951. Bionomics of the prawn, *Pandalus kessleri. J. Tokyo Univ. Fish.* 38:1–26.

Lane, E. A. and T. S. Hyde. 1973. Effect of maternal stress on fertility and sex ratio: a pilot study with rats. *J. Abnormal Psych.* 82:73–80.

Lang, K. 1958. Protogynic bei zwei Tanaidacean-Arten. *Ark. Zool. Bd.* 11-32:535–539.

Lavenda, N. 1949. Sexual differences and normal protogynous hermaphroditism in the Atlantic sea bass, *Centropristes striatus. Copeia 1949* (3):185–194.

Lawrence, P. S. 1941. The sex ratio, fertility, and ancestral longevity. *Quart. Rev. Biol.* 16:35–79.

LeGall, P. and W. Streiff. 1975. Protandric hermaphroditism in prosobranch gastropods. *In:* Reinboth, R. (ed.), *Intersexual-*

322

ity in the Animal Kingdom. Springer-Verlag, Berlin, pp. 170–178.

Legner, E. F. 1969a. Distribution pattern of hosts and parasitization by *Spalangia drosophilae* (Hymenoptera: Pteromalidae). *Can. Ent.* 101:551–557.

———. 1969b. Adult emergence interval and reproduction in parasitic Hymenoptera influenced by host size and density. *Ann. Ent. Soc. Amer.* 62:220–226.

Leigh, E. G. 1970. Sex ratio and differential mortality between the sexes. *Amer. Natur.* 104:205–210.

Leigh, E. G., Charnov, E. L. and R. R. Warner. 1976. Sex ratio, sex change and natural selection. *Proc. Natl. Acad. Sci.* 73:3655–3660.

Lemen, C. 1980. Allocation of reproductive effort to male and female strategies in wind-pollinated plants. *Oecologia* 45:156–159.

Lepori, N. C. 1980. *Sex Differentiation, Hermaphroditism, and Intersexuality in Vertebrates, Including Man.* Piccin Editori, Padua, Italy.

Levin, D. A. 1974. Spatial segregation of pins and thrums in populations of *Hedyotis nigricans. Evolution* 28:648–655.

Levins, R. 1968. *Evolution in Changing Environments.* Princeton University Press.

Lewis, C.L.A. 1975. Reproductive biology and development of the gooseneck barnacle, *Pollicipes polymerus.* Ph.D. Thesis, University of Alberta.

Lewis, D. 1941. Male sterility in natural populations of hermaphrodite plants. *New Phytol.* 40:56–63.

———. 1979. *Sexual Incompatibility in Plants.* Edward Arnold, London.

Liem, K. F. 1963. Sex reversal as a natural process in the synbranchiform fish *Monopterus albus. Mar. Biol.* 36:359–367.

———. 1968. Geographical and taxonomic variation in the pattern of natural sex reversal in the teleost fish order Synbranchiformes. *J. Zool. Lond.* 156:225–238.

Lloyd, D. G. 1972a. Breeding systems in *Cotula* L. (Compositae, Anthemideae). I. The array of monoclinous and diclinous systems. *New Phytol.* 71:1181–1194.

———. 1972b. Breeding systems in *Cotula* L. (Compositae, Anthemideae). II. Monoecious populations. *New Phytol.* 71:1195–1202.

———. 1974a. Theoretical sex ratios in dioecious and gynodioecious angiosperms. *Heredity* 32:11–34.

———. 1974b. The genetic contributions of individual males and females in dioecious and gynodioecious angiosperms. *Heredity* 32:45–51.

———. 1975a. The maintenance of gynodioecy and androdioecy in angiosperms. *Genetica* 45:325–339.

———. 1975b. Breeding systems in *Cotula*. III. Dioecious populations. *New Phytol.* 74:109–123.

———. 1976. The transmission of genes via pollen and ovules in gynodioecious angiosperms. *Theor. Pop. Biol.* 9:299–316.

———. 1979a. Some reproductive factors affecting the selection of self-fertilization in plants. *Amer. Natur.* 113:67–79.

———. 1979b. Parental strategies of angiosperms. *New Zeal. J. Bot.* 17:595–606.

———. 1979c. Evolution towards dioecy in heterostylous populations. *Plant Syst. Evol.* 131:71–80.

———. 1980a. The distribution of gender in four angiosperm species illustrating two evolutionary pathways to dioecy. *Evolution* 34:123–134.

———. 1980b. Sexual strategies in plants III. A quantitative method for describing the gender of plants. *New Zeal. J. Bot.* 18:103–108.

———. 1980c. Demographic factors and mating patterns in Angiosperms. *In:* Solbrig, O. T. (ed.), *Demography and Evolution of Plant Populations*. Blackwell, Oxford, pp. 67–88.

Lloyd, D. G. and A. J. Myall. 1976. Sexual dimorphism in *Cirsium arvense*. *Ann. Bot.* 40:115–123.

Lloyd, D. G. and C. J. Webb. 1977. Secondary sex characters in seed plants. *Bot. Rev.* 43:177–216.

Longhurst, A. R. 1965. The biology of West African polynemid fishes. *J. Cons., Cons. Perm. Int. Explor. Mar.* 30:58–74.

Lovett Doust, J. 1980. Floral sex ratios in andromonoecious Umbelliferae. *New Phytol.* 85:265–273.

Lovett Doust, J. and J. L. Harper. 1980. The resource costs of gender and maternal support in an andromonoecious Umbellifer, *Smyrnium olusatrum* L. *New Phytol.* 85:251–264.

Lovett Doust, J. and P. B. Cavers. 1981. Floral resource allocation in hermaphrodites. *Can. J. Bot.* (in press).

_____. 1982. Sex and gender dynamics in Jack-in-the-Pulpit, *Arisaema triphyllum* (L.) Schott (Araceae). *Ecology* (in press).

Lucchesi, J. C. 1978. Gene dosage compensation and the evolution of sex chromosomes. *Science* 202:711–716.

MacArthur, R. H. 1965. Ecological consequences of natural selection. *In:* Waterman, T. H. and H. Morowitz (eds.), *Theoretical and Mathematical Biology.* Blaisdell, N.Y., pp. 388–397.

MacKauer, M. 1976. The sex ratio in field populations of some aphid parasites. *Ann. Ent. Soc. Amer.* 69:453–456.

Maekawa, T. 1924. On the phenomena of sex transition in *Arisaema japonica. J. Coll. Agr., Hokkaido Imp. Univ.* 13:217–305.

Marine Biol. Assn. India. 1967. *Proc. Symp. on Crustacea.*

Marwick, N. P. 1974. A comparative study of four housefly parasites. Ph.D. Thesis, University of Wellington, New Zealand.

Maynard Smith, J. 1964. Group selection and kin selection. *Nature* 201:1145–1147.

_____. 1976. Evolution and the theory of games. *Amer. Sci.* 64:41–45.

_____. 1978. *The Evolution of Sex.* Cambridge University Press.

_____. 1980. A new theory of sexual investment. *Behav. Ecol. Sociob.* 7:247–251.

Maynard Smith, J. and N. C. Stenseth. 1978. On the evolutionary stability of the female biased sex ratio in the wood lemming (*Myopus schisticolor*): the effect of inbreeding. *Heredity* 41:205–214.

McArthur, E. D. 1977. Environmentally induced changes of sex expression in *Atriplex canescens*. *Heredity* 38:97–103.

McArthur, E. D. and D. C. Freeman. 1981. Sex reversal in *Atriplex canescens*. In manuscript.

McClure, P. A. 1981. Sex-biased litter reduction in food-restricted wood rats (*Neotoma floridana*). *Science* 211:1058–1060.

McCracken, G. F. and R. K. Selander. 1980. Self-fertilization and monogenic strains in natural populations of terrestrial slugs. *Proc. Natl. Acad. Sci.* 77:684–688.

McCullough, D. R. 1979. *The George Reserve Deer Herd: Population Ecology of a K-Selected Species.* University of Michigan Press, Ann Arbor.

McEnroe, W. D. 1969. Spreading and inbreeding in the spider mite. *Heredity* 60:343–345.

_____. 1970. A natural outcrossing swarm of *Tetranychus urticae. J. Econ. Ent.* 63:822–823.

McErlean, A. J., and C. L. Smith. 1964. The age of sexual succession in the protogynous hermaphrodite, *Mycteroperca microlepis. Trans. Amer. Fish. Soc.* 93:301–302.

McGugan, B. M. 1955. Certain host-parasite relationships involving the spruce budworm. *Can. Ent.* 87:178–187.

McKinley, J. M. 1980. Offspring size, sex, and number in the Northern watersnake, *Nerodia sipedon*. Paper submitted for M.S. degree, University of Utah, Salt Lake City.

McLaughlin, P. A. and D. P. Henry. 1972. Comparative morphology of complemental males in four species of *Balanus* (Cirripedia: Thoracica). *Crustaceana* 22:13–30.

Minina, E. G. 1952. Sex shifts in plants induced by environmental factors. Moscow Acad. Sci. USSR Publishing House. Translated from the Russian.

Mistakidis, M. N. 1957. The biology of *Pandalus montagui* Leach. *Fish. Invest. Ser. II. Mar. Fish. G. B., Minist. Agric. Fish. Food.* 21:1–52.

Mitchell, R. 1972. The sex ratio of the spider mite, *Tetranychus urticae. Ent. Exp. Appl.* 15:299–304.

_____. 1973. Growth and population dynamics of a spider mite (*Tetranychus urticae;* Acarina: Tetranychidae). *Ecology* 54:1349–1355.

Moe, M. A., Jr. 1969. Biology of the red grouper *Epinephelus morio* (Valenciennes) from the eastern Gulf of Mexico. *Florida Dept. Nat. Res. Prof. Paper Ser. 10.*

Montalenti, G. 1958. Perspectives of research on sex problems in marine organisms. *In:* Buzzati-Traverso, A. A. (ed.), *Perspectives in Marine Biology.* University of California Press, Berkeley, pp. 589–602.

Moyer, J. T. and A. Nakazono. 1978a. Protandrous hermaphroditism in six species of Anemonefish genus *Amphiprion* in Japan. *Jap. J. Ich.* 25:25–39.

Moyer, J. T. and A. Nakazono. 1978b. Population structure, reproductive behavior and protogynous hermaphroditism in the Angelfish *Centropyge interruptus* at Miyake-jima Japan. *Jap. J. Ich.* 25:25–39.

Müller, H. 1962. Über die Sexualität des Polychaeten *Ophryotrocha puerilis,* ihre Determination and ihren Einfluss auf Drüsentätigkeit und Kauapparatentwicklung. *Z. Morph. Ökol. Tiere* 52:1–32.

Myers, J. H. 1978. Sex ratio adjustment under food stress: maximization of quality or numbers of offspring. *Amer. Natur.* 112:381–388.

Nanmov, S. P., Gibet, L. A. and S. P. Shatlova. 1969. Dynamics of sex ratio with respect to changes in number of mammals. In Russian. *Zh. obshch. Biol.* 30:673–680.

Napier, K. M. and P. D. Mullaney. 1974. Sex ratio in sheep. *J. Reprod. Fert.* 39:391–392.

Nelson-Rees, W. A. 1960. A study of sex predetermination in the mealy bug, *Planococcus citri* (Risso). *J. Exp. Zool.* 144:111–137.

Newman, W. A. 1980. A review of extant *Scillaelepas* (Cirripedia: Scalpellidae) including recognition of new species from the North Atlantic, western Indian Ocean, and New Zealand. *Tethys.* 9:379–398.

Newman, W. A., Zullo, V. A. and T. H. Withers. 1969. *Cirripedia. In:* Moore, R. C. (ed.), *Treatise on Invertebrate Paleontology, Part R (Arthropoda 4),* pp. R207–R295.

Newton, I. and M. Marquiss. 1979. Sex ratio among nestlings of the European Sparrowhawk. *Amer. Natur.* 113:309–315.

Nichols, J. D. and R. H. Chabreck. 1980. On the variability of alligator sex ratios. *Amer. Natur.* 116:125–137.

Nishida, S., Otsuka, J., Yamagishi, T. and T. Sugaya. 1977. Sex ratio of offspring in domestic animals. (7) Pigs. *Jap. J. Anim. Reprod.* 23:55–59.

Nishida, S., Otsuka, J., Kano, Y., Yamagishi, T. and M. Kondo. 1974. Sex ratio of offspring in domestic animals. Swine (5). *Bull. Azabu Veterinary College* 28:50–54.

Nozato, K. 1969. Biology of *Itoplectis cristatae* (Hym.: Ichneumonidae), a pupal parasite of pine shoot moths in Japan. *Kontyû* 37:75–82.

Ogden, J. C., and N. S. Buckman. 1973. Movements, foraging groups, and diurnal migrations of the striped parrotfish, *Scarus croicensis* Bloch (Scaridae). *Ecology* 54:589–596.

Omar, O. B. and K. M. Graham. 1974. Selection for sex ratio in local cucumber. *Mal. Agric. Res.* 3:196–203.

Opler, P. A., Baker, H. G. and G. W. Frankie. 1975. Reproductive biology of some Costa Rican *Cordia* species (Boraginaceae). *Biotropica* 7:234–247.

Orians, G. H. 1969. On the evolution of mating systems in birds and mammals. *Amer. Natur.* 103:589–603.

Ornduff, R. 1964. The breeding system of *Oxalis suksdorfii. Am. J. Bot.* 51:307–314.

_____. 1976. The reproductive system of *Amsinckia grandiflora*, a distylous species. *Syst. Bot.* 1:57–66.

_____. 1979. Pollen flow in *Primula vulgaris*. *Bot. J. Linn. Soc.* 78:1–10.

_____. 1980. Heterostyly, population composition, and pollen flow in *Hedyotis cacrula*. *Am. J. Bot.* 67:95–103.

Orton, J. H. 1912. An account of the natural history of the slipper limpet (*Crepidula fornicata*) with some remarks on its occurrence in the oyster ground on the Essex coast. *J. Mar. Biol. Assn. U.K.* 9:437–478.

_____. 1920. Sex phenomena in the common limpet (*Patella vulgata*). *Nature* 104:373.

_____. 1928. Observations on *Patella vulgata*, Pt. I. Sex phenomena, breeding and shell growth. *J. Mar. Biol. Assn. U.K.* 15:851–862.

_____. 1946. The biology of *Patella* in Britain. *Nature* 158:173.

Orton, J. H. and A. J. Southward. 1961. Studies on the biology of limpets IV. The breeding of *Patella depressa* Pennant on the North Cornish Coast. *J. Mar. Biol. Assn. U.K.* 41:653–662.

Orton, J. H., Southward, A. J. and J. M. Dodd. 1956. Studies on the biology of limpets II. The breeding of *Patella vulgata* L. in Britain. *J. Mar. Biol. Assn. U.K.* 35:149–176.

Orzack, S. H., Sohn, J. J., Kallman, K. D., Levin, S. A. and R. Johnston. 1980. Maintenance of the three sex chromosome polymorphism in the platyfish, *Xiphophorus maculatus*. *Evolution* 34:663–672.

Owen, D. F. 1966. Predominantly female populations of an African butterfly. *Heredity* 21:443–451.

Owen, D. F. and D. O. Chanter. 1969. Population biology of tropical African butterflies. Sex ratio and genetic variation in *Acraea encedon*. *J. Zool. Lond.* 157:345–374.

Palenichko, Z. G. 1941. The distribution and life history of the shrimp *Pandalus borealis* (Kr.) in the Barents Sea. *Zool. Zh.* 20:398–414.

Parkes, A. S. 1926. The mammalian sex ratio. *Biol. Rev.* 2:1–51.

_____. 1971. Mythology of the human sex ratio. *In:* Kiddy, C. A. and H. D. Hafs (eds.), *Sex ratio at birth—prospects for control.* Symp. pub. by Amer. Soc. Anim. Science, pp. 38–42.

Petersen, J. J. 1972. Factors affecting sex ratios of a Mermithid parasite of mosquitoes. *J. Nemat.* 4:83–87.

_____. 1973. Factors affecting mass production of *Reesimermis nielseni,* a nematode parasite of mosquitoes. *J. Med. Ent.* 10:75–79.

_____. 1977. Effects of host size and parasite burden on sex ratio in the mosquito parasite *Octomymermis muspratti. J. Nemat.* 9:343–346.

Petersen, J. J., Chapman, H. C. and D. B. Woodward. 1968. The bionomics of a Mermithid nematode of larval mosquitoes in southwestern Louisiana. *Mosq. News* 28:346–352.

Petrusewicz, K. 1960. Some regularities in male and female dynamics in mice populations. *Acta Theriologica* 9:103–137.

Pfannenstiel, H.-D. 1975. Mutual influence on the sexual differentiation in the protandric polychaete *Ophryotrocha puerilis. In:* Reinboth, R. (ed.), *Intersexuality in the Animal Kingdom.* Springer–Verlag, Berlin, pp. 48–56.

Poinar, G. O. 1979. *Nematodes for Biological Control of Insects.* CRC Press, Boca Raton, Florida.

Policansky, D. 1981. Sex choice and the size advantage model in jack-in-the pulpit (*Arisaema triphyllum*). *Proc. Natl. Acad. Sci.* 78:1306–1308.

_____. 1982. Sex change, differential sex-specific mortality and a puzzle: Why don't more organisms change sex? In manuscript.

Policansky, D. and B. B. Dempsey. 1978. Modifiers and "sex ratio" in *Drosophila pseudoobscura. Evolution* 32:922–924.

Policansky, D. and J. Ellison. 1970. Sex ratio in *Drosophila pseudoobscura:* spermiogenic failure. *Science* 169:888–889.

Popper, D., and L. Fishelson. 1973. Ecology and behavior of *Anthias squamipinnis* (Peters, 1855) (Anthiidae, Teleostei) in the coral habitat of Eilat (Red Sea). *J. Exp. Zool.* 184:409–424.

Population Report. 1975. (Series 1, #2) Pub. by Dept. of Medical and Public Affairs, The George Washington University Medical Center, 2001 S Street, N.W. Wash., D.C., 20009.

Potter, D. A. 1978. Functional sex ratio in the carmine spider mite. *Ann. Ent. Soc. Amer.* 71:218–222.

———. 1979. Reproductive behavior and sexual selection in Tetranychine mites. *Rec. Adv. Acarology* 1:137–145.

Potter, D. A., Wrensch, D. L. and D. E. Johnston. 1976a. Guarding, aggressive behavior and mating success in male two-spotted spider mites. *Ann. Ent. Soc. Amer.* 69:707–711.

Potter, D. A., Wrensch, D. L. and D. E. Johnston. 1976b. Aggression and mating success in male spider mites. *Science* 193:160–161.

Poulson, D. F. 1963. Cytoplasmic inheritance and hereditary infections in *Drosophila. In:* Burdette, W. J. (ed.), *Methodology in Basic Genetics.* Holden-Day, San Francisco.

Preer, J. R. 1971. Extrachromosomal inheritance: hereditary symbionts, mitochondria, chloroplasts. *Ann. Rev. Genet.* 5:361–406.

Primack, R. B. and D. G. Lloyd. 1980. Sexual strategies in plants IV. The distribution of gender in two monomorphic shrub populations. *New Zeal. J. Bot.* 18:109–114.

Pyke, G. H. 1978. Optimal foraging in bumblebees and coevolution with their plants. *Oecologia* 36:281–293.

Randall, J. E. and H. A. Randall. 1963. The spawning and early development of the Atlantic parrotfish, *Sparisoma rubripinne,* with notes on other Scarid and Labrid fishes. *Zoologica* 48:49–60.

Rasmussen, B. 1969. Variations in protandric hermaphroditism in *Pandalus borealis. F.A.O. Fish. Rep.* 57:1102–1106.

———. 1953. On the geographical variation in growth and sexual development of the deep sea prawn (*Pandalus borealis*). *Rep. Norw. Fish. Mar. Invest.* 10(3):160 pp.

331

Rechav, Y. 1978. Biological and ecological studies of the parasitoid *Chelonus inanitus* (Braconidae) in Israel IV. Oviposition, host preference and sex ratio. *Entomophaga* 23:95–102.

Reinboth, R. 1970. Intersexuality in fishes. *Mem. Soc. Endocrinology* 18:515–543.

――――. 1973. Dualistic reproductive behavior in the protogynous wrasse *Thalassoma bifasciatum* and some observations on its day-night changeover. *Helgoländer wissenschafliche Meersuntersuchungen* 24:174–191.

――――, ed. 1975. *Intersexuality in the Animal Kingdom.* Springer-Verlag, Berlin.

Reish, P. J. 1957. The life history of the polychaetous annelid *Neanthes stauronereis,* including a summary of development in the family Nereidae. Pacif. Sci. 11:216–228.

Reznick, D. and J. Endler. 1982. The impact of predation on life history evolution in Trinidadian guppies (*Poecilia reticulata*). *Evolution* 36:160–177.

Richards, C. S. 1973. Pigmentation variations in *Biomphalaria glabrata* and other Planorbidae. *Malacol. Rev.* 6:49–51.

――――. 1976. Genetics of the host-parasite relationship between *Biomphalaria glabrata* and *Schistosoma mansoni. In:* Taylor, A.E.R. and R. Muller (eds.), *Genetic Aspects of Host-Parasite Relationships.* British Soc. Paras. Symp. 14, Blackwell, Oxford, pp. 45–54.

Ricker, W. E. 1973. Linear regressions in fishery research. *J. Fish. Res. Bd. Can.* 30:409–434.

Rivers, J. and M. A. Crawford. 1974. Maternal nutrition and the sex ratio at birth. *Nature* 252:297–298.

Roberts, R. A. 1933. Biology of *Brachymeria fonscolombie,* a hymenopterous parasite of blowfly larvae. *U.S. Dept. Agr. Tech. Bull. 365.*

Robertson, D. R. 1972. Social control of sex reversal in a coral-reef fish. *Science* 177:1007–1009.

――――. 1974. A study of the ethology and reproductive biology of the Labrid fish, *Labroides dimidiatus* at Heron Island, Great

Barrier Reef. Ph.D. Thesis, Queensland University, Australia.

Robertson, D. R., and J. H. Choat. 1974. Protogynous hermaphroditism and social systems in Labrid fishes. *Proc. Second International Symposium on Coral Reefs.* 1(Biology):217–225.

Robertson, D. R., and R. R. Warner. 1978. Sexual patterns in the Labroid fishes of the western Caribbean, II: The Parrotfishes (Scaridae). *Smithsonian Contrib. Zool.* 255:26 pp.

Robertson, D. R. and G. Justines. 1982. Protogynous hermaphroditism and gonochorism in four Caribbean reef gobies. *Envir. Biol. Fishes* 7:137–142.

Robinette, W. L., Baer, C. H., Pillmore, R. E. and C. E. Knittle. 1973. Effects of nutritional change on captive mule deer. *J. Wildlife Mgt.* 37:312–326.

Robinson, R. W., Munger, H. M., Whitaker, T. W. and G. W. Bohn. 1976. Genes of the Cucurbitaceae. *Hortoscience* 11:554–568.

Roede, M. J. 1975. Reversal of sex in several Labrid fish species. *Pubbl. Stn. Zool. Napoli* 39 (Suppl.):595–617.

Rose, M. and B. Charlesworth. 1980. A test of evolutionary theories of senescence. *Nature* 287:141–142.

Ross, R. M. 1978. Reproductive behavior in the anemonefish *Amphiprion melanopus* on Guam. *Copeia 1978*:103–107.

Runham, N. W. and P. J. Hunter. 1970. *Terrestrial Slugs.* Hutchinson, London.

Ryan, R. B. and J. A. Rudinsky. 1962. Biology and habits of the Douglas-fir beetle parasite, *Coeloides brunneri* (Hymenoptera: Braconidae) in western Oregon. *Can. Entomol.* 94:748–763.

Rychlewski, J. and K. Zarzycki. 1975. Sex ratio in seeds of *Rumex acetosa* as a result of sparse or abundant pollen. *Acta. Biol. Cracov.* 18:101–114.

Salt, G. W. 1936. Experimental studies in insect parasitism: IV. The effect of superparasitism on populations of *Trichogramma evanescens. J. Exp. Biol.* 13:363–375.

Sandlan, K. 1979. Sex ratio regulation in *Coccygomimus turionella* Linnaeus (Hymenoptera: Ichneumonidae) and its ecological implications. *Ecol. Entomol.* 4:365–378.

Sastry, A. N. 1977. Pelecypoda (excluding Ostreidae). *In:* Giese, A. C. and J. S. Pearse (eds.), *Reproduction of Marine Invertebrates,* Vol. 5. Academic Press, N.Y., pp. 113–292.

Schaffner, J. H. 1922. Control of sexual state in *Arisaema triphyllum* and *A. dracontium. Am. J. Bot.* 9:72–78.

Schemske, D. W. 1978. Evolution of reproductive characteristics in *Impatiens* (Balsaminaceae): The significance of cleistogamy and chasmogamy. *Ecology* 59:596–613.

Schenk, L. 1898. *Schenk's Theory: The Determination of Sex.* The Werner Co., N.Y.

Schoch-Bodmer, H. 1938. The proportion of long-, mid- and short-styled plants in natural populations of *Lythrum salicaria* L. *J. Genetics* 36:39–43.

Schoen, D. J. 1981. The evolution of self-pollination in *Gilia achilleifolia* (Polemoniaceae). Ph.D. Thesis, University of California, Berkeley.

Schroeder, P. C. and C. O. Hermans. 1975. Annelida:Polychaeta. *In:* Giese, A. C. and J. S. Pearse (eds.), *Reproduction of Marine Invertebrates,* Vol. 3. Academic Press, N.Y., pp. 1–214.

Schulton, G.G.M., Van Arendonk, R.C.M., Russell, V.M. and F.A. Roorda. 1978. Copulation, egg production and sex ratio in *Phytoseiulus persimilis* and *Amblyseius bibens* (Acari: Phytoseiidae). *Ent. Exp. Appl.* 24:145–153.

Schwarz, A. L. 1980. Almost all *Dascyllus reticulatus* are girls! *Bull. Mar. Sci.* 30:328 (abstract).

Scrivener, J. C. and T. H. Butler. 1971. A bibliography of shrimps of the family Pandalidae, emphasizing economically important species of the genus *Pandalus. Fish. Res. Board. Can. Tech. Rep.* 241.

Seger, J. 1982. Bivoltinism may cause alternating sex-ratio biases that favour eusociality. *Nature* (in press).

Seiler, J. 1920. Geschlechtschromosomenuntersuchungen as Psy-

chiden. I. Experimentelle Beinflussung der Geschlechtsbesti-
menden Reifeteilung bei *Talaeporia tubulosa* Retz. *Arch.
Zellforsch.* 15:249–268.

Shapiro, D. Y. 1977a. Social organization and sex reversal of the
coral reef fish *Anthias squamipinnis* (Peters). Ph.D. Thesis,
Cambridge University.

———. 1977b. The structure and growth of social groups of the
hermaphroditic fish *Anthias squamipinnis* (Peters). *In: Proc.
Third International Symposium on Coral Reefs.* 1(Biology):571–577.

———. 1979. Social behavior, group structure, and sex reversal in
hermaphroditic fish. *Adv. Study Behav.* 10:43–102.

———. 1980. Serial female sex changes after simultaneous
removal of males from social groups of a coral reef fish.
Science 209:1136–1137.

———. 1981. Size, maturation and the social control of sex
reversal in the coral reef fish *Anthias squamipinnis* (Peters).
J. Zool. 193:105–128.

Shapiro, D. Y. and Lubbock, R. 1980. Group sex ratio and sex
reversal. *J. Theor. Biol.* 82:411–426.

Shaw, R. F. 1958. The theoretical genetics of the sex ratio.
Genetics 93:149–163.

Shaw, R. F. and J. D. Mohler. 1953. The selective advantage of
the sex ratio. *Amer. Natur.* 87:337–342.

Shen, S., Lin, R. and F. Liv. 1979. Redescription of a protandrous
hermaphroditic moray eel (*Rhinomuaena guaesita*). *Bull.
Inst. Zool., Acad. Sinica* 18:79–87.

Shiga, M. and A. Nakanishi. 1968. Variation in the sex ratio of
Gregopimpla himalyensis (Hymenoptera: Ichneumonidae)
parasitic on *Maracosoma neustria testacea* (Lepidoptera:
Lasiocampidae) with considerations on the mechanism. *Kontyû* 36:369–376.

Shine, R. and J. J. Bull. 1977. Skewed sex ratios in snakes.
Copeia 1977:228–234.

———. 1979. The evolution of live-bearing in lizards and snakes.
Amer. Natur. 113:905–923.

Shuster, D. H. and L. Shuster. 1972. Speculative mechanisms affecting sex ratio. *J. Genet. Psychol.* 121:245–254.

Skinner, S. W. 1982. Maternally inherited sex ratio in the parasitoid wasp, *Nasonia vitripennis*. *Science* 215:1133–1134.

Smith, C. C. 1981. The facultative adjustment of sex ratio in lodgepole pine. *Amer. Natur.* 118:297–305.

Smith, C. L. 1965. The patterns of sexuality and the classification of Serranid fishes. *Amer. Mus. Novitates* 2207:20 pp.

――――. 1967. Contributions to a theory of hermaphroditism. *J. Theor. Biol.* 17:76–90.

――――. 1972. A spawning aggregation of Nassau Grouper, *Epinephelus striatus*. *Trans. Amer. Fish. Soc.* 101:257–261.

――――. 1975. The evolution of hermaphroditism in fishes. *In:* R. Reinboth (ed.), *Intersexuality in the Animal Kingdom*. Springer-Verlag, Berlin, pp. 295–310.

Smith, R. H. and M. R. Shaw. 1980. Haplodiploid sex ratios and the mutation rate. *Nature* 287:728–729.

Snyder, R. L. 1962. Reproductive performance of a population of woodchucks after a change in sex ratio. *Ecology* 43:506–515.

――――. 1976. *The Biology of Population Growth*. Croom Helm, London.

Speith, P. T. 1974. Theoretical considerations of unequal sex ratios. *Amer. Natur.* 87:337–342.

Starkweather, G. B. 1883. *The Law of Sex*. J. and A. Churchill, London.

Stenseth, N. C. 1978. Is the female-biased sex ratio in wood lemming *Myopus schisticolor* maintained by cyclic inbreeding? *Oikos* 30:83–89.

Stephen, W. P. and C. E. Osgood. 1965. Influence of tunnel size and nesting medium on sex ratios in a leaf-cutter bee, *Megachile rotundata*. *J. Econ. Ent.* 58:965–968.

Stromberg, L. 1977. *Sexing All Fowl, Baby Chicks, Game Birds, Cage Birds*. Stromberg Pub. Co., Pine River, Minn.

Stubbins, H. G. 1975. *Balanus balanoides*. Liverpool University Press, U.K.

Stubblefield, J. W. 1980. Theoretical elements of sex ratio evolution. Ph.D. Diss., Harvard University.

Suzuki, Y. and Y. Iwasa. 1980. A sex ratio theory of gregarious parasitoids. *Res. Pop. Ecol.* 22:366–382.

Taylor, F. 1979. Convergence to the stable-age distribution in populations of insects. *Amer. Nat.* 113:511–530.

Taylor, L. W., ed. 1949. *Fertility and Hatchability of Chicken and Turkey Eggs*. John Wiley, N.Y.

Taylor, P. D. 1981. Intra-sex and inter-sex sib interactions as sex ratio determinants. *Nature* 291:64–66.

Taylor, P. D. and A. Sauer. 1980. The selective advantage of sex-ratio homeostasis. *Amer. Natur.* 116:305–310.

Taylor, P. D. and M. G. Bulmer. 1980. Local mate competition and the sex ratio. *J. Theor. Biol.* 86:409–419.

Teitelbaum, M. S. 1972. Factors associated with the sex ratio in human populations. *In:* Harrison, G. A. and A. J. Boyce, (eds.), *The Structure of Human Populations*. Oxford University Press, pp. 90–109.

Thompson, R. and J. L. Munro. 1978. Aspects of the biology and ecology of Caribbean reef fishes: Serranidae (hinds and groupers). *J. Fish. Biol.* 12:115–146.

Thomson, J. D. and S.C.H. Barrett. 1981. Selection for outcrossing, sexual selection, and the evolution of dioecy in plants. *Amer. Natur.* 118:443–449.

Thresher, R. E. 1979. Social behavior and ecology of two sympatric wrasses (Labridae:*Halichoeres* spp.) off the coast of Florida. *Mar. Biol.* 53:161–172.

Tomlinson, J. T. 1953. A burrowing barnacle of the genus *Trypetesa* (order Acrothoracica). *J. Wash. Acad. Sci.* 43:373–381.

———. 1967. *The Burrowing Barnacles*. Bull. 296, U.S. National Museum, Smithsonian Inst., Wash. D.C.

Torchio, P. F. and V. J. Tepedino. 1980. Sex ratio, body size and seasonality in a solitary bee, *Osmia lignaria propinqua*

Cresson (Hymenoptera: Megachilidae). *Evolution* 34:993–1003.

Triantaphyllow, A. C. 1973. Environmental sex differentiation of nematodes in relation to pest management. *Ann. Rev. Phytopathology* 11:441–462.

Trivers, R. L. 1972. Parental investment and sexual selection. *In:* Campbell, B. (ed.), *Sexual Selection and the Descent of Man, 1871–1971.* Aldine, Chicago, pp. 136–179.

———. 1974. Parent-offspring conflict. *Amer. Zool.* 14:249–265.

Trivers, R. L. and D. E. Willard. 1973. Natural selection of parental ability to vary the sex ratio of offspring. *Science* 179:90–92.

Trivers, R. L. and H. Hare. 1976. Haplodiploidy and the evolution of the social insects. *Science* 191:249–263.

Trudgill, D. L. 1967. The effect of environment on sex determination in *Heterodera rostochiensis. Nematologica* 13:263–272.

Turner, R. D. 1966. *A survey and illustrated catalogue of the Teredinidae.* Museum of Comparative Zoology, Harvard University.

Uyenoyama, M. K. and M. W. Feldman. 1978. The genetics of sex ratio distortion by cytoplasmic infection under maternal and contagious transmission: an epidemological study. *Theor. Pop. Biol.* 14:471–497.

Van den Ende, H. 1976. *Sexual Interactions in Plants: The Role of Specific Substances in Sexual Reproduction.* Academic Press, N.Y.

Vasek, F. 1966. The distribution and taxonomy of three western junipers. *Brittonia* 18:350–372.

Velich I. and Satyko, L. 1974. Possibilities of increasing earliness in melon by means of the genetics of sex and floral biology. *Agrartudomanyi Kozlemenyek* 33:459–472.

Velthuis, H.H.W., Velthuis-Kluppell, F. M. and G.A.H. Bossink. 1965. Some aspects of the biology and population dynamics of *Nasonia vitripennis* (Walker) (Hymenoptera: Pteromalidae). *Ent. Exp. Appl.* 8:205–227.

Venge, O. 1953. The sex ratio in farm mink. *Acta Zool.* 34: 293–302.

Verme, L. J. 1965. Reproduction studies on penned white-tailed deer. *J. Wildlife Mgt.* 29:74–79.

_____. 1969. Reproductive patterns of white-tailed deer related to nutritional plane. *J. Wildlife Mgt.* 33:881–887.

Verner, J. 1965. Selection for the sex ratio. *Amer. Natur.* 99:419–421.

Viktorov, G. A. 1968. Effect of population density on sex ratio in *Trissolcus grandis* Thoms. (Hymenoptera, Scelionidae). *Zool. Zh.* 47:1035–1039.

Viktorov, G. A. and N. I. Kochetova. 1973a. The role of trace pheromones in regulating the sex ratio in *Trissolcus grandis* (Hymenoptera, Scelionidae). *Zhur. obshch., biol.* 34:559–562.

Viktorov, G. A. and N. I. Kochetova. 1973b. On the regulation of the sex ratio in *Dahlbominus fuscipennis* Zett. (Hymenoptera, Eulophidae). *Entom. obozr.* 52:651–657.

Vinson, S. B. and G. F. Iwantsch. 1980. Host suitability for insect parasitoids. *Ann. Rev. Ent.* 25:397–419.

Volkmann-Rocco, B. 1972. The effect of delayed fertilization in some species of the genus *Tisbe* (Copepoda). *Biol. Bull.* 142:520–529.

Vuilleumier, B. S. 1967. The origin and evolutionary development of heterostyly in angiosperms. *Evolution* 21:210–226.

Waage, J. K. 1982. Sib-mating and sex ratio strategies in Scelionid wasps. *Ecol. Ent.* 7:103–112.

Walker, G. 1977. Observations by scanning electron microscope (SEM) on the oviducal gland sacs of *Balanus balanoides* at egg laying. *J. Mar. Biol. Assn. U.K.* 57:969–972.

_____. 1980. A study of the oviducal glands and ovisacs of *Balanus balanoides* (L.), together with comparative observations on the ovisacs of *Balanus hameri* (Ascanius) and the reproductive biology of the two species. *Phil. Trans. Roy. Soc. London (B)* 291:147–162.

Walker, I. 1967. Effect of population density on the viability and fecundity in *Nasonia vitripennis* Walker (Hymenoptera, Pteromalidae). *Ecology* 48:294–301.

Wallace, B. 1948. Studies on sex-ratio in *Drosophila pseudoobscura*. I. Selection and sex ratio. *Evolution* 2:189–217.

Waller, D. M. 1979. The relative costs of self- and cross-fertilized seeds in *Impatiens capensis* (Balsaminaceae). *Am. J. Bot.* 66:313–320.

Walley, L. J. 1967. The cirral glands: a new type of epidermal gland in cirripedes. *Crustaceana* 12:151–158.

Walley, L. J., White, F. and K. M. Brander. 1971. Sperm activation and fertilization in *Balanus balanoides*. *J. Mar. Biol. Assn. U.K.* 51:489–494.

Warner, R. R. 1975a. The adaptive significance of sequential hermaphroditism in animals. *Amer. Natur.* 109:61–82.

———. 1975b. The reproductive biology of the protogynous hermaphrodite *Pimelometopon pulchrum* (Pisces: Labridae). *Fish. Bull.* 73:262–283.

———. 1978. The evolution of hermaphroditism and unisexuality in aquatic and terrestrial vertebrates. *In:* E. Reese (ed.), *Contrasts in Behavior*. Wiley Interscience, N.Y., pp. 78–101.

———. 1982. Mating systems, sex change and sexual demography in the rainbow wrasse, *Thalassoma lucasanum*. *Copeia* (in press).

Warner, R. R. and I. F. Downs. 1977. Comparative life histories: growth vs. reproduction in normal males and sex-changing hermaphrodites in the striped parrotfish *Scarus croicensis*. Proc. Third International Symposium on Coral Reefs. 1(Biology):275–282.

Warner, R. R. and D. R. Robertson. 1978. Sexual patterns in the labroid fishes of the western Caribbean, I: The wrasses (Labridae). *Smithsonian Contrib. Zool.* 254:27 pp.

Warner, R. R. and S. G. Hoffman. 1980a. Local population size as a determinant of mating system and sexual composition in

340

two tropical marine fishes (*Thalassoma spp.*). *Evolution* 34:508–518.

Warner, R. R. and S. G. Hoffman. 1980b. Population density and the economics of territorial defense in a coral reef fish. *Ecology.* 61:772–780.

Warner, R. R., D. R. Robertson, and E. G. Leigh. 1975. Sex change and sexual selection. *Science* 190:633–638.

Warwick, E. J. and J. E. Legates. 1979. *Breeding and Improvement of Farm Animals.* McGraw-Hill, N.Y.

Waser, N. W. 1981. Sex ratio variation in populations of two desert perennials. In manuscript.

Webb, C. J. 1979. Breeding systems and the evolution of dioecy in New Zealand apioid Umbelliferae. *Evolution* 33:662–672.

_____. 1981. Test of a model predicting equilibrium frequencies of females in populations of gynodioecious angiosperms. *Heredity* 46:397–405.

Webber, H. H. 1977. Gastropoda: Prosobranchia. *In:* Giese, A. C. and J. S. Pearse (eds.), *Reproduction of Marine Invertebrates,* Vol. 4. Academic Press, N.Y., pp. 1–114.

Weir, J. A. 1971. Genetic control of sex ratio in mice. *In:* Kiddy, C. A. and H. D. Hafs (eds.), *Sex ratio at birth—prospects for control.* Symp. pub. by Amer. Soc. Anim. Science, pp. 43–54.

Welch, H. E. 1965. Entomophilic nematodes. *Ann. Rev. Ent.* 10:275–302.

Welch, S. M. 1979. The application of simulation models to mite pest management. *Rec. Adv. Acarology* 1:31–40.

Weller, S. G. 1976. Breeding system polymorphism in a heterostylous species. *Evolution* 30:442–454.

Weller, S. G. and R. Ornduff. 1977. Cryptic self-incompatibility in *Amsinckia grandiflora. Evolution* 31:47–51.

Wenner, A. M. 1972. Sex ratio as a function of size in marine Crustacea. *Amer. Natur.* 106:321–350.

Werren, J. H. 1980a. Sex ratio adaptations to local mate competition in a parasitic wasp. *Science* 208:1157–1159.

341

————. 1980b. Studies in the evolution of sex ratios. Ph.D. Thesis, University of Utah, Salt Lake City.

————. 1982. Sex ratio evolution under local mate competition in a parasitic wasp. *Evolution* (in press).

Werren, J. H. and E. L. Charnov. 1978. Facultative sex ratios and population dynamics. *Nature* 272:349–350.

Werren, J. H., Skinner, S. W. and E. L. Charnov. 1981. Paternal inheritance of a daughterless sex ratio factor. *Nature* 293:467–468.

Westergaard, M. 1958. The mechanism of sex determination in dioecious flowering plants. *Adv. Genet.* 9:217–281.

Wethey, D. 1979. Demographic variation in intertidal barnacles. Ph.D. Thesis, University of Michigan, Ann Arbor.

White, M.J.D. 1973. *Animal Cytology and Evolution*. Cambridge University Press.

Whiting, A. R. 1967. The biology of the parasitic wasp, *Mormoniella vitripennis. Quart. Rev. Biol.* 42(3):333–406.

Wildish, D. J. 1976. A selected bibliography of invertebrate sex ratio data. *Fish. Res. Bd. Can. Tech. Rep.* 630.

Wilkes, A. 1963. Environmental causes of variation in the sex ratio of an arrhenotokous insect, *Dahlbominus fuliginosus* (Nees) (Hymenoptera: Eulophidae). *Can. Ent.* 95:183–202.

Williams, G. C. 1957. Pleiotropy, natural selection, and the evolution of senescence. *Evolution* 11:398–411.

————. 1966. *Adaptation and Natural Selection*. Princeton University Press.

————. 1975. *Sex and Evolution*. Princeton University Press.

————. 1979. The question of adaptive sex ratio in outcrossed vertebrates. *Proc. Roy. Soc. London (B)* 205:567–580.

Williamson, D. L. and D. F. Poulson. 1979. Sex ratio organisms (Spiroplasmas) of *Drosophila. In: The Mycoplasmas,* Vol. 3. Academic Press, N.Y., pp. 176–208.

Williamson, M. H. 1959. Studies on the colour and genetics of the black slug. *Proc. Roy. Soc. Edinb.* 27:87–93.

Willson, M. F. 1979. Sexual selection in plants. *Amer. Natur.* 113:777–790.

———. 1981. Sex expression in fern gametophytes: some evolutionary possibilities. *J. Theor. Biol.* 93:403–410.

Wilson, D. S. 1980. *The Natural Selection of Populations and Communities.* Benjamin/Cummings, Menlo Park, Calif.

Wilson, D. S. and R. K. Colwell. 1981. The evolution of sex ratio in structured demes. *Evolution* 35:882–897.

Wilson, K. A. 1960. The genera of the Arales in the southeastern United States. *J. Arnold Arboretum* 41:47–71.

Wittenberger, J. F. 1981. *Animal Social Behavior.* Duxbury Press, Boston.

Wong, A. Y.-C. 1967. Studies on mating behavior and maximum distance for copulation in the barnacles *Balanus glandula, Balanus tintinnabulum* and *Chthamalus dalli.* Paper for Biol. 175h, Hopkins Marine Station, California.

Wrensch, D. L. 1979. Components of reproductive success in spider mites. *Rec. Adv. Acarology* 1:155–164.

Wrensch, D. L. and S.S.Y. Young. 1978. Effects of density and host quality on rate of development, survivorship and sex ratio in the carmine spider mite. *Environ. Ent.* 7:499–501.

Wu, H. W. and C. K. Lin. 1942. On the breeding habits and larval metamorphosis of *Monopterus javanensis. Scinensia* 13:1–13.

Wylie, H. G. 1958. Factors that affect host finding by *Nasonia vitripennis* (Walker) (Hymenoptera: Pteromalidae). *Can. Ent.* 90:597–608.

———. 1963. Some effects of host age on parasitism by *Nasonia vitripennis* (Walker) (Hymenoptera: Pteromalidae). *Can. Ent.* 95:881–886.

———. 1965. Some factors that reduce the reproductive rate of *Nasonia vitripennis* (Walk.) at high adult population densities. *Can. Ent.* 97:970–977.

———. 1966. Some mechanisms that affect the sex ratio of *Nasonia vitripennis* (Walk.) (Hymenoptera: Pteromalidae) reared from superparasitized housefly pupae. *Can. Ent.* 98:645–653.

343

Yampolsky, E. and H. Yampolsky. 1922. Distribution of sex forms in phanerogamic flora. *Bibl. Genet.* 3:1–62.

Yonge, M. 1960. *Oysters.* Collins, London.

Zaher, M. A., Shehata, K. K. and H. El-Khatib. 1979. Population density effects on biology of *Tetranychus arabicus,* the common spider mite in Egypt. *Rec. Adv. Acarology* 1:507–509.

Zei, M. 1949. Typical sex-reversal in Teleosts. *Proc. Zool. Soc. Lond.* 119:917–920.

Ziser, S. W., Wojtowicz, J. A. and W. C. Nettles, Jr. 1977. The effects of the number of maggots per host on length of development, puparial weight and adult emergence of *Eucelatoria sp. Ann. Ent. Soc. Amer.* 70:733–736.

Taxonomic Index (Genera)

Author Index

Subject Index

353

LIBRARY OF CONGRESS CATALOGING IN PUBLICATION DATA

Charnov, Eric L., 1947–
    The theory of sex allocation.

    (Monographs in population biology ; 18)
    Bibliography : p.
    Includes indexes.
    1. Sex (Biology) 2. Sex differences. I. Title.
II. Title: Sex allocation. III. Series.
QH481.C5   1982   574.2′248   82-47586
ISBN 0-691-08311-8   AACR2
ISBN 0-691-08312-6 (pbk.)